THE PIAGETIAN LANGUAGE NURSERY

An Intensive Group Language Intervention Program for Preschoolers

Elizabeth B. Johnston
Andrew V. Johnston

Miami University of Ohio

AN ASPEN PUBLICATION®
Aspen Systems Corporation
Rockville, Maryland
Royal Tunbridge Wells
1984

Library of Congress Cataloging in Publication Data

Johnston, Elizabeth B.
The Piagetian language nursery.

An Aspen publication.
Includes bibliographies and index.
1. Language disorders in children—Treatment.
2. Cognitive therapy. 3. Piaget, Jean, 1896—
I. Johnston, Andrew V. II. Title. [DNLM: 1. Language
therapy—In infancy and childhood. 2. Child, Preschool.
WL 340 J72p]
RJ496.L35J64 1984   618.92′855   83-17396
ISBN: 0-89443-890-5

Publisher: John Marozsan
Editorial Director: Margaret M. Quinlin
Executive Managing Editor: Margot Raphael
Editorial Services: Jane Coyle
Printing and Manufacturing: Debbie Collins

Library of Congress Catalog Card Number: 83-17396
ISBN: 0-89443-890-5

Printed in the United States of America

1 2 3 4 5

This book is affectionately dedicated
to all the children who have shared the magic of their language with us,
especially Denis, Paula, and Mark;
Patrick and Kim;
and Amy, Jason, Gregory, and William.

Table of Contents

Preface

This is not a book about Piaget, nor is it a book about language or child management. It is not specifically about education or therapy. Extensive treatises could be written about each of these subjects, which we have not attempted to do.

Rather, this book is about severely language-impaired preschool children in a program designed especially for them. It presents theories and philosophy that the authors have formed into a cohesive program. We are aware that numerous other theories and ideas are left out of this discussion. Many of these may be quite valid and compatible with our philosophical base, with much to be said for them. However, many others do not appear to be compatible with the program we have established.

The program that serves as a model for this book consists of two preschool language group sessions—one sensorimotor and one preoperational—each of which meets for eight hours a week. It is based on Piagetian principles of cognitive development, expanded to include a developmental language intervention model. The areas of pragmatics, semantics, syntax, and phonology are approached in a developmental manner, utilizing experience therapy along with modeling and expansion. The child management theories of Alfred Adler (implemented by child psychologist, Dr. Rudolf Dreikurs) are used since they are compatible with the philosophical base of the program and parents of children who have undergone the program find them effective.

The program has grown over the years and has served severely language-impaired preschoolers, most of whom have since gone on to regular classes in public schools and many of whom are speaking and reading several years above their age levels. We expect it to continue growing and evolving. We sincerely believe this model for intensive language intervention to be the most appropriate one available for most children who are very severely language impaired. We hope it will work for users of this book.

A note about how to best utilize this book:

One basic premise of effective reading that has been demonstrated again and again is that the most efficient readers have a systematic approach to new material. One approach that has proved beneficial over many years is the study skills approach. Using that method with this book, readers should:

1. Read over the objectives for each chapter and consider what they already know about the subject.
2. Read the key ideas, fitting them into the framework they are bringing to the exercise.
3. Read each subheading throughout the chapter, forming each into a question to be answered while reading. These headings will help to support the framework being built since they serve to identify major topics or divisions of topics.
4. Read the summary at the end of the chapter to see what the authors consider the major points made.
5. Read the discussion questions at the end of the chapter to complete the mapping or survey of the material.
6. Return to the beginning of the chapter and read the first section, keeping in mind the questions readers asked themselves.
7. Pause after reading the section to answer the questions raised, then proceed to the next chapter, and so on throughout the book.

A final note: All tables, exhibits, and figures are by the authors unless credited otherwise.

Elizabeth B. Johnston, Ed.D.
Andrew V. Johnston, Ph.D.
Oxford, Ohio

Chapter 1

Philosophical Bases of the Program

CHAPTER OBJECTIVES

After completing this chapter, readers will be able to:

1. Describe the basic elements of Piaget's theory of development of the intellect of children.
2. Relate various aspects of the development of language in children to appropriate stages of intellectual development.
3. Relate the area of interpersonal development to those of language and intellectual development.

KEY IDEAS

1. Children with language impairments need early, systematic, cognition-based intervention to help them achieve their communicative potential.
2. The Piagetian model of intellectual development seems best suited for articulating with the language development model deemed most appropriate for this intervention.
3. Language growth in all individuals is powered by the expansion of the intellect and, in turn, is instrumental in refining and guiding that growth.
4. Nonverbal children seem to respond better to a management approach that is nonpunitive, does not depend upon language for implementation, and helps them achieve socially acceptable levels of behavior.

THE PROGRAM DESCRIBED

Throughout this book, mention of "the program" refers to a Piagetian Language Nursery, an intensive group experience designed for preschool-aged children that focuses heavily on language development and is organized around the constructionist theories of Piaget. It was founded on sets of principles chosen from the areas of cognitive development, language development, and behavior management because they are compatible and because they offer a cohesive way of working with the youngsters.

The prototype program is not a complete nursery school. It is a format for intensive group language therapy for children with severe communicative impairment, although it could be incorporated into a regular nursery school. The program is modeled on Piagetian principles of learning in the sensorimotor and preoperational periods. It primarily uses experience-based language therapy and Adlerian child management procedures, in which an understanding of the child's goals is used to modify the goals and improve the behavior (See Appendix D). This Adlerian philosophy has been implemented and expanded in the United States by his former student and associate, the late Dr. Rudolf Dreikurs.

The children are in the setting for two hours a day, four days a week, and are not enrolled in other programs. Many of the activities, both group and individual, have goals and implementation much like traditional nursery school programs. While some of this program is appropriate only for severely language-impaired children, much of it is fully appropriate for the normal nursery school population.

The language nursery program is offered by Miami University, Oxford, Ohio, and is housed in the Speech and Hearing Clinic. The therapy is performed by student clinicians under the supervision of university supervisors with Certificates of Clinical Competence from the American Speech-Language-Hearing Association. A ratio of one student to each two or three children is maintained. Youngsters are enrolled in the nursery groups based upon their need for the services. They attend the program until they either have no further need for intervention or until some other more appropriate placement can be made.

The parents of all children meet weekly as a group, led jointly by a graduate clinic assistant and the university supervisor, a fully certified speech pathologist. The vast majority of counseling relates to communication and is within the training capabilities of the staff. However, counseling occasions do arise that are beyond the range of the speech pathologist or trainee. At such times, other fully qualified professionals are invited into the group or referrals are made for specific parents to be counseled according to their individual needs.

THE NATURE OF LEARNING

There are many notions about the nature of learning and the importance of various factors to it that are basic to the school and/or preschool. The important element is now, as it always has been, finding the most appropriate ways to interact with the children to make their early years as productive as possible.

From Behaviorist to Developmentalist

A shift has been observed from an emphasis based primarily on behaviorism (learning as the result of operant conditioning in a stimulus-response-reinforcement model), which has appeared to dominate American educational theory, to focus on developmental theory (learning as the result of children's interaction with the environment from which they construct meaning). As the basic philosophy changes, the axioms that support it also change and the newer notions come to support the newer paradigm.

One field of research is leading in a new direction—away from the behaviorist view in which children are seen as a passive element in learning upon whom information is impressed by various types and amounts of conditioning. It also is leading away from the empiricist notion "that reality can be reduced to its observable features and that knowledge must limit itself to transcribing these features" (Inhelder & Chipman, 1976, p. 24), and away from the tabula rasa in which the body of information is taught to the children from without and the youngsters are assumed to have no innate characteristics (Houston, 1972; Skinner, 1957; Sloane & MacAulay, 1968). This research is examining many elements involved in and growing out of the constructionist views of Jean Piaget (Piaget, 1974, 1977).

All of Piaget's works were originally in French and translations vary in their adequacy. Many times the most useful references to Piaget's theories are interpretations (which relate to the subject matter of this book) found in the works of his associates, such as Inhelder, Kamii, Sinclair, etc.). In addition, Piaget concentrated on normal children and information relating his theories to children with problems has been extrapolated by his associates and others.

> Piaget is an interactionist-relativist who believes in the construction of knowledge by the indissociable interaction between sensory experience and reason . . . [Piaget's] interactionist views . . . lead to an emphasis on what is internal to the child. Methods reflecting this view use indirect ways of encouraging the child's own development of his or her reasoning. (Kamii & DeVries, 1977, p. 366)

Piaget teaches that children construct their knowledge from their experiences by the combined processes of assimilation and accommodation. He holds that learning is mediated by interaction with persons and things in the environment. In this combined view, children may be born with considerable innate ability and a biological predisposition that fosters learning (Lenneberg, 1967). They are seen as the active element in the interaction and their learning comes about as they interact with and experience their environment and formulate various schemata upon which they subsequently build more schemata, the blueprints of their concepts (Ginsburg & Opper, 1969; Inhelder & Chipman, 1976; Kamii & DeVries, 1977).

This new direction highlights a number of questions and even more subquestions that become central to the search for improved ways to help children gain the optimum results from their preschool experiences. Professionals become concerned with:

- the nature of learning
- the nature of early communication and the role of early mother-child interactions in it
- effective ways to build desired behavior in children.

It seems evident that the focus now is on identifying a number of basic components that lie at the core of early development. The study of these elements provides useful information upon which to base efforts at mediation and remediation whenever the process goes wrong.

In normally developing children the three areas are complexly interrelated at every level of development. The threads of this interrelationship weave the fabric of cognition and interpersonal communication upon which everything else is based. Each area is composed of sequential developments in a hierarchical pattern. At numerous points, combinations of these developmental levels must be achieved to serve as prerequisites for further development. These often transcend their areas, producing such things as sensorimotor schemata that are prerequisites for specific language development. For these reasons the authors of this book have discussed normal cognitive development, normal language development, normal play behavior, and the behavior of normally developing children (in each of the chapters that follow) to furnish a base upon which to discuss the special population served in the language nursery program.

For example, the normal process would have children roll and bounce a ball (sensorimotor) before they would be able to symbolize or talk about it (linguistic). At a more advanced level, sensorimotor patterns continue to provide the basis for later normally developing language arts functions. Greg, 15 months old, lying on his back having his diaper changed, is "reading" one of his books. While this action is not yet linguistic, it does furnish a sensorimotor base upon which later reading can be built. At another time, 14-month-old Amy sits in the big chair "reading to her dolly" from a book, babbling and showing the pictures to the doll, also laying the sensorimotor foundation for later reading activity.

While it is true that severely physically handicapped children often do construct symbols for things they cannot experience physically, these are more difficult to establish and the resulting schemata probably are not as complete as those that result from the normal sensorimotor experiences of the nonhandicapped. Certainly language development is a more arduous process for the severely physically handicapped, often requiring a great deal of specific speech and language therapy and many times a nonoral adaptation of expressive language, i.e., communication board, electronic device, or some combination.

The Heuristic Approach

A significant number of educational settings, especially those dealing with special problems, has been based on the behavior modification notions of B.F. Skinner (1957), which stated that stimulus, followed by desired response, followed immediately by an operant (reward) increased the likelihood that the behavior would recur. An oft-used description of the "learning mechanism" as a small computer that processes information in a mechanical fashion left from this more behavioral approach (Glucksberg & Danks, 1975; Kirk & McCarthy, 1968; Stevens, 1972) is at variance with developmental theories discussed by Kamii and DeVries (1977), who comment that "cognitive development is not a matter of improving 'cognitive skills' as one would program a computer or build an information processing machine" (p. 367).

The operant system for developing language was seen by behaviorists as somehow "mechanical" in that this description was based on mechanical terms and notions. They regarded the system as highly complex and said it could be expected to malfunction at times. It would be possible, of course, for a variety of discrete mechanical items to fail to function, were these items really discrete or simply parts of a system, thereby throwing it out of adjustment. Here the analogy runs into trouble, however, because even if some flaw appears, it is not possible to take out a discrete bit of human behavior and work on it in isolation.

Whatever is done diagnostically (when the system has failed to function) must be done to the entire system, on site, and the operation of each portion must be evaluated in its context. In addition, whatever intervention is administered to remediate a poorly functioning operation also must be done to the entire system and may have not only the planned effects on the error but also a variety of other effects on this and many other parts. The conclusion seems warranted that working with human systems is nothing at all like working with mechanical systems and that the common analogy is not appropriate since what is being dealt with is an unknown number of human traits that act jointly and/or independently and are capable of a variety of actions and reactions in unlimited combinations.

In planning intervention strategies and individual lessons, it is necessary to identify the problem areas and attempt to remediate them. While the notion of remediation never is presented by Piaget in his considerations of normally developing children, it is not necessarily contrary to developmental constructionist views. The extension of these theories to language-impaired children requires only that the professional choose intervention models that are amenable to the theoretical basis of the program.

Many clinicians, however, have adopted the behaviorally written objective, a model borrowed from more behavioral views. In this mode, plans are written in terms of the behavior to be demanded of the children. Success of the remediation program is judged in terms of the number of repetitions of counted behaviors that meet the specifications of these behaviorally written objectives. While it is possible to count or identify specific aspects or examples of a behavior, it is not possible to count or delineate cognition, which is the goal of the activity.

So professionals have become counters of behaviors, expecting children to abstract out of the repetitions the essential element and to assimilate it into an existing schema, regardless of how this element is related to the youngsters' cognitive processes. In terms of the goals of building understanding, reasoning, thinking, and ideas (Kamii & DeVries, 1977) the scores and tallies that result from this model generally are irrelevant. Perhaps a new way of writing plans can be suggested for this program that will be more compatible with the present construc-tionist approach (see Exhibit 4-1 and Tables 4-1 and 4-2, infra) and yet can be made sufficiently accountable for work situations. The plans must build upon teachers' knowledge of how cognitive processes are developed and what experiences will be most useful for the children to enable them to construct the desired knowledge.

PIAGET'S DEVELOPMENTAL THEORIES

"Each time Piaget comes across a behavior, however trivial it may seem, he seeks to explain it with reference to his theoretical framework, which is thus continuously being refined and enriched" (Inhelder, 1969, p. vii).

In describing the emergence and development of intelligence, Piaget (1957, 1963, 1969a, 1973, 1974; Piaget & Inhelder, 1969b) has provided a workable way to explain a complex, lifelong action, and to organize attempts to enhance it. His observations lead to an explanation of his theories for learning. Piaget made major contributions to the understanding of intelligence. These have been widely extrap-olated for use in schools and preschools. His division of the development of intelligence into four periods (Exhibit 1-1) has provided an organizational frame-work on which to base instructional efforts. (Piaget sometimes divided this development into three, four, or six periods or stages. The four-stage (-period) division appears to the authors to be the most consistent with this work and therefore has been chosen arbitrarily.) Of the four stages: sensorimotor, preopera-tional, concrete operational, and formal operational, the first two are of primary importance in dealing with preschool language learners.

Philosophically the preschool language nursery group is based on Piagetian notions. The choice of activities, the language modeling, the questioning, and the feedback all are designed to encourage the children to construct knowledge and, with it, language.

Exhibit 1-1 Piaget's Stages of the Development of the Intellect

Period I	*Sensorimotor* (0 to 18–24 months)
	Stage 1—Reflexive
	Stage 2—Initial Differentiations
	Stage 3—Reproduction
	Stage 4—Coordination of Schemata
	Stage 5—Experimentation
	Stage 6—Representation
Period II	*Preoperational* (18–24 months to 7 years)
Period III	*Concrete Operational* (7 to 11–12 years)
Period IV	*Formal Operational* (11–12 years to adult)

Source: Adapted from *Piaget's Theory of Cognitive Development* by B.J. Wadsworth, published by David McKay Co., Inc., New York, copyright © 1975, and from *Piaget's Theory of Intellectual Development: An Introduction* by H. Ginsburg and S. Opper, published by Prentice-Hall, Inc., Englewood Cliffs, N.J., copyright © 1969, both by permission of the respective publishers.

According to Piaget (1963, 1974, 1976, 1977) each person constructs knowledge (intelligence) through the process of acting upon and interacting with objects, actions, and others in the individual's world. The constructs are identified as scheme (pl., schemes), operational activities or schema (pl., schemata), figurative aspects of thought (Inhelder & Chipman, 1976). Individuals bring their maturity level, motivation, personal discipline, biological endowment of innate abilities, and predisposition or style of learning to the job of constructing schemata from their interactions with their environment. As this process goes on, children develop internalized structures or operations that form an organizational superstructure and act as the tools with which knowledge is constructed.

The process used implies an equilibration, or balance, between assimilation and accommodation. In this process, the children assimilate or take new information into their existing schemata, adding to them as appropriate and possible. When a new bit of information cannot be assimilated into an existing schema because it is not a fit, then the individuals must accommodate or reorganize that material either by reorganizing existing schemata or by forming a new category.

At times when the children are doing more assimilating than accommodating (as youngsters with so much information to take in and catalog), the process will be more egocentric or autistic in nature (Inhelder & Chipman, 1976). For example, children with a schema for horse are able to assimilate numerous instances of horses they have seen into their mental plan without problems. If, however, they see a Great Dane (which fails to fit into the schema because it neither neighs nor eats grass), they must accommodate this nonfitting information by forming a schema that will accept it, so the category of nonhorse is created. (Professionals always risk error by producing examples because at the same time that the illustration is showing what they mean to show, it also may be confounding what they have said.)

Initially children assimilate their own actions and viewpoints and essentially are egocentric or autistic, states where they see the world from their own viewpoint alone (Wadsworth, 1975). As they accommodate more and become less egocentric, they become capable of decentration—the ability to look at things from more than one point of view, a very necessary stage for later emerging objectivity (Inhelder & Chipman, 1976).

The Sensorimotor Period (0 to 18–24 Months)

This first period is the time during which children begin to form their first sensorimotor schemata. It is divided into six stages (Exhibit 1-1, supra). These initial efforts are constructed from the children's experiences in and interactions with their world. They must learn basic operations with which to relate to that world. Here the theory of operativity is essential to understanding Piaget: "Operativity, the heart of Piaget's theory, refers to the basic structuring aspect of intelligence (understanding . . . reasoning . . . thinking . . . ideas)" (Kamii & DeVries, 1977, p. 367).

The infants' first task is to begin to establish their own ego boundary—to begin to get some sense of where they themselves begin and the outside world leaves off, the lifelong process of realizing what the dimensions of their person are. They learn about objects in the world by manipulating, tasting, throwing them, etc. By this interaction with objects in relation to self and other people, they begin to organize time and space (Kamii & DeVries, 1977). As they progress, they begin to show evidence of intentionality (doing things by intent rather than by accident). Intentionality can be credited when the causes of the behavior are not reflexive or repetitive of immediate stimuli. Intentionality of behavior indexes the initial step in children's emerging intelligence (Wadsworth, 1975).

With this beginning, children are on the way to sensorimotor development, which they will construct by building four understandings: object constancy, coordinated space, causality, and temporality.

Object Constancy

The children must develop the understanding that objects have a stable existence of their own. In the beginning, they do not understand that the object they see has an existence apart from themselves and continues to exist when not in their presence. They assume that each instance in which they see an item represents a new object. Thus, they may examine or play with an object, toy, tool, or utensil again and again. They are learning more about the constancy of the item each time and are reinforcing their perceptions of its various characteristics—as it were, refining their assimilations of it.

As children's experience with the objects grows, they acquire an understanding that it is permanent, that it has the same substance when they are not looking at it as when they are. They begin to realize that the blanket on the bed at night is the same one that was in the laundry basket in the morning.

With this growing understanding of the permanence of objects, children become capable of generating nouns, an understanding that gives rise both to the ability to classify objects using oral categories and to relate to nouns, for this is what the nouns reflect—the objects of the world. Before children can generate the use of nouns, they must understand the permanence of objects in their world.

Coordinated Space

Children's understanding of how they relate to objects and other people in space also is an essential component of the sensorimotor period. With growing under-standing of the relationships in the world between objects, children come to comprehend the prepositional constituents of the language. Until they understand the physical manipulations that will let them put the "tooth under the pillow" and the Tooth Fairy will put the money "under the pillow," they will not be able to relate to the linguistic (prepositional) forms that represent this action, such as "in," "on," "under," "beside," etc.

Causality

The knowledge that one action causes another and so on—that one action can cause a chain of others—also is necessary for sensorimotor development. In learning schemata for these actions (causes and results), children will be beginning to think in terms of agent (doer of the action)—action—and sometimes patient (receiver of the action). As they comprehend this relationship among people, objects, and events, they become able to generate words such as "because," "until," "before," etc., that refer to coordination and subordination in language.

It can be seen that unless children understand actions, causes, and results, their language will not contain the linguistic elements that signal it, nor will they be able to express the semantics of agent-action-patient (or complement), subordination, or coordination. Certainly they will not reach these levels during the sensorimotor period but the levels' antecedents lie in the causality of the sensorimotor period.

In addition, this is an important phase because at this point children begin to envision themselves as the agents (causers of events), the active participants in the construction of their own knowledge.

Temporality

This knowledge as it relates to children's growing understanding of continuing activity also is a prerequisite of language development. As the youngsters con-struct their knowledge of sequence and time, they are establishing the cognitive base upon which they can build the linguistic elements of verb tense. While they do not develop this far during the sensorimotor period, they do begin to formulate such knowledge during this time. With the development of temporality, children have the beginnings of the basic cognitive prerequisites for language.

The action (which is the basic verb) comes in very early. Children relatively quickly pay attention to "where the action is," developing the motoric aspect of the sensorimotor level. As language begins to develop, verbs and verb tenses are among the first meaningful constituents to appear.

The Importance of Cognition

Inherent in any definition of language is the inference that a message is exchanged. This message implies that meaning is transferred from one person to another. It is this meaning, grounded in cognition, that gives language its essential quality. If children transmit meaningless signals to the "other," they cannot be said to have used language. The idle chatter was merely vocalization that carried no information. Consequently, it can be said that the essential base for later development of language is cognition that the children will have begun to construct during the sensorimotor period.

Piaget (1969) believed that language merely translated what children already understood, that word meaning was dependent on internalized representations. At a conference in Berkeley, California, in 1964 he said, "Words are probably not a short cut to a better understanding . . . The level of understanding seems to modify the language that is used . . . language serves to translate what is already understood . . . language may even present a danger if it is used to introduce an idea which is not yet accessible." (Duckworth, 1964, p. 73.) The ability to form symbols is inherently dependent on cognition. The roles of both parties in a language exchange must be grounded in cognition if meaning is to be transferred from one to the other.

"The language a child is exposed to and taught must be based on what he comprehends. Matching language to the child's knowledge and concepts is the name of the game" (Streng, Kretschmer, & Kretschmer, 1978, p. 23). If the various elements of sensorimotor knowledge are not emerging, there seems to be little or no prospect that the children will develop language normally.

Symbolic Formation

As children near the end of the sensorimotor period (18 to 24 months old), they become able to form internal representations of objects and actions. They move from sensorimotor intelligence to representational intelligence (Wadsworth, 1975). They begin to symbolize: to form symbols that they then can begin to use to transmit messages to others.

This transitional phase between the sensorimotor period and the preoperational period is a prerequisite for language. It is to be hoped that the children will have been communicating with the important people in their world for some time via protoperformatives (basic gestures), suprasegmentals (prosody—in this context, the rate, pitch, and inflectional patterns of the stream of speech), and some single-word utterances. When they have developed sufficient sensorimotor schemata they will begin to form verbal symbols to represent them. It is this transitional time that indexes the beginning of "language." For example, children will come to know that when they produce the phonetic string /əwʌnət'/ (I want that) or /gɪmɪmɪk'/ (give me milk), it will mean the same thing to a listener as it did to them, and the desired "milk" will be forthcoming.

Armed with their sensorimotor schemata and their newfound ability to share the meaning of vocal symbols with others, the children now are ready to embark on the preoperational period. This actually is the time of language learning and the point at which they seem to "bring it all together," to show the great advances they have made in the cognitive, linguistic, motoric, and social realms.

Children with sensorimotor abilities have intelligence of an extremely practical nature, based on manipulation of objects and development of action plans. The emergence of verbal behavior (at the end of this period) increases the powers of thought in range and speed. With this development, thought can be greatly speeded up and is not limited to a format of one step at a time (Wadsworth, 1975).

For example, instead of the elaborate ritual of normally developing 15-month-old Greg going to the children's bookshelf, taking a book, going to his grandfather, taking him by a trouser leg, pulling him over to the couch, turning him around, pushing against his legs to seat him, then climbing up to be read to, Greg at 18 months accomplishes the desired result from any point in the room by choosing a book and saying firmly, "read." The results are exactly the same but less time and effort have been expended. But later, when he is 21 months old, Greg arrives where his father is reading the evening paper, climbs onto his lap, pushes the paper away and says, "Read Growly Bear," referring to his book, which is on an adjacent shelf. For him, language has become a tool. "For Piaget, the development of language is based on the prior development of sensorimotor operations" (Wadsworth, 1975, p. 69).

Preoperational Period (18–24 Months to 7 Years)

This rather long phase in the development of the intellect is a time when many hierarchical bits of knowledge are constructed and organized into increasingly complex mental structures. The children build upon and expand whatever techniques they have established during the sensorimotor period. With the increasing usefulness of the symbolic process, mental activity has increased and they now are capable of learning to perform mental operations.

Since this is an additive process, each new development presents a multiplicity of new possibilities. Constructional patterns are laid down as the children begin to construct cognitive operations such as sequencing (putting in order), coordination (joining equal elements), embedding (inserting one element into another), intersection (point of meeting of two elements), and correspondence (relationship of one element to another). Mainly through play, they gain experience with imagery, immediate imitation, and deferred imitation (Inhelder & Chipman, 1976). In this period, they develop language, logicomathematical schemata, and socioemotional style. While logical thinking will be hindered by their egocentrism (the inability to see from any point of view but one's own) and centration (the inability to separate self from the environment) and their difficulty with transformation (an operation that changes the properties of something) and reversibility (action that can be done can be undone) (Wadsworth, 1975), children will begin to learn to reason in an orderly manner.

According to Piaget, children learn in three ways: from physical experience, concrete manipulation, and interaction with others (Ginsburg & Opper, 1969). As far as the children are concerned, all their knowledge comes as a result of their own activity. What they learn by interaction with objects in the world is destined to become physical knowledge. What they construct from their mental activity will become logicomathematical knowledge, and what they learn from interaction with other people will become socioemotional knowledge (Kamii & DeVries, 1977, p. 368).

During the preoperational period, children construct these operations in one direction, i.e., actions can be done but not undone. At this point they are ready to understand conservation, the idea that an amount of matter stays the same regardless of changes in shape (Wadsworth, 1975). The ability to do conservation problems is worthy of note. It marks the end of the preoperational period and continues into the formal operational period. When they can use decentration (i.e., can separate self from environment), reversibility, and transformation, they can conduct the mental interactions between two dimensions, e.g., height and diameter of a glass. They begin to work their way through the series of hierarchical conservation problems (Figure 1-1) (Wadsworth, 1975).

Thus children's formation of intellectual operations (tools they will use during the final two periods) nears completion and they are ready to move to the concrete operation period.

Concrete Operational Period (7 to 11–12 Years)

Once children have learned the set of activities that are characteristic of the preoperational period, they are able to continue construction of knowledge by using all those learned during performance of logical operations on concrete things.

Figure 1-1 Developmental Order of Conservation Abilities and Age of Acquisition

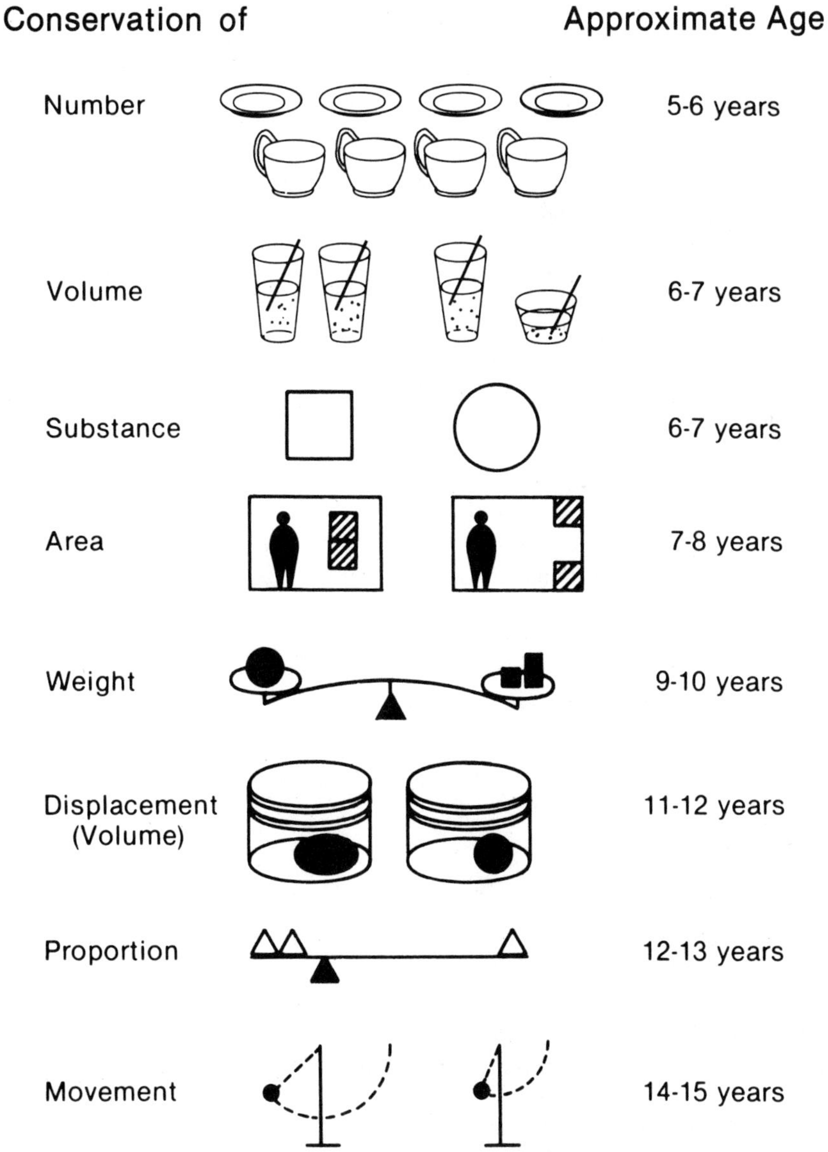

Conservation of   Approximate Age

Number		5-6 years
Volume		6-7 years
Substance		6-7 years
Area		7-8 years
Weight		9-10 years
Displacement (Volume)		11-12 years
Proportion		12-13 years
Movement		14-15 years

Source: Adapted from *Piaget's Theory of Cognitive Development* by Barry J. Wadsworth, published by David McKay Co., Inc., New York, copyright © 1975, and from *Piaget's Theory of Intellectual Development: An Introduction* by Herbert Ginsburg and Sylvia Opper, published by Prentice-Hall, Inc., Englewood Cliffs, N.J., copyright © 1969.

By this time the language structure and speech of the adult world have been assimilated or accommodated but the children continue to refine usage in communication and their vocabulary continues to grow. They now have a set of operations that allows them to interact with the world. During the elementary school years, children construct their basic concepts, structures, and processes in reading, writing, arithmetic, science, and social science and in interpersonal relationships. They establish the scholastic and social patterns and attitudes that will guide their behavior for a lifetime.

Formal Operational Period (11–12 Years to Adult)

Once adolescents become capable of consciously and consistently using the operations they have developed by now to an advanced level, they can perform logical operations on abstract or hypothetical elements. Here they acquire the ability to deal with the advanced content areas and thinking models of the academic world. They can cope with combinational thought, verbal problems, hypothetical problems, and more abstract conservation tasks (Wadsworth, 1975).

Examination of the order of children's development leads to the conclusion that there are specific common stages of development and that it is possible to know how to expect the youngsters to think during each. This is important for teachers of young children because it enables them to deal with each pupil in terms of the appropriate stage of thinking and level of construction of knowledge and thinking processes.

All individuals like to think of themselves as formal operational thinkers. While most adults are capable of formal operations in content areas in which they are prepared, it seems unlikely that many function at such a level at all times. It is more likely that there is considerable interplay between levels as they interact with the various realities of life.

THE NATURE OF LANGUAGE

Lack of ability to communicate with the world is devastating for children. Without it, they cannot ask or answer questions, express their own feelings, or relate to the feelings of others. Those who have language problems when they begin school are at a distinct disadvantage in formal training. They may be isolated both socially and academically from their peers and their teachers. The focus of this book is intervention to assist these children to a fuller, more meaningful preschool experience based on language and communication.

Since Piaget mainly studied normally developing children and since he believed that some basic knowledge (at a motor level) can develop without verbal language, he did not write extensively in this area. His *Language and Thought of the Child* (1923, 1969) emphasizes his belief that language serves to mediate and facilitate the construction of knowledge and the development of the intellect does acknowledge the importance of language but he did not generally extend his insights to the large group of communication-impaired children who are the focus here. Like many basic researchers, he has provided theory, which has then been implemented successfully in a variety of contexts. This has been done by Piaget's associates, and has provided a valuable way of organizing language intervention programs.

According to one Piagetian thinker, children's sensorimotor development simply follows its course until the youngsters have acquired enough knowledge to need some sort of symbolic representational system, i.e., spoken language, their cognitive development is sophisticated enough to allow them to form the appropriate symbols, and they are generating enough intellectual output to require a more efficient system (Sinclair, 1970).

Intellectual development thus can be seen as emerging not from language but from the sensorimotor period. However, with the increase of mental activity, some representational system becomes necessary. It should be remembered that this system may not be verbal (Sinclair, 1970). While a verbal system is the most natural, others may develop to meet the needs of persons with specific limitations, i.e., the deaf or the severely physically handicapped.

The children for whom this program has been designed are those who have not and/or are not developing communication normally. They often demonstrate that they have many other capabilities in excess of their language development and that their specific deficits are not causative of their language problems. They should have developed more language than they have, given the strengths and weaknesses they possess.

Intensive study of children's communication development and/or failure to develop language, both in the literature and in the authors' Speech, Language, and Hearing Clinic, verifies the theory that early intervention is essential and very profitable for these youngsters and that their problems usually can be helped, and often corrected, so that they begin school better able to deal with the language tasks there. Exhibit 1-2 outlines the assumptions on which the Piagetian Language Nursery group is based.

Receptive and Expressive Language

Communication is a two-sided coin or a record on which one side is expression and the flip side is reception. The two are intricately bound together in an essential relationship.

Children acquire receptive language first; it is the cornerstone upon which further communication must be developed. Youngsters must hear, discriminate, and attach meaning to the language they hear to begin to make sense of their world.

Exhibit 1-2 Bases of Piagetian Language Nursery Group

The Piagetian Language Nursery group is based on the following assumptions:

1. Communication is composed of two interrelated and highly critical areas: reception of language and expression of language.
2. Children develop their communication through the combination of rule induction and hypothesis testing and interaction with the environment.
3. Four universals of language can be studied or described developmentally and form the basis around which this program can be organized:

   • pragmatics, the relations between signs and their human users
   • semantics, the relations between signs and their referents
   • syntax, the relations between signs
   • phonology, the relations between referents and the sound system that represents them.

4. Children develop sets of rules to govern each of these four areas and sets of rules to interrelate the various areas.
5. Very young children with extremely impaired communication may be impossible to diagnose definitively because they actually have characteristics that resemble all the diagnostic categories.
6. Early intervention is appropriate if children have failed to develop the expected language; if severely involved, they need intensive therapy.
7. Children can benefit jointly from being in a group where meaningful group language therapy is the focus.
8. A group language nursery experience plus specific appropriate individual language therapy is beneficial to all.

Gradually they begin to perceive meanings of words and combinations of them. Hearing is essential to language development for two reasons: (1) children are introduced to the vocabulary of their language family (cultural group) by hearing what people say to them and (2) the hearing mechanism actually provides the tools through which the language is learned. Hearing is the main vehicle for language stimulation, for appropriate feedback, and for half of the meaningful exchange of spoken language. Children hear the structures used in the language family and it is almost certain that these are among the first structures they learn to say.

Development of Language

Difficult as it is to pin down assumptions when it is not possible to actually look at the object in question, many researchers nevertheless have concentrated their efforts on the goal of identifying the way humans develop language. This has been a long and arduous process of watching children intently, recording their productions during the language acquisition years, and relating them back to the possible techniques and styles related to their learning (Bloom, 1970, 1973; Brown, 1973, and others).

A study by Bloom, Miller, and Hood (1975) explored the adequacy of various explanations of child language development: pragmatic, semantic, action-based or grammatical, the adequacy of various linguistic schemata to represent grammar, and whether the notion of competence or performance better accounts for some of the variations in this language. They conclude that while none of the previous attempts to explain child language have been entirely incorrect, none have been entirely correct either. They report that the relationships between the pragmatic, semantic, syntactic, and phonemic aspects of the language clearly are present but could not determine their exact nature.

Researchers (Brown & Bellugi, 1974; Dale, 1976; Houston, 1972) identify the twin processes of rule induction and hypothesis testing as the most important central technique for learning language. These are compatible with Piaget's assumption about learning (that man is an inductive animal). In this view of language learning, children listen, watch, and interact with the environment. They induce a language rule that they then test (hypothesis testing) by using it. If it proves to be accurate in their minds because they get the desired feedback, they keep the rule in their repertoire and go on to induce another one. If their hypothesis is disproved, they abandon it and go on to try to induce another rule.

Another compelling factor in children's learning of language is interaction with the environment. Here the authors' belief coincides with Piaget's in that the interpersonal aspects of language, like the socioemotional development, must be constructed by the youngsters in interaction with others in their environment.

Children and major caregivers, usually their mothers, establish a specific relationship early and the interaction that comes from it gives form and function to the developing language and teaches the youngsters how to use it. This is done largely by the use of "motherese" (here defined as the specific register in which mothers instinctively talk to their young (Snow, 1972)). This motherese seems to follow the basic development, beginning at the most fundamental level of language and gradually growing more complex as the children advance in age and ability to understand and readiness to learn more complex language.

Initially this register contains only the simplest levels of the phonemics (phonology), structure (syntax), semantics, and pragmatics, with complexity added in a systematic way. It is left for the mother to model and expand the children's language experiences and to provide appropriate feedback so the youngsters will know when they have it correct. It thus can be said that children learn by abstracting rules from experiences within a language family, using the model and feedback given by the mother. This is a difficult task but one that normal humans seem well suited to.

The Representational System

As soon as children begin to make entries into the representational system, they start to use the three fundamental ways of representing information: the ikonic, the symbolic, and the enactive (Bates, 1976).

The Ikonic System

This system of representation accounts for information in the visual mode such as blueprints, photographs, or other likenesses. It represents something because it looks like it. This manner of representation continues to be used at all stages of development.

The Symbolic System

This system, which develops early in life, accounts for information in the auditory/language mode such as reading, writing, speaking, and listening. It is a highly abstract system in which signs are related to things by arbitrary symbols. The language represents the referents by arbitrary agreement of the language community that uses it.

The Enactive System

This essentially motor-based system, also called pragmatic indexes, accounts for information that involves motor behavior (or physical actions that they represent) by taking part in them, e.g., smoke indexes fire because it is part of it. The study of pragmatics is a study of the linguistic indexes (Bates, 1976).

Language Universals

The term language universal identifies elements that can be found in all languages. In preschool settings, there are four language universals: presentation mode (phonemics), structure, semantics, and pragmatics. Successful communication is built from the interaction of these elements at all levels and on a base of cognition.

Presentation Mode

Language has to be expressed in some medium. For most people, this presentation system is vocal/verbal, using the output of the modified air stream from the larynx. For some few, however, the system never is verbal because the children either are incapable of hearing the language and so do not relate to the spoken symbol or are physically incapable of using their vocal system (or some less common combination of causes). In such cases, the presentation mode may be sign language, communication board, or some more personal modification.

In ordinary circumstances, children learn to produce the sounds and inflectional patterns of the language they hear and build them into a predictable pattern for their own use. They produce a set of sounds (phonemes) whose use is governed by their own notion of a phonological (sound) system. This system consists of the phonology (its governing rules); the phonetics; the children's production of the phonemes of their system; and the suprasegmentals (prosody), the rate, pitch, and inflectional patterns of the stream of speech (Exhibit 1-3).

Structure

Language always has some predictable structure system that forms the common grammar used with any language. Children begin very early to build a sense of the use of the grammar of their language family. They begin to formulate specific ways of using the grammar as they learn to use the various constituents of the language. Of course, they do not yet know how to define the noun phrases, verb phrases, adjectives, or adverbs they use but they can develop a sense of what words and forms to use in specific places for specific meaning, at a using level.

The structure the children learn will consist of syntax (word order), morphology (word meanings and endings), and the combination area of morphophonemics (meaning interrelated with sounds). Children can be expected to continue the

---

Exhibit 1-3 Communication Universals

All Communication Has a . . .

Presentation Mode (usually a phonological system but may include sign language)
Phonology
Phonetics
Suprasegmentals
Structure System
Syntax
Morphology
Morphophonemics
Semantic System
Selection Restriction Rules
Concepts
Vocabulary
Pragmatic System
Performatives
Presuppositions
Conversational Postulates

usage of their language families and, as all clinicians and teachers know, it is very difficult to get them to learn the grammar of the school if it is different from the home.

Semantics

This can be defined as the system that organizes the meaning of the language. It contains three areas:

1. selection restriction rules, which identify which word to use in what context to transmit exactly the desired meaning
2. concepts, the understanding of the meaning related to specific words or ideas used
3. vocabulary, words the child can use.

These help children to know what words are necessary, and in what relationship, to transmit the intended meaning exactly. In this way a system of semantic relationships is constructed (Chafe, 1970; Fillmore, 1968; Schlessinger, 1971). The children learn to match the features of the nouns to the requirements of the verb they have chosen to express action, so the meaning of the speaker's language becomes ever more specific.

Pragmatics

This area provides for the use of language as a tool to accomplish specific purposes. It refers to the varying ways people use language to make it do what they want it to do (Bates, 1976). The area of pragmatics is crucial to the success of the system because no matter how good the language production is, if it is not used appropriately, the system fails. It does not matter whether a person can make sentences that are beautiful in every linguistic way; if they are not used appropriately, they are of no avail.

The pragmatic elements are:

1. performative, the persons' decision or intent to produce a specific type of modality or utterance
2. presupposition, the assumptions that speakers make about what the listener believes and toward which they adapt what they plan to say
3. conversational postulates (or implicature), the politeness conventions used by members of the language family.

All of these must be developed if speakers are to construct appropriate use of their language (Bates & Johnston, 1979).

Pragmatics is a working tool that interrelates thought, social motivation, and language but its workings can be interpreted only within the context at the time (Bates, 1976).

Children develop sets of rules for each of the areas of pragmatics, semantics, syntax, and phonology. They also formulate sets of rules for interrelating one group of rules with another.

The pragmatic and phonological systems begin earliest and continue to develop for some time. The path to pragmatic appropriateness begins when infants first begin to use correct gestures and vocalizations for a communicative purpose. Pragmatic development is learned largely from social feedback, similar to Piaget's socioemotional learning, and is the work of a lifetime—from young children's first protoperformative gesture modality to the finishing touches constructed by adult politicians or actors and actresses.

A child of 2½ to 3 years old can be expected to have a functional use of pragmatics while the system continues to develop. Because of its prime importance and early emergence, pragmatics might be the first remediation target selected by a clinician in laying the foundations for the appropriate use of language.

Next in importance and in time of emergence is semantics. This embodies meaning, without which communication ceases to exist. A child of 3 or 3½ can be expected to have a basic grasp of the necessary semantic elements of the language. If deficient, this area might represent the second remediation target.

Third both in order of emergence and in importance to children's communication is the structure area. Youngsters can be expected to have this organized by the age of 3½ to 4, by which point they seem to have about 80 percent of the adult grammar. This then would be the next possible remediation area.

Fourth in order of completion and immediacy (even though it obviously starts first) is the presentation mode, most often the sound system—but under some circumstances may be either sign language, some form of communication board, or electronic device. In developing the sound system, children go through stages in the process of gradually making sense of what they can do with their vocal tract (Ingram, 1978; Oller, Weiman, Doyle, & Ross, 1974).

This system can be expected, by most norms (Poole, 1934; Templin, 1953 and others), to be complete by age 7 or 8 although in many children it never really contains errors and, once developed at about 4½ years, is correct. However, since it develops last among the elements and since the message usually does not depend for content and meaning on the articulation or phonology, this probably would be the last area chosen for emphasis.

With some children, the phonemic rule system can be so deviant that it constitutes the major language disorder and they fail to induce appropriate rules for the sound system, to the point that they cannot be understood. In these cases, the area of phonemics/phonetics might acquire a much higher priority in the hope that once the words could be understood, the language could be worked on more productively.

The authors' experience demonstrates that if children fail to develop language in the expected order or at the normal time, given a ± range of several months (the consideration is more properly mental age than chronological age), immediate help is needed. It seems clear that if the ordinary means for the development of language were sufficient, children would use them successfully. However, if the normal processes are not sufficient, the youngsters obviously need the extraordinary means provided by specific language intervention.

It will not do to simply wait until such children begin public school and hope a teacher or other school official will remediate the language dysfunction, for several reasons:

- The other pupils by this time may be several years ahead in linguistic activity, placing the handicapped child at an extreme disadvantage in school.
- Knowing what we do about the relationship between language and reading (discussed fully in Chapter 10), professionals know that if children do not speak the language reasonably well, they will be unable to accomplish many of the tasks that are a part of the school curriculum, and probably cannot learn to read.
- Attention can be paid to a communication breakdown as early as possible, so a more specific diagnosis can be made and both intervention and school placement can be optimized.

According to Piaget's theory (1970, 1977), children must progress through a set of hierarchical stages as they learn to use mental operations. The structures they establish form the building blocks of their growing operativity. This network provides a base for earliest language; continuing language growth links the other operations that children construct during the sensorimotor and preoperational periods. If this has not occurred, the normal development of language is unlikely. The authors have found that early intervention with such children is effective and often can ensure better use of communication by the time they enter school.

In planning preschool language nursery groups, the authors focus on two things:

1. The children are grouped according to their cognitive level. Sensorimotor children (who still must learn the prerequisites of language and some of the pragmatic elements) are placed together. Preoperational children (who are ready to construct their language) also are placed together—in a different group. In this way, the cognitive and language activities can be unified and a more appropriate and cohesive plan can be developed for each individual child.

2. The children are placed in a context where they will benefit from interaction with teachers/clinicians and other children. They learn to play, add to their cognitive and motor development, and are assisted in language growth. They participate in a variety of group and individual language experiences. These provide extra-organizational structure for learning language, appropriate models, encouragement to practice using the language, and feedback to let them know when they are succeeding.

Educators should not overestimate what children, in a group, can gain from each other. The variety of activities possible in any group can be enhanced if it contains a variety of types of members. When children have different strengths, temperaments, and needs, their group will offer a richer blend of interpersonal potential. It has not seemed desirable to the authors to attempt to place children with like problems in the same group. The rationale for the heterogeneous grouping is that so long as cognitive stimulation and language targets remain individually appropriate, each child will have strengths from which to give to the others and weak areas in which to gain from the strengths of the others.

INTERPERSONAL DEVELOPMENT

In both the cognitive and language realms, heavy emphasis is placed on individual children, constructing important elements from their experience and with feedback from the environment. The method of child management used must promote the construction of stable emotional ability to interact appropriately with others while remaining consistent with the basic philosophy underlying the entire program.

In dealing with one or more children in any context, it is mandatory to have a philosophical base to guide the interactions among the faculty members and to control, monitor, and facilitate the development of the children. The Adlerian approach of Dreikurs meets the criterion for effective management and provides teachers and clinicians with an effective, logical way of dealing with any contingency. It also offers a practical means of counseling and guiding parents in this confusing area. It has the advantage for these nonverbal children of not being a highly oral approach so its main focus does not itself fall into the problem area.

In a time when autocratic child-rearing methods have fallen from favor, yet democratic methods too often yield only confusion, appropriate ways are sought to teach children to get along with each other. Parents are on the horns of a dilemma, finding that they no longer can make their children obey them by the only methods they know—those used by their parents—and that their efforts to be more democratic yield only chaos. Thus parents are frustrated and children are without direction.

Piagetian Views

Piaget's theories regarding children's socioemotional development are compatible with those of Dreikurs. For Piaget, growth of morality (like other development) must be constructed from within. Only by their own developing of internal controls will children construct the autonomy of social, emotional, and moral responses (Kamii and DeVries, 1969b, 1977). This knowledge is incorporated into the socioemotional objectives Piaget sets for the child:

1. To feel secure in noncoercive relationships with adults,
2. To respect the feelings and rights of others and to begin to coordinate different points of view (decentering and cooperation),
3. To be independent, alert, and curious, to use initiative in pursuing curiosities, to have confidence in his ability to figure things out for himself, and to speak his mind with conviction (Kamii & DeVries, 1977, p. 393).

Even as children construct their social/emotional/moral responses, there inevitably will be times when adults must exercise authority. When this must be done, Piaget urges that children be allowed to make some choices, thus using the time to add to their constructs.

For example: "We are having mushroom soup for lunch. I'm sorry that you don't like it. You will have to eat it anyway. Would you rather have it in the blue plastic bowl or the red china one?"

If the adult can prevent the situation from becoming punitive and coercive and offer some voluntary choices, a more positive learning situation can be maintained. Piagetian theory appears to favor a more reciprocal arrangement. Kamii and DeVries suggest six possible forms it might take:

1. Excluding the child from the social group,
2. Allowing the logical or natural material consequence to follow a misdeed,
3. Depriving a child of the thing he has misused,
4. Doing to the child what he has done,
5. Encouraging the child to make restitution,
6. Censuring the child without further punishment (Kamii & DeVries, 1977, p. 379).

The appropriate form of response would be chosen to fit the particular child, the youngster's needs, and the nature of the transgression. It should be noted that Items 2 and 3 will work only in situations where the child cares about the consequences.

The high level of emotion that often exists between parent and child (such as when the youngster does not meet the family's expectations) can be at the base of the conflict. When children act out, parents react, and at least some of the time the interactions serve only to worsen the situation. It is important that parents make the effort always to see their children not as an extension of their own lives or as a reflection on their credibility but as new human beings who are being guided along to maturity: humans with their own potentials, strengths, weaknesses, and frustrations. In this way they can avoid becoming helplessly involved in parent-child issues.

Adlerian (Dreikurs) Views

According to Dreikurs (1964), all human behavior is goal directed. People do what they do in the world because of their perceptions of themselves, their positions in the society and the world itself, and the ends they desire to achieve.

Children's goals and their means of achieving them often are in direct conflict with parents' objectives and attempts to achieve them, and the ensuing battle damages everyone involved. The result: angry parents and discouraged children, frustrated because they are thwarted in their efforts to achieve autonomy. "To encourage a child we must allow him to take risks. It is better to have ruined furniture than a ruined child" (Dreikurs & Grey, 1970, p. 27). One of the most important elements parents can provide is encouragement for children as they learn. Parents and children must approach this task with mutual respect and honesty if they are to succeed.

Parents also must be careful in providing the social context that in turn will require that the children develop appropriately. According to Dreikurs (1964), it is crucial that parents understand the children's motives before they can plan to deal effectively with the behavior. The youngsters' actions must be seen in context if parent response is to be appropriate. Dreikurs believes that with parents' careful planning, kindness, and firmness, children can learn to make their lives fit into the social system around them (Dreikurs & Grey, 1970).

Since parents are not able to make children do or prevent them from doing whatever their physical ability allows, the parents must teach them to be responsible in their actions. It already has been noted that all actions have motivation and while children cannot be expected to be aware of their motivation, and should not be made aware of it (Dreikurs, 1964), parents and teachers must identify those motives if they are to plan appropriate interaction. Dreikurs and Grey cite four general goals children may have for their behavior patterns, each of which requires a different adaptation from the parents:

1. getting attention
2. struggle for power

3. revenge
4. using a disability (real or assumed) as an excuse (Dreikurs & Grey, 1970, p. 20).

Attention Getting

It is doubtful that any children ever feel that they have too much (or even enough) attention so they devote much of their time to getting more. Most of them would like to gain positive attention but, failing that, would rather have negative attention than none at all so they find themselves acting out, if necessary, to win the recognition they desire.

When their goal is attention getting, it would appear to be most effective to help them learn to obtain it by the most positive of the means available and perhaps to modify the need for so much. This may involve helping them find rewards other than parental attention for being good.

Power Struggle

In this type of situation the children are more discouraged than those with an attention-getting mechanism (AGM). Their goal is to assert themselves by involving the parents in a struggle for power. However, ''once the battle has been joined, the child has already won it'' (Dreikurs & Grey, 1970, p. 18). Parents and teachers will need to use encouragement as well as techniques of disinvolvement that will allow the parents to stay out of the struggle.

Revenge

When revenge has become the motive for behavior, the children already have become more discouraged than the previous two types discussed. Discouraged youngsters are likely to take their revenge against society in various forms of delinquency. Effective treatment here involves providing them with encouragement and confidence so they can obtain their satisfactions in a more socially acceptable way, in combination with parental disinvolvement in power struggles with them.

Assumed Disability

The most discouraged children of all are those who assume disability (whether real or imagined) and use it to excuse the failures of an unhappy life. The management of these serious problems requires much time, understanding, and encouragement. Parents and teachers need to use all available techniques and, indeed, should not hesitate to seek professional assistance when indicated.

The three most effective techniques presented by the Dreikurs' approach involve logical consequences, encouragement, and disinvolvement and are compatible with Piaget. They must be operated together, each contributing to the children's development and growing independence. These are not as easy or as natural as yelling, threatening, and spanking, which frustrated parents so often resort to.

The premise of logical consequences is that children can learn how to choose their actions once they become aware that they will experience the results of what they do—whether that outcome is pleasant or unpleasant. While youngsters are learning that they and they alone will reap the fruits of their actions, the parents are responsible for the logical arrangement of those learning consequences. The parents can cease to scold and argue and can afford to be truly sorry when their children's choice of actions brings unpleasant consequences. This is where encouragement comes in. The youngsters need to be encouraged when they fail; this same encouragement can be used to change their motivation.

The concept of logical consequences, while not hard to explain, can be quite difficult to administer and, when done improperly, can become no more than the reward and punishment routine that already has proved unsuccessful. It is essential that adults remain aware of the differences between these approaches.

Both reward and encouragement are positive, but encouragement is a much more productive response. The main difference is in when they are applied. *Reward* comes when the children have succeeded (rewards for success make the fear and the pain of failure that much worse) while *encouragement* provides positive strokes when children are faltering and need the assist.

Punishment and consequences (Table 1-1) both follow when children make a poor choice of action and may be highlighted mainly by parent or teacher tone of voice. In punishment, the parents take a personal (and negative) role in the punitive action. In consequence, while parents administer the consequences, they

---

Table 1-1 Comparison of Logical Consequences and Punishment

Logical Consequences	*vs.*	*Punishment*
1. Express the reality of the social order, not the person.		Expresses the power of a personal authority.
2. Are intrinsically related to the misbehavior.		Does not include a logical, only an arbitrary, connection between misbehavior and consequences.
3. Involve no element of moral judgment.		Inevitably involves some moral judgment.
4. Are concerned only with what will happen now.		Deals with the past.

Source: Reprinted from *A Parent's Guide to Child Discipline* by Rudolph Dreikurs and Loren Grey with permission of E.P. Dutton, Inc. © 1970, p. 45.

have no role in the punitive element and can be truly "sorry" the youngsters have brought unpleasantness on themselves (Dreikurs & Grey, 1970).

Dreikurs and Grey (1970) recommend "problem solving through democratic transactions" and declare:

1. All conflicts can be resolved only on the basis of mutual respect.
2. In any conflict situation one has to pinpoint the issue,
3. Conflicts can be resolved only by agreement,
4. Conflicts can be resolved only through participation in decision making through shared responsibility. (pp. 46, 47)

To these ends, they recommend the use of the family council, which can organize and make other techniques goal directed.

The third technique, disinvolvement, can be used effectively any time children plan to engage their parents in a struggle. The main requirement in using this technique is parents' restraint. They must be able to refrain from struggles the youngsters are trying to draw them into; the parents need to learn how to withdraw from the power struggle but at the same time not from the children.

The Adlerian approach implemented by Dreikurs does focus on the same elements as the rest of the authorities used to guide the Piagetian program. It is possible to organize children's experiences so they will acquire appropriate, realistic knowledge in this area. They will come to know what consequences will be brought about by their actions and will realize that they are the agents, bringing the logical consequences on themselves. Their actions cause the sequence of activities that follows.

They learn to view themselves as potential doers of the activity and as a force in their own lives. Thus, they build improved motivation, which in turn builds better interactions, leading to more social acceptance. They learn that antisocial activity usually brings unpleasant logical consequences that they would rather not live with, and so they learn restraint.

The philosophy is exacting in its demands for logical planning and consistency of approach. It becomes a fundamental attitude toward child management and as such second nature to teachers, clinicians, and parents.

This approach allows the teacher to assume the role of guide, helping children sort out various elements of behavior. Since the consequences are seen as coming from the social context, the teacher is not required to assume a punitive role with the youngsters and therefore can give assistance as the children work their way through the various courses of action.

Since this program is action based, it is quite effective with language-impaired children who seem unable to relate to more verbal approaches. (Exhibit 1-4 lists the general guidelines for parents and teachers in implementing this program.)

Exhibit 1-4 Do's and Don'ts with Handicapped Preschoolers

Do learn when *not* to talk.
Do not threaten.
Do avoid competition between children.
Do not feel sorry for the child.
Do avoid overprotecting the child.
Do not overemphasize children's fears.
Do pick one area to work on.
Do not use physical punishment any more than necessary.
Do use the family council.

Source: Reprinted from *A Parent's Guide to Child Discipline* by Rudolph Dreikurs and Loren Grey with permission of E.P. Dutton, Inc. © 1970, pp. 26–34.

SUMMARY

The three elements expected to be mediated in a language group such as described here—cognition, language, and interpersonal behavior—have been outlined and a rationale described for severely language-impaired preschoolers that is compatible with the ultimate goal of intervention. The constructionist/interactionist scenario outlined places heavy emphasis on the children as active learners, experience as the medium of instruction, feedback as the gauge of success, context as the arena of learning, and the teacher as guide through the process.

The theories of Piaget that are most applicable to the age level and focus of this study have been reviewed. It has been seen that in the view of Piaget and his associates in Geneva children can be expected to construct their speech and language competence through the same complex hierarchical interactions with which they construct intelligence (Sinclair, 1970), and that language and speech furnish a viable medium for expressing that which they know.

It is exactly this that the language nursery set out to do for its special population.

Since Piaget did not write specifically about handicapped children, those of his principles chosen here have been modified and adapted to meet their special needs. It must be remembered that this constitutes a new application of Piaget and care must be taken to remain flexible in both direction and expectations.

Once the Piagetian philosophy was chosen as a preferred operational format, it was necessary to choose other specific models that would round out the program and would be compatible with his approach. Those chosen were the developmental/experiential approach to language intervention and the Adlerian child management approach of Dreikurs. These three models are operated together to form a cohesive program for helping young language-impaired children develop cognitive, language, and interpersonal abilities.

DISCUSSION QUESTIONS

1. What are the goals of the language nursery compared to the traditional nursery school?
2. How do the three strands of the Piagetian nursery coordinate and mutually reinforce each other?
3. What are the implications of nonintervention with language-impaired preschoolers on communication development? . . . on reading? . . . on academic and social adjustment?

REFERENCES

Bates, E. *Language in context: The acquisition of pragmatics.* New York: Academic Press, Inc., 1976.

Bates, E., & Johnston, J. Paper presented to the Southwestern Ohio Speech and Hearing Association, Cincinnati, January 1979.

Bloom, L. *Language development: Form & function in emerging grammars.* Cambridge, Mass.: The MIT Press, 1970.

Bloom, L. *One word at a time.* The Hague: Mouton Publishers, 1973.

Bloom, L.; Miller, P.; & Hood, L. Variation and reduction as aspects of a competence in language development, *Minnesota Symposia on Child Psychology* (Vol. 9). Minneapolis: University of Minnesota Press, 1975.

Brown, R. *A first language: The early stages.* Cambridge, Mass.: Harvard University Press, 1973.

Brown, R., & Bellugi, U. Three processes in the child's acquisition of syntax. *Harvard Educational Review,* 1964, *34,* 133–151.

Chafe, W.L. *Meaning and the structure of language.* Chicago: The University of Chicago Press, 1970.

Dale, P.S. *Language development: Structure and function* (2nd ed.). New York: Holt, Rinehart & Winston, Inc., 1976.

Dreikurs, R. *Children: The challenge.* New York: Hawthorn Books, Inc., 1964.

Dreikurs, R., & Grey, L. *A parent's guide to child discipline.* New York: E.P. Dutton, Inc., 1970.

Duckworth, E. Piaget rediscovered. *Journal of Research in Science Teaching,* 1964, *2,* 172–175.

Fillmore, C.J. The case for case. In E. Bach & R.T. Harms (Eds.), *Universals in linguistic theory.* New York: Holt, Rinehart & Winston, Inc., 1968.

Ginsburg, H., & Opper, S. *Piaget's theory of intellectual development: An introduction.* Englewood Cliffs, N.J.: Prentice-Hall, Inc., 1969.

Glucksberg, S., & Danks, J.H. *Experimental psycholinguistics: An introduction.* Hillsdale, N.J.: Lawrence Erlbaum Associates, Inc., Publishers, 1975.

Houston, S.H. *A survey of psycholinguistics.* The Hague: Mouton Publishers, 1972.

Ingram, D. *Phonological disability in children.* New York: Elsevier, 1978.

Inhelder, B. in H. Ginsburg & S. Opper (Eds.), *Piaget's theory of intellectual development: An introduction.* Englewood Cliffs, N.J.: Prentice-Hall, Inc., 1969.

Inhelder, B., & Chipman, H.H. In C. Zwingman (Ed.), *Piaget and his school: A reader in developmental psychology.* New York: Springer-Verlag, 1976.

Kamii, C., & DeVries, R. Piaget for early education. In M.C. Day & R.K. Parker (Eds.), *The preschool in action: Exploring early childhood programs* (2nd ed.). Boston: Allyn & Bacon, Inc., 1977.

Kirk, S., & McCarthy, J. *The Illinois test of psycholinguistic abilities* (Rev. ed.). Urbana, Ill.: University of Illinois Press, 1968.

Lenneberg, E. *Biological foundations of language.* New York: John Wiley & Sons, Inc., 1967.

Oller, K.D.; Weiman, L.A.; Doyle, W.J.; & Ross, C. Child speech, babbling and phonological universals. *Papers and Reports on Child Language Development* (PRCLD), 1974, *8*, 33–41.

Piaget, J. *The child in reality.* New York: The Viking Press, Inc., 1973.

Piaget, J. *The construction of reality in the child* (M. Cook, trans.). New York: Ballantine Books, 1974.

Piaget, J. In H.E. Gruber and J.J. Vonèche (Eds.), *The essential Piaget.* New York: Basic Books, Inc., Publishers, 1977.

Piaget, J. *[The language and thought of the child]* (M. Gavain, trans.). Cleveland and New York: The World Publishing Co., 1969(a).

Piaget, J. *Logic and psychology,* New York: Basic Books, Inc., Publishers, 1957.

Piaget, J. *The origins of intelligence in children* (M. Cook, trans.). New York: W.W. Norton and Co., Inc., 1963.

Piaget, J. Piaget's theory. In B. Inhelder & H. Chipman (Eds.), *Piaget and his school: A reader in developmental psychology.* New York: Springer-Verlag, 1976.

Piaget, J. *Structuralism* (C. Maschler, Ed. and trans.). New York: Basic Books, Inc., Publishers, 1970.

Piaget, J. & Inhelder, B. *The psychology of the child* (H. Weaver, trans.). New York: Basic Books, Inc., Publishers, 1969(b).

Poole, E. Genetic development of articulation of consonant sounds in speech. *Elementary English Review,* 1934, *11*, 159–161.

Schlesinger, I.M. Production of utterances and language acquisition. In D.I. Slobin (Ed.), *The ontogenesis of grammar.* New York: Academic Press, Inc., 1971.

Sinclair, H. The transition from sensorimotor behavior to symbolic activity. *Interchange,* 1970, *1*(3), 119–126.

Skinner, B.F. *Verbal behavior.* New York: Appleton-Century-Crofts, Inc., 1957.

Sloan, H.N., Jr., & MacAulay, B.D. *Operant procedures in remedial speech and language training.* Boston: Houghton Mifflin Co. 1968.

Snow, C.E. Mother's speech to children learning language. *Child Development,* 1972, *43*, 549–565.

Stevens, K.N. Segments, features and analysis by synthesis. In J.F. Kavanaugh & I.G. Mattingly (Eds.), *Language by ear and eye.* Cambridge, Mass.: The MIT Press, 1972.

Streng, A.H.; Kretschmer, R.R.; & Kretschmer, L.W. *Language, learning, & deafness.* New York: Grune & Stratton, Inc., 1978.

Templin, M.C. Norms on a screening test of articulation for ages three through eight. *Journal of Speech and Hearing Disorders,* 1953, *18*, 323–331.

Wadsworth, B.J. *Piaget's theory of cognitive development.* New York: David McKay Co., Inc., 1975.

Chapter 2

Normal Language Development

CHAPTER OBJECTIVES

After completing this chapter, readers will be able to:

1. Describe whether a child appears to be normal in language development, is delayed in that ability, or shows a deviant growth pattern.
2. Distinguish between language performance and language competence.
3. Describe the sequence of growth for a normally developing child.
4. Describe the stages in acquisition of the four basic systems comprising language and the interrelationships among them.
5. Describe eight techniques for learning language and suggest some relationships between them in working with children on language acquisition.

KEY IDEAS

1. Language acquisition in children follows a very specific, highly predictable order.
2. Children who are not on schedule in developing the language of the society in which they live are in need of assistance.
3. Various strategies exist for guiding children in the development of aspects of any language system that seems to be delayed.

LANGUAGE DEVIANCY OR DELAY

In dealing with deviancy or delay in children's language development, it is essential that the teacher or clinician fully understand the range of normal behavior. This chapter traces the development of expressive and receptive communication in normal preschool children. It should be used as a guide for comparing the conditions and growth (or lack of it) among language-impaired children.

According to Sinclair (1976), language is but one aspect of symbolic function, albeit a very important one. While individuals do not have to have language for intelligence to operate, they do have to have symbolic function. Language, based on symbolic function, serves to speed up and augment the construction of knowledge.

Language is defined here as "an organized set of symbolic relationships mutually agreed upon by a speech community to represent and facilitate communication" (Kretschmer & Kretschmer, 1978, p. 1). It is a "set" of symbols chosen arbitrarily by the members of a language family to stand for specific referents in the group experience. There is a systematic way to operate these symbols known to all members of the speech community. This community (language family) encompasses all those who share the common bonds represented by the life style and, consequently, the language. This code system is then used to transmit thoughts, feelings, ideas, and questions from one person to another.

Put another way, language is a code constructed by the members of a language community to be operated by a set of rules known to all. Members decode (listen to) the vocal messages of others and encode (respond to them), using the code (the language).

When all aspects of this definition are considered, it becomes obvious that some types of language that do not conform to the norm, or do not meet the established requirements for language, classify as language disorders while others do not. Some types of language would be adjudged nonstandard or different. This determination rests on whether or not the children have learned the language of their speech community. If they have, indeed, learned the language to which they were exposed, they have done what they were expected to do.

Such children may speak a dialect but in no way should they be considered to have language problems. They simply are members of a dialect-speaking group. If, on the other hand, they have not been able to learn the language to which they were exposed, any problem they demonstrate may be considered a possible language disorder.

Chapter 1 discussed the construction of intelligence and the nature of language and how they emerge in a highly systematic way. Children interact with their environment, in the process of formulating schemata, inducing rules and forming and testing hypotheses about the way language acts.

Consideration of the definition of language should make it clear that it involves a basically two-sided phenomenon: Language, the code system, must be both expressed and received. These two sides of the coin are interdependent and both are essential to satisfactory communication. Both the receptive and expressive systems begin early in children's lives and continue to develop throughout it.

LANGUAGE DISORDERS DEFINED

A number of terms identify children with language disorders and the exact nature of their problems. For purposes of the Preschool Language Nursery Program, language disorder, language delay, and language deviancy are the terms used.

Language disorder refers to all the problems that occur when one child's language does not develop at the rate and level of others the same age. The term does not identify the nature of the disorder or the reason for it, only the fact that language development has not been adequate for age.

Language delay refers to language that develops in the normal order but either begins much later or grows more slowly than normal, or both. Children who have delayed language will take longer to develop it than age peers and may also begin later. If they should reach puberty, generally seen as the end of the most favorable language development period, before their language reaches its full maturity, they may not fully reach that maturity.

Language deviancy designates what does not develop in a normal order or is not used in a normal manner. It may be deviant in content, structure, amount, or use patterns, or in any combination of these. Such children may progress in therapy but the level and nature of their language or language use patterns may never fall within the normal range.

A practical and philosophical discussion has sought for some time to answer the question, "Does children's disordered language differ quantitatively or qualitatively from normal language?" The results of related research vary substantially because of wide differences in methodology, populations used, relationship of populations to control group, and researcher designs and definitions of terms. Bloom and Lahey (1978) report that while a number of researchers (Leonard, 1972; Menyuk, 1968) concluded that deviant language does differ in quality from normal language, others (deVilliers & deVilliers, 1973; Lackner, 1968; Morehead & Ingram, 1973) draw the opposite conclusion. Both positions probably are valid, depending on what measures and criteria were used.

The authors hypothesize that the possibility of extreme delay at some stages of growth could result in a profile that differs from the normal language development profile. When this occurs and further gains are added to the better developed areas, greater unevenness could result. If this goes on sufficiently long, the profile and the functioning of the existing language could become so distorted that it would be identified as deviant in nature. Thus, in at least some cases, deviant language actually could be a product of extreme delay over time. In other cases the development of deviant language is more closely related to an overriding cause, e.g., deafness, cerebral palsy, etc., that could produce the language deviancy as well as other related problems.

This may be useful information for clinicians under some specific circumstances. For the most part, they seek to identify and remediate the problems rather than to classify their type because classification may not help in choosing an intervention model or planning the intervention. It must be left to individual clinicians to seek this information if they believe it can enhance the intervention they can offer.

LANGUAGE COMPETENCE AND PERFORMANCE

It is clear that language exists at two levels (competence and performance) that represent ways of describing it.

First, it exists at the level of intention to communicate, where it consists of innate knowledge about language and the mental actions required to use it. Language competence refers to individuals' store of knowledge about their language. This is used as an overview or master plan of language organization for all pragmatics, semantics, syntax, and phonology. Here adjustments of meaning are made and children use mental operations to manipulate the semantic elements to be conveyed. In effect this is an ability to deal with the deep structure of the language, the level of meaning and operations.

Second, it exists at the level of actual production of language, where it produces the spoken words. The term language performance refers to actual production at the surface level, in effect the language of the surface structure. At this level all questions relating to the production of the utterance are resolved.

Transformational linguists, who believe that a transformation process exists to provide language complexity (Chomsky, 1965), point to the differentiation between deep structure, the mental operations needed to understand and produce a given sentence, and the surface structure, the actual string of phonemes produced and understood (Kretschmer & Kretschmer, 1978). While the meanings of deep structure and language competence or surface structure and language performance are not necessarily equated, some overlapping implications are discernible. Efforts that enrich the deep structure (the language competence) relate to the semantic areas of language. Efforts that support the surface structure (the language performance) add complexity to what actually is said and relate more to the syntactic areas. In general they delete redundancy, substitute words, and reorganize elements of the surface sentence.

Clinicians should work to improve language at the deep structure/competence level to give children the most flexible and creative use of the system.

This deep structure emphasis becomes important in planning language intervention, when the goal is to expand and enhance competence or, in other words, to build language at the deep structure level. This is the point at which meaningful changes in children's language ability must be made. Clinical experience indicates to the authors that therapy based on the cognitive, semantic, developmental realm of experience therapy does in fact act on language competence by enriching the schema with which children build language. If the goal of the intervention should happen to be simply to change the language performance at the surface level, this could be done just as easily by an operant model since it would modify only the surface structure and need not be based on meaning. This kind of learning, however, would not generalize to other language uses in the same way as what children learned more meaningfully.

RECEPTIVE LANGUAGE

When a problem with their ears prevents children from hearing, it is called a peripheral hearing loss. Deaf children, who need special training, or those with reduced hearing acuity, who may need hearing aids or other special help, are in this category. Children with problems of associating and using what they hear are considered to have central hearing problems at the level of the brain; these affect the auditory processing and auditory association skills. Developmental aphasic children or those with severe learning disabilities can be in this category.

Initially normally developing children must hear the signal adequately if they are to learn it for later communicative use. The deaf or hearing impaired have a difficult time learning to communicate with others in the world and may depend on other senses to receive and give communication, with an end result that often is far from satisfactory. These children need special help from birth on if they are to reach their true potential.

Even for those with adequate ability to hear the signal or who have a corrected loss of acuity (i.e., a hearing aid, PE (pressure equalization) tubes, etc.), disorders of hearing and/or listening ability constitute sources of language and learning disorders. Research now indicates that children who have serous otitis media are at high risk for hearing-related language and learning problems (Clark, 1980). They appear likely to be identified in school as having central auditory processing problems (Protti, Young, & Byrne, 1980).

It is becoming evident that a hearing threshold of even -15 dB during the critical period of language learning is enough to interfere with normal auditory perceptual processing development and can cause continuing school problems (Battin, 1980). During these years, children must be picking up a variety of semantic, syntactic, pragmatic, phonological, and cognitive information. Since this learning is hierarchical in nature, depressed or fluctuating hearing can cause significant disruptions in the patterns the children were supposed to be learning. As discussed earlier, extreme delay or uneven progress based on a faulty foundation is likely to produce distortions in development.

Reception of the language code and attachment of meaning to it are necessary first steps in the growth of verbal communication; these must be developed before language can be useful. Thus language reception is part cognition and part processing. In the early stages, children must learn to identify sound patterns, attach meaning to them, and eventually store them in memory for retrieval when needed. They must construct a system that receives language in its many forms and is capable of responding to the messages received. Eventually these youngsters will need to develop more abstract auditory skills that will help them function in school.

For the authors, the term receptive language refers to the ability to receive and perform operations on symbols within the contextual frame. Implied in this definition is possession of adequate schemata and pragmatic appropriateness for the children's age and situation.

Auditory Processing Skills

However, many behaviorists and psycholinguists such as Kirk and McCarthy (1968) place the highest importance on the learning of the auditory processing skills: auditory figure ground, auditory sequencing, memory, auditory motor production, auditory closure, sound blending, etc., and focus most of their effort on teaching these under the assumption that this will remediate the language. This has resulted in an entire intervention model based on identifying specific weaknesses and teaching to them directly, a method espoused by many professionals.

Contrary to this viewpoint, continued research has failed to support this as the most efficient way to remediate language. Sabatino (1969) and other researchers, including Bloom and Lahey (1978) conclude that children must possess meaningful language before being able to respond to these tests of processing that were being used to differentiate between those with neurological problems and normal youngsters. If this is true, it is not known whether these test instruments actually measure language or processing.

It is true that research indicates a relationship between perceptual dysfunction and language problems but it is not known whether this is linear and, if so, in what direction it goes (Bloom & Lahey, 1978). It also is not known whether the children failed to learn the language because they had faulty processing, or could not organize and demonstrate processing ability because they lacked the language for it, or even whether both the language disorder and the processing problem were related to some more abstract causal third factor.

It is known that: (1) it cannot be stated for sure that the auditory processing abilities identified, and they alone, are necessary for language, (2) it is not certain that these discrete bits of processing ability have been positively identified and tested, and (3) it cannot be shown conclusively that remediating these defective areas has improved children's language at all. The authors do have the notion (as yet not fully tested) that these auditory processing skills are more necessary for reading and writing than for speaking and listening. It is speculated that the further abstraction of language usage represented by reading and writing requires a different level of processing. Perhaps this higher level of abstraction becomes possible only after sufficient successful use of language. (This is considered further in Chapter 10.)

Developmentalists such as Bloom and Lahey (1978) tend to believe that while the basic ability to hear and discriminate is necessary for development of spoken language, attainment of higher levels of the so-called auditory processing or perceptual skills lacks a proved relationship with success in language. They decry the teaching of splinter skills as useless exercises in the process of language intervention. However, data indicate that at least some children in remedial reading programs who were trained specifically in language and pragmatic skills also show specific gains in reading, processing, and language (Armstrong, 1981).

The Piagetian Perspective

Students of Piaget who read the entire collection of his work in search of some definite statement about the necessity for children to possess auditory processing skills will find that he does not discuss these as a discrete set of skills. Instead, he appears to see them as elements (like other discrimination the children learn) that are adapted and assimilated into the early sensorimotor efforts, then transferred to the preoperational stage. According to Piaget (1969a, 1977) children's early thinking is autistic to egocentric and this self-orientation probably also is a part of their perceptual awareness.

Their thoughts and language are perceptually bound and the authors have not been surprised to see young children use variable word order in sentences to generate word and phrase reversals (as well as semantic order reversals). Certainly, children who fail to incorporate the basics of auditory perception into their sensorimotor schema would show deficits of both operational and figurative knowledge and of symbolic formation as well. Hence, those with a severe language problem (who probably have conceptual, interactional, and play difficulties as well), may be the ones who have basic perceptual problems; however, the reverse of this situation is not necessarily true.

For normally developing children, the time of learning the oral language probably corresponds with the egocentric period of life. When they no longer are perceptually bound but are social in thought and speech, they can be expected to have learned a higher, more abstract set of schemata that incorporate auditory ability in the form of the auditory processing skills. It does appear that these specific skills may be necessary as foundations upon which to base reading and writing.

According to Protti, Young, and Byrne (1980), children reach auditory maturity by about 10 years of age yet their language will have developed at least five years before that. It may be about this time that they have progressed to the stage in reading where they need a complete set of auditory processing skills. At that point, specific training in these skills might aid significantly in the acquisition of reading and writing.

The fact that there is a relationship between the auditory perceptual area and the language arts can be proved but the exact nature of that linkage eludes the authors, prompting their speculation that the sequence may be as follows:

1. Development of basic auditory discrimination, storage, and retrieval. Children who cannot perform these early tasks may be those identified as developmental aphasic who in fact do not learn language normally.
2. Development of the spoken language. Those who develop problems at this point may have the idiopathic language problem of distorted but present language.
3. Learning of the set of auditory processing skills. Those who fail at this level may be the children with learning disabilities or severe idiopathic reading problems.
4. Natural and effortless learning of the higher forms of the language arts. This is the progression made by normally developing children.

The suggestion appears warranted that perhaps the development of refined auditory perceptual skills follows the basic development of language, which in turn is prerequisite to learning to read and write. Thus a realistic view of language intervention would emphasize the development of language per se and would expect the processing skills to follow. Viewed in this sequential order, the learning of the auditory perceptual skills can be seen as fitting into the sequence of language arts learning that runs from children's first attending to the auditory signal to adults' final high-level uses of reading, writing, and spelling.

LANGUAGE PERSPECTIVES

The order in which the elements of language appear to reach a reasonably mature level of usage has been identified as:

1. pragmatics (the use of the language as a tool)
2. semantics (the meaning of relationships contained in the linguistic message)
3. syntax (the structure of the language)
4. phonology (the sound system of the language).

Even as phonology is identified as being the last area to reach functional maturity, it must be recognized that this system is the earliest in which the beginning of development can be seen, making its appearance in early infancy (Oller, 1981).

For normal children and their parents, the period of developing communication is a time of rapid growth and tremendous generation and expansion of ideas. The children go from helpless infant to moving force and communicator in the world in about three and a half years. Their ultimate successes in the later school years are built upon this foundation.

During the time children are developing sensorimotor abilities, they also should be acquiring the other prerequisites of language: linguistic experience, nonlinguistic experience, and a desire to communicate with others. They need sensorimotor knowledge to understand how they, the language, and physical facts are related to each other in time and space. There must be some notion of object permanence, realized as nouns in the language; coordinated space, realized as notions of relationship and of prepositions; causality, realized as the concept of agent (or self as agent) and the words that show this; and temporality, as reflected by ideas of verb tense and designations of various ways of representing time.

In addition, children need linguistic experience if they are to realize the potential of language, for if they never hear it spoken, they have no way of constructing it. Those who are deaf or hearing impaired may be lost to the system at this point unless they receive amplification and appropriate language models.

Nonlinguistic experience also is essential if the children are to have anything to communicate. If they have not gone anywhere or done anything, they have nothing to talk about. Those who are blind, cerebral palsied, or otherwise barred from normal experience may be lost at this point unless more and varied experiences are provided. The handicapped need more experiences, not fewer, than normal children.

It may well be that these experiences must be carefully structured to make the essential language-stimulating elements more available. If children have failed to construct the language foundation as others do, it may be necessary to reduce their cognitive load by simplifying the essential elements and eliciting their production. Unfortunately, this is a much slower process, with less generalization, as it becomes more direct and more highly structured; therefore, it should be avoided where possible.

Children who do not build an interpersonal desire to communicate may know many things but fail to develop the interest or ability to show what they know, think, or feel. For them, the knowledge and the linguistic ability do not become communication so they lose out on the world around them.

When these prerequisites are attained, however, the children will have the necessary cognition, will know how language can sound, will have things they want to say, and will realize that communicating with others gives numerous satisfactions. They are ready to begin.

DEVELOPMENT OF LANGUAGE

During the first four to five years of children's development, language emerges and grows to be a flexible, functional, interpersonal tool. Initially, youngsters are cognitively and perceptually tied to the here and now, and the content of their language is correspondingly linked to an egocentric view of the world. As pragmatic ability grows and they learn to produce communicative utterances, language becomes more complex until eventually they are capable of the variety of modulations used in mature language (Exhibit 2-1).

The study of child language usually begins at the one-word level. At that point a controversy emerges about the extent of meaning in one-word and/or two-word utterances. Bloom and Lahey (1978) reflect a view that a one- or two-word utterance, which they do see as communicative, must contain a verb at least by implication, a factor they term reduction transformation. Accordingly, children reduce a sentence component when they do not know the word they need or when they do not have ready functional use of a desired or needed word in their repertoire (Greenfield & Smith, 1976). It appears to the authors that the reduction transformation, if it occurs at all, probably also appears when children have more meaningful words in their utterance than they are able to handle at one time.

DeVilliers and deVilliers (1973) note that children's reception and comprehension of language exceed their ability to express it (see the earlier section on

---

Exhibit 2-1 Possible Order of Language Emergence

- Cry
- Coo
- Babble
- Jargon
- Inflected jargon (containing occasional words)
- Chained one-word utterance (not fully symbolic)
- Holistic one-word utterance (carries symbolic meaning)
- Successive one-word utterances
- Two-word utterances (often utilizing the reduction transformation). These are instances of noun phrase plus verb phrase (NP + VP). The following semantic relationships are the earliest developed: existence, nonexistence, recurrence, agent-action-patient, possession, location, attribute.
- Three-word utterances. These consist of three-word production of kernel (most basic) sentences, easy transformations, and elaborated nodes (complexity coming from deep structure).
- Four-word or longer utterances. These continue to expand and become more complex as children learn to use all forms of grammatical complexity to produce more specific meanings.

competence and performance). Their limited ability to encode language produces the holophrase, the one-word "sentence," the topic-comment with the topic deleted. Greenfield and Smith (1976) add that the holophrase must be interpreted in light of the existing context if it is to have the meaning the children intended. Greenfield and Smith support the view that these holophrases do not really represent entire sentences but only the portion or idea the children both want to express and can control. While the words said at this level are not simply sentence components or parts of speech but represent entire utterances, Greenfield and Smith maintain that there are insufficient data to prove that the children have any more complex linguistic abilities than those that appear on the surface. They believe that words that do not occur in a sentence simply are not there.

Bowerman (1973) also concludes that young children, while they may possess much information about the structure of the language, need not necessarily do so in order to produce the utterances on some other basis such as semantic function or cognitive understanding. For example, the very young child who produces "no spank" may be doing it from a semantic or cognitive base. The child may not yet have the syntactic information that would produce the correct, "Don't spank me."

Piaget expresses interest in how much linguistic knowledge is implied by young children's one-word utterances. In his view, as interpreted by Sinclair, these are a combination of topic and comment, the verbal manifestation of a schema (Sinclair, 1970).

In line with this Piagetian view, deVilliers and deVilliers (1978) point to the necessity of the youngsters' achieving certain cognitive prerequisites that appear to be the precursors of various levels of language development. They believe that some levels of cognitive development constrain the onset of language or the rate or order of acquisition. As the children's language grows along with their cognitive development, they focus on rules identified by Slobin (1973) as a series of language operating principles that tell them how their language is supposed to behave (Exhibit 2-2) and how they are supposed to attend to it. These principles are universally used by children to guide their language development.

Exhibit 2-2 Language Operating Principles of Slobin

> A. Pay attention to the ends of words.
> B. The phonological forms of words can be systematically modified.
> C. Pay attention to the order of words and morphemes.
> D. Avoid interruption or rearrangement of linguistic units.
> E. Underlying semantic relations should be marked overtly and clearly.
> F. Avoid exceptions.
> G. The use of grammatical markers should make semantic sense.
>
> *Source:* Reprinted from "Cognitive Prerequisites for the Development of Language" by Dan I. Slobin, with permission of Dr. William Dingwall, 1971.

Once children have progressed through the developmental stages to the point that language becomes an available avenue, they use it to speed up, streamline, and expand the potential of both the thought processes and the language. In Piagetian terms: "(1) verbal behavior permits representation of many acts very quickly, (2) language behavior may range beyond the here and now, and (3) language permits the child to handle several elements and actions at once" (Wadsworth, 1975, p. 68).

Pragmatics

Pragmatic development, children's growing ability to use language effectively and to make it do what they want it to do, was discussed earlier. This pragmatic advancement stimulates additional growth for as the children acquire and improve their ability to use language to effect change, their linguistic complexity increases (Lucas, 1980, p. 44).

This area of pragmatics can be disrupted in any of four areas, to varying degrees. Lucas (1980) writes of possible disruptions that could cause breakdowns in pragmatic growth, with telling effects on general communication development. She notes that the children could fail at:

1. developing the rules,
2. establishing a desire or motivational cause for having an intent to linguistically express,
3. having a need to communicate to a hearer, and/or
4. being capable of participating in the active process. (p. 45)

Failure in any one of these areas, at any level, could cause a lag in development and a consequent failure of communication. It would make a significant difference in all subsequent development—intellectual, linguistic, and interpersonal.

Semantics

This development, related to the meaning of the utterances, cannot be separated from pragmatics on the one hand (Lucas, 1980) and syntax on the other. The meaning of the language is intimately bound up in the pragmatics (the uses the language is put to) and the structure (the word order and endings used to specify meaning). Neither can meaning be separated from the orchestration of the sound system (phonology) that itself carries the meaning in prelinguistic children. They early learn to "mean something" by their utterances. They probably learn to use the most necessary semantic relationships at this early age by interacting with the environment and their environmental models (Lucas, 1980) in a sort of motor-based language experience.

As noted previously, there is a philosophical dilemma involving how much linguistic (syntactic) knowledge to credit children with when they produce one- and two-word utterances. It is possible that instead of syntax, recognition of semantics as the base for these utterances would eliminate this dilemma since it does appear that the semantic base could be identified more surely in early language (Greenfield & Smith, 1976).

Syntax

Both pragmatic and semantic development precede children's active development of syntax. However, at the time two-word semantic relationships are being produced, their flip side, two-word syntactic utterances, also are being said. Chomsky, the father of transformational grammar, believes that grammar is innate in infants, that the structure of the language is present in their genetic makeup, and that they need only develop it (Chomsky, 1965).

The many language universals that have been identified enhance this view and many linguists support this philosophy to some extent. This theory appears compatible with that of Piaget. Greenfield and Smith (1976) quote French linguist Guillaume to support this combination of philosophies: "The child does not invent grammatical categories . . . he must learn to use them by the direct relation of the sentence to the concrete situation" (p. 21).

Certainly this is not possible until children understand the cognitive principles to which the linguistic forms are related. However, as soon as they do comprehend the prerequisite principles, they can and do develop the semantic and syntactic forms appropriate to them. The similarity between Piaget's (1963, 1974, 1977) notion of children's sensorimotor construction and Chomsky's 1965 discussion of the innate quality of the deep structure accentuates the parallel between embedding in action and embedding in grammar (Sinclair, 1971). This also can be seen in children's adherence to the operating principles of Slobin (Exhibit 2-2, supra).

Phonology

While children may not finish learning their phonological system until the last of the four communication areas, they begin it very early. Infants' only means of producing order out of auditory chaos is listening to the sound of the adult voice, something they show a significant preference for among auditory signals (deVilliers & deVilliers, 1978). Infants are quick to recognize the natural rhythm and inflectional pattern of the voices in the language family and to equate specific patterns with particular emotional states of the speakers.

Babies receive information about the attitudes implied by adult utterances: resignation, disappointment, disapproval, anger, pleasure, fear, boredom, etc., and from the prosody used (deVilliers & deVilliers, 1978). From these beginnings they build basic patterns that represent the way their native language is supposed to sound. They receive and send communications, beginning with the basics and using the suprasegmentals of the language to carry the meaning.

At the same time they are receiving and interpreting auditory stimuli, children experiment with the vocal tract, finding out what sounds they can produce. They extrapolate a set of rules for themselves about how language operates and their experiences modify it until it eventually conforms to adult phonology. Children make progressively more accurate approximations of the sounds in the phonetic repertoire until ultimately they become mature users of the particular system.

THE BEGINNINGS IN INFANCY

Earlier views that held that infants were either a bundle of reflexes waiting to develop or a blank slate waiting to be written on have been modified by research. It now is possible to identify certain preferences and abilities in infants within the first few days of life and to begin to see where the possible cognitive beginnings of the construction of intelligence lie.

For example, it is known that infants can discriminate among several auditory stimuli (Eisenberg, 1970), that they respond characteristically to intensity of sound (Eisenberg, 1970; Steinschneider, Lipton, & Richmond, 1966), and that they can discriminate one phoneme from another (Eimas, Siqueland, Jusczyk, & Vigorito, 1971).

DeVilliers and deVilliers (1978) note the increasing number of infant studies being done. They refer to the 1978 study by Butterfield and Siperstein of neonates younger than 3 days old and conclude that speech sounds engage children's attention early. The studies show that babies will continue to maintain nonnutritive sucking if being able to listen to speech is contingent upon it. They report research by Hutt, Hutt, Leonard, Benuth, and Muntjewereff (1968), with neonates less than ten days old. They note that these infants are highly sensitive to sound frequencies which the adult speaking range uses.

Research by Eimas et al. (1971) finds that infants have categorical perception of speech sounds very early in life. Even in the first few hours after birth, they are not without preferences and expectations of how they are to be treated, and by simply fussing until the parents ''get it right'' can inadvertently cause changes in the environment.

Motherese

When infants go home from the hospital, if there are no sensory problems or other risk factors, they are ready to begin interacting with a ''significant other'' in the language environment, usually the mother. The ''other'' also appears to be programmed to provide the child with the highly organized and greatly simplified motherese that forms the structure of the earliest language learning/teaching (Kretschmer & Kretschmer, 1978; Snow 1972; Snow & Ferguson, 1977).

Motherese involves: carefully maintained eye contact, easy direct conversational model, redundant structures, fluent delivery, slower rate, long pauses, exaggerated inflectional pattern, short correct sentences, no transformations, no elaborated nodes, correct sentence order, no consonant blends or clusters, controlled vocabulary, etc.

It is clear that, given this type of language stimulation, infants would have enough information available to begin to implement the rule induction and hypothesis testing process.

THE NORMAL DEVELOPMENT OF COMMUNICATION

During these communication learning years, children progress through a series of hierarchical developments. In order to understand children with language problems, the professional must have a thorough understanding of normal language development. The authors have observed many normal preschool children as they progress through sequential developmental stages in a manner exemplified by the following developmental schedule. As must be expected, normal children show considerable overlap from one age level to the next. Nevertheless, it is possible to note the appearance of receptive items preceding expressive ones and to follow the interrelated threads of cognitive, pragmatic, semantic, syntactic, and phonological development.

Age: Birth to 6 Months

It is motherese that organizes the latent language structure so children can learn it. It focuses on such things as eye contact, turn taking, and short, repetitive utterances that are semantically and syntactically simple. Prosodically, motherese contains relatively longer pauses and exaggerated inflection. It is very fluent, phonetically simple, and presents the customary inflection of the language.

In form, it contains a high proportion of imperative and question modalities. Questions often are followed immediately by the answers: "Where is baby's nose? There it is! Show me your nose," etc. All of this is appropriate for the job infants must do at this time if they are to begin to organize the learning of the language (Bloom & Lahey, 1978; Snow, 1972, 1981).

During this infant stage, communication emerges and becomes identifiable. The infants use all elements at their command—body and facial tonus and gestures, sound, gaze, and facial expression. By three or four months, they can coordinate these elements to make basic communication (Stern, Joffe, Beebe, &

Bennett, 1975). The motoric elements of the communicative context function independently and begin earlier than vocal language, but when the vocalization and its accompanying prosodic patterns are added, a "communicative act is created" (Stern et al., 1975). Through these acts, infants begin to form notions of identity and joint reference. Infants and mothers build a communication dyad.

Cognition

During this period, neonates progress from egocentric creatures possessed mainly of reflexive activity to babies capable of causing "their" adults to do things. They have achieved some eye-hand coordination, can reproduce a motor action they already have performed, and can play peek-a-boo. They begin to understand and anticipate the motion an object (once in motion) will take (Wadsworth, 1975, p. 36). This appears to be a first step in developing the essential concept of object constancy.

Pragmatics

During this period children are learning many things that are closely related to language. They are learning to look mother in the eye and maintain interpersonal contact. They are learning to take verbal turns with mother in which she talks, they "talk," and a pattern is formed for conversation. They learn to associate the referent to the words they hear. This development of a repertoire of meaningful referents is crucial to children's language development (Lucas, 1980) and can begin toward the end of this stage. They are learning that communicating with the "other" can be rewarding and that both the communication and the reward exist when they are the receiver as well as the talker (Bloom & Lahey, 1978; Snow, 1981).

Semantics

As noted earlier, pragmatic and semantic elements are not separable. While children are performing the early pragmatic act of referring, they are laying down the semantic basis for referring and by the end of this first period may begin to identify what they regard as the meaning of certain common utterances, inflections, etc., such as "Here is your bottle," "OK baby," and "I'm coming." While they do not understand individual structures, they are beginning to get a feel for the "action" and may be learning that an action can be anticipated from vocal expression.

For example, children cry because they want to be out of the playpen and when they hear mother say "OK, I'm coming," they may come to know that this response signals that gratification is forthcoming—that mother will take them out—so they stop fussing, in anticipation. Throughout this time, most of the initial meaning they attach to utterances is via the inflectional patterns of the language they hear, for this inflection is the first carrier of meaning (Kaplan & Kaplan, 1971).

Syntax and Phonology

The children are internalizing patterns of the grammar that later will come naturally in their spoken language. These elements are inseparable in the very early stages, so they obviously must be considered together. Children are learning to produce the prosodic utterances that signal the vocal counterparts of sentence modality. They can produce the imperative of cry, the declarative of coo. They begin to explore the parameters of their vocal tract to find out what they can do. They learn to produce open vowels and begin to form and differentiate consonants (Table 2-1). They produce cooing sounds and modify voice onset time (VOT) to utter voiced and devoiced sounds. Meaning begins to be expressed by their use of inflectional pattern (Lewis, 1951).

Age 6 to 12 Months

Motherese

If mother and infant have synchronized their time clocks, both the motherese and the child's responses have advanced, maintaining the previous elements and expanding and adding new ones. Motherese now may contain longer but still very

---

Table 2-1 Phonological Development in Infancy

Infant Age (months)	Infant Vocal Behavior	Metaphonological Trait
0–1	Quasi-resonant nuclei	Normal phonation
2–3	Quasi-resonant nuclei plus velar consonant-like elements	Open and close vocal tract (articulation)
4–6	Fully resonant nuclei Raspberries Squeals and growls Yells Marginal babbles	Resonance Front and back closure Pitch Loudness Full open and close vocal tract
7–10	Reduplicated babbling	Timing
11–12	Variegated babbling	Vocalic and consonantal contrasts

Source: Reprinted from D. Kimbrough Oller. "Infant Vocalizations and Speech Sound Development," presented at the convention of Ohio Speech & Hearing Association, Cincinnati, 1981, by permission of the author.

simple utterances. Mother may be presenting the same object in more than one utterance, e.g., "Here is the ball. Roll the ball. Oh! Oh! Where did the ball go? There is the ball!" The objects used are those that occur in the environment. It is hoped that parents will concentrate on presenting agents in relationships with actions and patients. When they give the children feedback for any response, the focus is the semantic accuracy of the utterances.

In view of observations of infant vocal development, such as those of Delack (1976); Oller, Weiman, Doyle, and Ross (1976); and Stern et al. (1975), it appears that sufficient information is available to support the notion of continuity from the babbling stage to speech. Current authorities believe infant communication can be studied even before adult speech patterns develop.

As the infant/mother dyad develops, a dyadic interaction—a reciprocal social interaction between the two—is produced (Lucas, 1980). This interaction helps children develop a knowledge of referents. They learn to associate the linguistic term with the referent. As this shared mother-infant attention is used in the natural social order, it becomes increasingly more complex and each becomes more dependent upon the other for continuance of the interaction.

Cognition

Many things happen during this time as schemata are begun and expanded. The infants come to a fuller understanding of object constancy. They begin to look for an object that no longer is in view and organize a search following logical sequences of displacement. When the ball rolls under the bed, they begin to follow it with their eyes and mark where they expect it to reappear (Wadsworth, 1975).

Spatially, infants begin to experience the fact that things can be "in" and "out" of containers and spend long hours putting things in and out of boxes, bottles, etc. They also learn that they like to be picked "up" and dislike being put "down." They come to know that they can prevail on others to do something such as pick them up. In this understanding are the seeds of causality. In infants' emerging understanding of the rituals of life, a beginning of serial order can be seen that ultimately will become a part of their sense of time and number.

Pragmatics

By the time children are 12 months old, they have passed through the initial stages of communication development so a considerable amount of pragmatic growth can be observed. The first of a number of stages, perlocutionary, carries meaning, not by the children's design but more by the fact that they feel impelled to utter a string of vocalizations and gestures that are interpreted by mother as having meaning. The meaning during the perlocutionary stage is largely accidental as far as the infants are concerned. This stage generally is completed before they are 10 months old (Bates & Johnston, 1979).

At about 10 months, the second stage in the development of pragmatics can be seen. This, the illocutionary stage, appears to lay the seeds of the performatives and the modalities: question, imperative, declarative, negative, etc. They may be entirely gestural or a combination of gestural and vocal production. The gesture behavior of 12-month-olds carries the illocutionary force of the interrogative, declarative, imperative, negative, and/or possessive utterances (Bates & John-ston, 1979).

Semantics

By the time they are 12 months old, children probably can produce at least a couple of appropriate single-word utterances, either chained or holistic. These are a culmination of previous cognitive and pragmatic development and start the children on a new path of development motivated by their desire to code meaning into symbols.

Chaining, defined here as the ability to produce the name of an object while in its presence, begins an active process in which the children go on to build a vocabulary of familiar words.

When they can produce these names, although the object is not in their presence, the stage known as the holistic (which is true symbolism) can be said to occur and the one-word utterance can be used meaningfully (Bloom, 1970). If a holistic utterance is used at this level, it usually represents the comment portion of the topic/comment structure, with the topic present in the context. This stage of holistic (one-word symbolic) language appears to correspond with the first emergence of the earliest Piagetian stage of symbolic development.

Syntax and Phonology

The children still are storing the syntactic and phonological information they are taking in. They also continue to organize their utterances and expand pitch, stress, and juncture from the prosody and suprasegmentals they hear. While doing this, they build the various schemata necessary for communication.

Phonologically, they have followed the early sequence of developmental steps in finding out what their vocal tract will do. They have passed through the "coo" and "goo" and variegated babbling stages (Table 2-1, supra) and are pho-nologically ready to produce single words, albeit not very clearly (Oller, 1981).

Age 12 to 18 Months

Motherese

Both parties to this interaction have become more sophisticated in their ability to interact. The parents find it natural to present increasingly more complex linguistic structures as the children show they are capable of processing and reacting to the information (Snow, 1981). While keeping input simple, parents provide more semantic relationships, more syntactic structure, and a broader vocabulary.

Cognition

In this period, while the children are completing their sensorimotor development, they can be expected to have object constancy quite well organized. As cognition continues to expand, early concepts of time, space, and causality emerge to provide a base for later preoperational learning. While not yet able to encode these elements into language, the children can respond receptively to much of what they hear. Cognitively, this is the point at which the focus shifts to the all-important ability to classify objects. From that will eventually come the form classes so important to early language learning and the essential ability to form symbols (Ginsburg & Opper, 1969).

Pragmatics

Assuming both mother and child have expanded their basic communication, advances can be expected in the ability to establish joint references and exchange communications regarding it. Children are building their ability for meaningful eye contact and verbal turn taking. They have become more sophisticated users of basic communication—part verbal, part gestural, and part vocal. Here it appears that the seeds of topicalization have been sown.

Semantics

Single-word utterances, both chained and holistic, develop, embedded in the variegated jargon of the age. Successive single-word utterances, identified as two words in close proximity to each other that are not in a sentence constituent relationship, also may be noted (Bloom, 1970).

Syntax and Phonology

Input into syntax and phonology, still inseparable from each other, develops as the children continue to organize and store receptive information, to be used at a later date. At this time, they appear to focus on developing vowel sounds and continuing the process of phonetic differentiation that results in the emergence of the consonant inventory. The period of babbling and jargon associated with this stage allows practice time for production and refining of skills. Research (Oller, Weiman, Doyle, & Ross, 1976) indicates that there is a sequential relationship between the babbled language and the spoken language that follows.

Age 18 to 24 Months

Motherese during this period continues to be slightly simplified and redundant but mother now employs a richer vocabulary, containing more function words. Her assumption that certain cognitive capabilities have been developed leads her to use terms that signal causality and temporality, i.e., past tense verbs, etc.

This period is a coming together of all the realms with input into communication. Children are likely to be in transition to the preoperational stage of development described by Piaget (1969a, 1977).

Cognition

The children have a start on all sensorimotor areas and have formed sensorimotor schemata for numerous material objects and actions in the environment. These sensorimotor efforts yield nouns, prepositions, verbs, adjectives, etc., to serve as a medium for the emerging language. These are building blocks children use as they construct further knowledge (Inhelder & Chipman, 1976). They have had linguistic experiences and consequently, with the emergence of symbolic formation, have begun to try to produce language to express them.

Now the twin techniques of rule induction and hypothesis testing become very useful. The children have nonlinguistic experiences that give them something to talk about and they have begun to form word symbols that will give their communication economy in producing the building blocks to construct the sentences. The transmission of messages to others will be easier. The environment also is important as the source of motivation for the youngsters to use this new-found communication ability.

Pragmatics

The children have learned that their utterances are an effective mechanism for transfer of information. They can "converse" and use language to gain personal ends and register feelings about various happenings. They now are able to use most modalities in some rudimentary form. They are beginning to learn about topic and comment, the body of conversation. They also are learning that they can relate attribute to noun and transmit this information to another, so as to serve their own needs.

Semantics

The children probably are producing at least one or two utterances that are run-on one-word phrase approximations. This is not unusual. In all other phases of the study of language, the authors have espoused the belief that the meaningful unit (the phrase, sentence, even paragraph) is the base element. This probably is true as well in children's production of early utterances (although more difficult to identify).

The authors believe what probably occurs is that the children generate one or more word-phrases that sound like single words but carry the semantic intent of the entire phrase. As the expected responses, questions, comments, plain misunderstandings, and inappropriate actions indicate lack of communication, the children subsequently differentiate these word-phrases into separate, distinct words. This permits language acquisition to follow the same model as postulated for other areas of language development, from the general to the specific.

In 12 years of interaction with very young children, the authors have yet to find one (who had reached this level of development) who did not have at least one such utterance during this earliest period of communication development. Some few had three or four such one-word phrases, e.g., /əwʌnət'/ ("I want that") /gɪmæʔ/ ("Gimme that"). Phrases at this level can be differentiated from true phrases by the fact that the children are unable during the earliest stage to use any part of the phrase meaningfully as separate from the entire production.

At the one-word phrase level, the emerging sentence combines with the production of single words and successive utterances, two or more single-word utterances in succession but with no semantic relationship between them, and semantic development and vocabulary development are visibly on their way.

Syntax and Phonology

The children are beginning to order elements in their output, which now consists of strings of inflected jargon containing occasional appropriate words. The first 20 words may be mastered—a corpus that reflects the children's environment, physiological ability to produce phonemes, and need to communicate. This early corpus of words appears to furnish the building blocks upon which they construct the earliest true two-word utterances (Ingram, 1978).

Age 2 to 2½ Years

By the time children have reached the age of 2, motherese gradually has become more complex. While maintaining its high level of structure, the focus has shifted gradually to uncomplicated use of a few transformations and elaborations on the basic sentence nodes and to higher levels of pragmatic, semantic, and phonological input.

Cognition

By this age, children have completed the basic sensorimotor development and have begun to formulate symbols that they can use to transmit information to others. They are communicating. In the preoperational stage, they begin to construct logicomathematical and socioemotional knowledge as well as the rules of language (Wadsworth, 1975).

Pragmatics

The children now have some basic ideas of conversation. They begin to generate some sense of the place of old and new information in their own and others' communications. They come to know that conversations have beginnings and ends. Their changes in tone of voice show that they have some ideas about register change and how and what they can say to various other people in the environment.

Amy, who is 2, orders her mother to "Give me that gum!" Her surprised mother asks, "What did you say?" After a moment, Amy responds with the demand, "I want some gum!" Her mother inquires, "Is that the way you ask for something?" After a few moments of thought and another register change, a quieter Amy again asks, "Can I have some gum, please?" She is learning to use her language to do what she wants it to do and is learning the effective use of politeness conventions.

Semantics

The children should be capable of some two-word or three-word utterances and begin to understand that certain semantic roles exist. During this time of mostly two-word statements, they master basic semantic relationships. While still experiencing difficulty with exact meanings, they begin to generalize uses of the semantic roles of agent (noun)-mover (noun)-action (verb)-state ("to be" verb)-attribute (adjective)-adverbials (adverbs) of time and place. They learn to talk of existence, nonexistence, reoccurrence, and agent-action-patient-possession-location and attribute (Bloom, 1970).

Syntax

It is at this point that syntax becomes identifiable as separate from phonology and the children begin to attend, slightly, to word order. They come to understand the subject-verb dichotomy and, with the advance to three-word utterances, begin to form basic kernel sentences. They may be able to add complexity to their language in the form of easy transformations and early elaborated nodes.

Phonology

The children probably have differentiated a number of vowels and consonants and use them to produce strings of utterances. They are formulating a set of phonological rules that begin to tell how the sound system of the language operates (Ingram, 1978). The primitive phonological rules are appropriate for the children's early sound inventory and ultimately will evolve into a more complete adult system. At this age, however, the youngsters have a partly developed phonetic inventory they can use for communication.

Age 2½ to 3 Years

During this time, motherese continues to keep pace with the children's development. Mother uses longer utterances that contain more complexities, a wider vocabulary, and more complex phonological structures. She introduces the intricacies of conversational exchanges.

Cognition

Children at 2½ are beginning to construct logicomathematical and socioemotional knowledge. While bound to egocentricity of thought and perception, they are learning much about social roles by role playing and modeling (Wadsworth, 1975).

Pragmatics

During this time, children can express all modalities in rudimentary verbal form. They can put utterances into a primitive sentence order and are beginning to sort out rules of discourse. They have formed a couple of basic speaking registers. Indeed, at this age, some advanced conversationalists have several registers—one for parents, one for playmates, one for baby sibling or cousin, and possibly one for emulating the oral patterns and reading patterns heard during story time.

Amy, almost 3, notes that Jay, about 1, has picked up one of her favorite toys and is using it to force two other toys into an unnatural or impossible relationship. She starts to grab her toy, stops, picks up one of Jay's toys, and hands it to him saying, "Jay, use this. It's better." She uses a voice half a tone higher than normal.

Jay, now 28 months old, carries an alphabet rhyming book to his grandmother and announces, "I read it," then begins, in a different tone and style, to intone a long, involved string of phonemes that carry the suprasegmental patterns of recognizable phrases—a reading register. It often seems to the authors that highly creative children also have a register (or more) that they use with their toys.

Semantics

Children at 2½ are adding new semantic roles to their repertoires. They now can handle experiences, processors, patients, and beneficiaries (direct object). They begin to understand the reciprocity of actions with the semantic relationships being used. The cognitive knowledge being constructed leads to more semantic understanding that is directly related to it.

These youngsters now are actually practicing matching features of nouns with verbs that express the meaning chosen. This gives rise to the entertaining "error" utterances characteristic of young children. In normally developing children, this phase passes quickly as they improve their feature-matching skill. Adults simply note the phase and enjoy it as it passes. In children with problems in developing language, however, this area may become one of major remedial focus.

Syntax

The young grammarians generate some orderly strings of words (kernel sentences), produce all modalities, and are beginning to delete the redundancy from their utterances. They are making their first efforts (often incorrect) at pronoun substitution and element coordination. They also may be starting to produce elaborated nodes in the kernel sentences, i.e., the elaborated noun phrase (ENP) containing embedded adjectives, e.g., "The big dog." For these youngsters, the language is becoming recursive.

Phonology

The phonological rules, the articulation system, and the supraesegmental system continue to expand toward the adult form and children learn how to use the inflectional pattern of language to signal syntactic, pragmatic, and semantic information.

By age 3, normally developing children have a good grasp of fundamental pragmatic and semantic elements and a growing understanding of the basic syntactic system, and are beginning to construct an adult phonological/phonetic system.

If they are not obviously developing in all these areas, it is the authors' opinion that thorough diagnostic evaluation is appropriate and any indicated intervention should be provided immediately.

Age 3 to 3½ Years

The motherese system has brought the children along to a fairly mature use pattern and begins to phase out some of its redundancy and structure, although mother continues to give organized introductions to the more complex elements of the language. She continues to provide feedback and to monitor the children's communication development. The feedback is based on cognitive and semantic correctness and on the pragmatic element of appropriateness. For example, a parent is much more likely to correct an utterance if it is semantically or cognitively incorrect or if it is inappropriate than if it is either ungrammatical or phonologically inaccurate (Dale, 1976).

Cognition

The 3-year-olds still have a long way to go but have made a substantial beginning in ability to symbolize and to use language. They now have the tools that make further construction of knowledge faster and more efficient. Cognitive abilities continue to serve as prerequisites for specific language skills throughout the preoperational period, as language enhances and facilitates cognitive development.

In their discussion of communicative development, Greenfield and Smith (1976) note that language acquisition is a basically cognitive endeavor. They maintain that language acquisition follows, and should be identified in terms of, cognitive development.

Pragmatics

The 3-year-olds appear to be functionally mature members of society. While they continue to expand and develop pragmatic skills, they have gained a level of appropriateness and conversational skill that enables them to make their language do what they want it to do in most circumstances. It now is a functional tool. (See Table 2-2, which shows what pragmatic observations can be expected at each age level, and their developmental order, for the normal population.)

Semantics

The 3-year-olds have the use of the major semantic relationships as shown by their ability to match the features of nouns to the verb frames they choose for their sentences. They continue to refine their semantic uses of one word in relation to another so as to make more discrete statements of meaning. They also are better able to understand shades of meaning in the conversations directed to them. (See Table 2-3, which shows what semantic relationships can be expected at each age level, and their developmental order, for the normal population.)

Syntax

The 3-year-olds probably have consistent use of an acceptable word order for ordinary sentences and produce all kernels, all modalities, some transformations, and some elaborated nodes, at least in simple contexts. They are beginning to know how and when to use these elements. Continued expansions increase their use of the syntactic forms that they now are learning in more complexity and those that are being generated over time from their experiences in the world and with language. (See Table 2-4, which shows what syntactic structures can be expected at each age level, and their developmental order, for the normal population.)

Table 2-2 Developmental Order of Pragmatic Abilities

For Normally Developing Population

Abilities	Ages 3-0/3-5	3-6/3-11	4-0/4-11	5-0/5-11
Acknowledge "Other"	x	x	x	x
Conversational Turns	x	x	x	x
Initiate Conversation	x	x	x	x
Respond to Conversation	x	x	x	x
Politeness	x	x	x	x
Label Objects	x	x	x	x
Answer Questions	x	x	x	x
Ask "Wh" Questions	x	x	x	x
Ask "Yes/No" Questions	x	x	x	x
Greet People	x	x	x	x
"Truth" Value	x	x	x	x
Appropriateness	x	x	x	x
Declarative Modality	x	x	x	x
Information (Sufficient)	x	x	x	x
Relevance	x	x	x	x
Indefinite Article	x	x	x	x
Definite Article	x	x	x	x
Negative Modality	x	x	x	x
Ask for Help	0	x	x	x
Verbalize Problem	0	x	x	x
Respond to Format	0	x	x	x
Imperative Modality	0	0	x	x
Give Names to "People"	0	0	x	x

x = structures to be expected
0 = not expected

Source: Reprinted from *Development of the Communicative Abilities Test for Young Children* by Elizabeth B. Johnston, unpublished doctoral dissertation, University of Cincinnati, 1978, with permission of the author.

Phonology

The children probably have figured out the major phonological rules of the adult language and are organizing personal production of the phonetic system (Exhibit 2-3), although the actual production of some phonemes may lag behind.

Table 2-3 Developmental Order of Semantic Relationships

For Normally Developing Population

Relationships	Ages			
	3-0/3-5	3-6/3-11	4-0/4-11	5-0/5-11
Mover-Action	x	x	x	x
Entity-State-Attribute	x	x	x	x
Agent-Action-Patient	x	x	x	x
Entity-State-Entity Equivalent	x	x	x	x
Part-Verb-Whole	x	x	x	x
Adverb of Location	x	x	x	x
Experiencer-Process	0	x	x	x
Adverb of Time	0	x	x	x
Adverb of Manner	0	x	x	x
Possessor-Verb-Possession	0	x	x	x
Ambient-Action	0	x	x	x
Agent-Action-Complement	0	x	x	x
Ambient-State-Attribute	0	0	x	x
Adverb of Reason	0	0	x	x
Beneficiary-Verb	0	0	x	x
Entity-State-Adverb	0	0	x	x
Adverb of Instrument	0	0	x	x
Patient-Passive-Instrument	0	0	0	0

x = structures to be expected
0 = not expected

Source: Reprinted from *Development of the Communicative Abilities Test for Young Children* by Elizabeth B. Johnston, unpublished doctoral dissertation, University of Cincinnati, 1978, with permission of the author.

Age 3½ to 4 Years

Motherese no longer is functional in the specific way it was and has ceased to be primarily for language learning. A mother-child register emerges and continues for an indefinite period. Following the motherese system, children generate more general language learning strategies.

Table 2-4 Developmental Order of Syntactic Structures

For Normally Developing Population

Structures	*Ages*			
	3-0/3-5	*3-6/3-11*	*4-0/4-11*	*5-0/5-11*
Present Progressive	x	x	x	x
Kernel 2	x	x	x	x
Indefinite Article	x	x	x	x
Kernel 1	x	x	x	x
Subjective Pronoun	x	x	x	x
Kernel 4	x	x	x	x
Contraction	x	x	x	x
Definite Article	x	x	x	x
Infinitive	x	x	x	x
Kernel 3	x	x	x	x
Regular Past	x	x	x	x
Adjective Embedding	x	x	x	x
Irregular Past	x	x	x	x
Conjunction	x	x	x	x
Objective Pronoun	0	x	x	x
Possessive Pronoun	0	x	x	x
Ellipsis	0	0	x	x
Particle	0	0	x	x
Adverb Shift	0	0	x	x
Indirect Object	0	0	x	x
Participle	0	0	x	x
Gerund	0	0	x	x
Kernel 5	0	0	x	x
Direct Discourse	0	0	x	x
Indirect Discourse	0	0	x	x
Interrogative Reversal	0	0	x	x
Noun Clause	0	0	0	x

x = structure to be expected
0 = not expected

Source: Reprinted from *Development of the Communicative Abilities Test for Young Children* by Elizabeth B. Johnston, unpublished doctoral dissertation, University of Cincinnati, 1978, with permission of the author.

Exhibit 2-3 Phonological Processes in Young Children

Syllable Reduction
Cluster Reduction
Prevocalic Singleton Omissions
Postvocalic Singleton Omissions
Stridency Deletion
Velar Deviations
Liquid Deviations   / l /
Liquid Deviations   /r, ɚ/
Nasal Deviations
Glide Deviations

Source: Reprinted from *The Assessment of Phonological Processes* by Barbara Hodson with permission of The Interstate Printers and Publishers, Inc., © 1980.

Cognition

By this time the children probably have an extensive supply of sensorimotor schemata, have acquired symbolic functioning, and have developed a language. Using a combination of all these, plus their experiences, they are constructing the socioemotional and logicomathematical knowledge of the preoperational stage (Wadsworth, 1975).

Pragmatics and Semantics

While 4-year-olds have functional use of basic pragmatics and semantics, both of these continue to develop. The children continue to use assimilation and accommodation to adapt them, to create their "style." It should be noted that some language-impaired and learning disabled children might be identified at this point by their failure to achieve the appropriate levels.

Syntax

Children at this age use the basic language structure of their language family. They may still be learning how to use transformations of blocking and transportation and probably do not use clausal embedding. By 4½ or 5, they may be functionally mature speakers of the grammar of their language family.

Phonology

The children continue to refine and add to their phonetic inventory. Gradually the primitive phonological rules previously induced are replaced by a functionally mature rule system (Ingram, 1978).

While their phonology and articulation should be understandable, it may not be until they reach the age of 6, 7, or 8 that the entire mature phonetic system of the language family finally develops. Table 2-5 identifies the earliest age levels at which 75 percent of children tested by Templin (1957) articulated correctly.

While all elements of communication continue to develop and refine, some for the entire lifetime, the system can be considered mature at this point. The children are free to use it to further their language arts development in reading and writing and in learning other material that is part of the school curriculum and of the social world.

LANGUAGE LEARNING STRATEGIES

This crucial process of language learning involves mapping (establishing the relationship of) the emergent language onto already constructed knowledge of the physical world (deVilliers & deVilliers, 1978) so as to enhance both the language itself and the cognition. The children build language learning strategies from their needs, the environment, and the models available. They act the role of the young linguist (Dale, 1976) in the entire process of rule induction and hypothesis testing identified previously. In doing this, they probably use a number of strategies, the most successful of which they modify, expand, and consolidate into an individual and unique language learning style.

Table 2-5 Articulation of Consonant Sounds

Earliest Age Levels at which 75 Percent of Children Tested Articulated Correctly

Age Levels Years	Consonants						
3.0	m	n	ŋ	p	f	h	w
3.5	j						
4.0	b	d	k	g	r		
4.5	s	ʃ	tʃ				
6.0	t	l	v	θ			
7.0	ɤ	z	ʒ	ʤ			

Sound tested but not articulated correctly by 75 percent of the subjects at the oldest age tested (8.): [w].

Note: Symbols used in this chart are from the International Phonetic Alphabet.

Source: Reprinted from *Certain Language Skills in Children* by M.C. Templin with permission of University of Minnesota Press, © 1957.

The literature is replete with accounts of the behavioral approach to learning language but these are seriously questioned by many linguists. Given the importance of cognition in communication, deVilliers and deVilliers (1978) feel that the nature of language learning, and of language itself, is not amenable to the reward-or-punishment approach. That approach does not appear to the authors to be compatible with the philosophical base of the Piagetian Language Nursery. While the authors have used, and will continue to use, some behavior modification techniques to build limited appropriate conduct in the group, they have not placed more specific therapy emphasis on it or on its chief technique—imitation.

Techniques for Learning Language

During this eventful period, the process of rule induction and hypothesis testing that was discussed earlier comes into operation. It depends on a variety of techniques such as imitation, motherese, self-talk, parallel talk, modeling, expansion, role playing, and experiences of all kinds.

The following language development and intervention techniques are not mutually exclusive. Some are discrete tactics while some more major ones incorporate some of the more limited techniques. They are listed in this way so that the salient elements will be easy to identify, regardless of the reference used as an entry.

Imitation

There obviusly is more to language learning than imitation, but it does appear to play some role. It is not certain exactly what this role is nor whether it remains constant. Some behaviorally oriented professionals see imitation as a primary way in which children learn language, while more developmentally oriented practitioners regard imitation as relatively unimportant as a teaching/learning technique.

There are several types of imitation, each reflective of somewhat different aspects of language use. Imitation can vary along at least three continua: one measuring the cognitive content (from rote imitation to imitation mediated by cognition), one measuring the time lapse (from immediate imitation to what is deferred over time), and the third measuring the amount of spontaneity (from elicited imitation to spontaneous). Each of these appears to have a different function (Bloom & Lahey, 1978; Dale, 1976; Kretschmer & Kretschmer, 1978; Singer & Reveson, 1978).

Rote imitation is simply the immediate repetition of a stimulus and does not necessarily reflect any cognitive activity. Children use more meaningful imitation often as they practice specific elements they may be learning (also see discussions of role playing[*infra*]). Some forms of imitation can be elicited from children and traditionally are used in various testing situations. It is generally believed that children's elicited imitation is unlikely to be advanced beyond their own competence (Brown & Bellugi, 1964; Slobin & Welsh, 1973).

This notion has diagnostic significance, although it also is clear that children may mediate this imitation according to their understanding of the discourse rules (Bates & Johnston, 1977; Prutting & Rees, 1977). A higher form, termed deferred imitation, occurs when behavior or language is imitated at a later time and/or a different context. This implies that the children not only can master the language involved but also can do so in another frame of reference. This is done often in symbolic play for mastery (Singer & Reveson, 1978).

While many assumptions have been made about imitation, the data are insufficient to make a definitive statement about exactly what children will imitate meaningfully. This choice appears to be theirs alone. They apparently use the knowledge they already possess as a base for imitation and in some individual way choose from among the possible forms of imitation to be used with it so as to enhance understanding and use of the language or of the play they may engage in (deVilliers & deVilliers, 1978).

Research by Bloom, Hood, and Lightbown (1974) seems to provide a clearer explanation of the role of imitation in language learning than was available previously. It appears from their research that children imitate the elements they are in the process of learning. The children are the ones who make this determination about what and when to imitate and how much use to make of it as a language learning technique.

If children thoroughly understand a linguistic structure, they can generate it any time they want it; they have no need to imitate it. If they do not understand it at all, they cannot imitate it. However, if they are in the process of learning a specific structure, they may elect to imitate adults' use of it to help them learn it more effectively. This would make imitation a learning technique used by the children rather than a teaching technique that can be controlled by the parent, instructor, or clinician.

When the teacher requires the children to imitate something of which they do not have some emerging understanding and some immediate need to imitate, the result probably is merely the rote repetition of long strings of meaningless utterances, in all probability adding nothing to the youngsters' learning process or to the sum of their knowledge. Too much language therapy appears to the authors to be based on this type of activity. Imitation can be an appropriate learning technique whenever and however children choose to use it but it probably cannot profitably be built into a lesson plan by the teacher/clinician.

Motherese

The motherese technique, already discussed, is highly effective in infancy and the one used most in mother-infant relationships. The major caregiver (whether mother, father, or other) appears to adopt this form innately with infants. As children grow more capable, motherese becomes more sophisticated, as if it were designed to keep pace with the youngsters' continuing development. It represents the earliest technique for communicating with infants and presenting language to them.

Motherese consists of a highly simplified, highly organized, highly inflected, and highly redundant manner of presenting the basic meaningful elements of pragmatics, semantics, syntax, and phonology of the language. The early focus often is on the interpersonal activities of joint activity, eye contact, and vocal turn taking that play such an important part in developing a conversational attitude. This specialized and organized introduction to language encourages babies to construct pragmatic and semantic knowledge upon which to build their communicative style.

Snow (1972) points to two major values children derive from motherese. The first, probably intended by mother, is that the children hear simplified and easily understood language (which in turn is related more easily to the referents and actions of the cognitive realm). The second benefit, probably not intentional, involves presenting the children with simplified speech well suited to the language learning task. This technique is appropriate for the infant level and on but becomes more complex for runabouts and toddlers, to the point where it diminishes to a characteristic mother-child register.

Self-Talk

This is a technique naturally employed with very young children that gives them an organized view of how others relate language to the true facts of the context, the entire situation. The mother/clinician talks aloud to the children about what she is thinking and doing. This allows the children to tune in on the thought and language processes appropriate to what she was doing in the context, which bears a strict relationship to what is true in the context. It is appropriate with infants and toddlers and with any children who must begin language intervention at this early level.

Parallel Talk

In this technique, often used with very young children, the parent or clinician talks to the youngsters about what they are doing and thinking (Muma, 1978). This gives them the opportunity to hear language and thought processes appropriate to what they were doing in the situation. This technique also is firmly related to what is true in the context. Both this and the self-talk help the children to see the essential relationship between language and truth. Because of this relationship, it is possible to give direct and repeatable stimulus closely related to fact. This technique also is appropriate for infants, toddlers, and/or any others whose language development is at this level.

Modeling

The modeling technique is suitable for all ages of children and is probably the main way both parent and clinician help them learn the language. This technique is defined here as the interaction that occurs when parents respond to the children's utterance by putting it in correct form and giving additional information (Hopper & Naremore, 1973). For example, a child says, "Doggie bite me," and the parent models, "Yes, the doggie might bite you if you pull his tail and make him angry." Parents focus primarily on the "truth value" of the utterances (Dale, 1976) and are quick to give the appropriate model, providing additional information, from which the children do learn both cognitive and linguistic elements (deVilliers & deVilliers, 1978).

Expansion

This technique is suitable for all children in situations where the parent or clinician takes their incorrect utterance and puts it in correct grammatical form, adding no new information (deVilliers & deVilliers, 1978; Hopper & Naremore, 1973). For example, the child says, "No gots shoe," and the parent expands with, "No, you do not have a shoe." In this instance the corrected utterance is uncomplicated by the addition of other information to be processed.

DeVilliers & deVilliers (1978) also support the view that children learn by the expansion technique. It appears from a review of the literature (Bloom & Lahey, 1978; deVilliers & deVilliers, 1978; Hopper & Naremore, 1973; Kretschmer & Kretschmer, 1978; and others) that the techniques of modeling and expansion are essential in children's language learning repertoire and that they function as cornerstones around which the other strategies are organized.

Role Playing

This technique is suitable for children of all ages and can be used effectively by parents, teachers, and clinicians. It allows the children to practice the roles and the language appropriate and important to them. This technique has other functions: it provides not only an opportunity for cognitive learning but also a primary way for children to develop pragmatic understanding and to construct socioemotional knowledge.

By role playing in social situations, children gain practice in seeing various situations in which they place themselves in another position (not to be confused with the emerging ability to see things from the viewpoint of another). They learn to play or live a situation to its logical conclusion. The social learning so acquired becomes part of their socioemotional adjustment. The portion that is communicative becomes part of their growing ability to use language as a tool—their pragmatic ability.

Language Experiences

These can provide direct input into the language at any level when children are beyond the emergence of symbolic function. They constitute the main technique used by many clinicians but also can be utilized effectively by parents and teachers at home and school, even at the reading level. In this technique, an ongoing experience is planned and the children are encouraged to use the appropriate language at each phase, either after the clinician's model or spontaneously. Thus, the youngsters are getting semantic and syntactic practice producing the true and expected language for a given event and are receiving the essential feedback to know when they have done so correctly.

This enables them to take advantage of their sensorimotor, logicomathematical, and socioemotional development. They are encouraged to use all possible input from modeling and expansion and their past experiences with self-talk and parallel talk.

All past knowledge and experience are brought together in a specific context, where they interact with the children's social environment or superstructure to produce their own language. The youngsters are helped to code or map the appropriate linguistic production throughout the activity. Prompts to encourage the target production and feedback to reinforce it are used liberally.

Because of the nature of the setting, the children cannot "fail." They simply hear the stimulus again with the needed prompt until they achieve success, at which point they have the self-rewarding knowledge that they have it right. This is augmented by parent/teacher/clinician response to the success. The total nature of the language experience has the children working simultaneously on semantics and syntax, from a cognitive base and within a pragmatic frame, much the way language operates in the nontherapeutic milieu.

ENCOURAGEMENT

In all phases of the language learning process, children who feel positive and encouraged are likely to do a better job. They are optimistic, listen better, and model more freely if they feel they have a good chance of succeeding.

Research by Nelson (1973) shows that negative interactions with mother or the caretaker are a significant factor in delaying child development. The job of encouraging youngsters, while unspecific in nature, is essential in the overall blueprint of language stimulation.

FEEDBACK

Fully as important as encouragement is appropriate feedback. Even if children are encouraged and feel good about their emerging language, the need for feedback is implied in the rule induction and hypothesis testing process and exists in every technique used there. Appropriate feedback is the element that makes hypothesis testing work; without it, while the children may induce a correct rule, they have little way of knowing they have done so, so the rule does not find its way into their personal system as quickly. Distortions produced by lack of feedback are difficult to erase because the children already have tried the rule and believe they have failed.

It often is very difficult to get youngsters to generate or induce that rule again, thus creating a specific area of deficit more deviant than developmental in nature. Similarly, the feedback implied when parents think children's immature utterances are cute and incorporate them into the family language may make these misproductions particularly resistant to change.

The language learning time is doubly important because it has far-reaching effects on children's education. It also is the point at which reading readiness begins. If youngsters are to be able to learn to read and write in first grade, they must have learned already to speak and listen and have had much time to practice using language in meaningful situations. If this is the case, reading and writing surely and naturally will follow the normal development of listening and speaking.

SUMMARY

Normal children develop the language of their social group in a specific order and in a less specific but still predictable time frame. Those who have not acquired a major portion of their communication abilities roughly on schedule may be penalized in all future language-related learning if intervention does not take place. The amazing rate of growth of children's language is such that six-month intervals can show distinct stages in acquisition.

Various language learning strategies and processes were described in relation to the stages of development of youngsters' communication and some attention was paid to the role of the primary care provider in interacting with the language learner during each of the stages. An introduction to the role played by the clinician and teacher in each of the techniques or strategies for learning language was provided, along with consideration of the essential motivating force of encouragement and feedback as adults interact with the new language learners.

DISCUSSION QUESTIONS

1. How do language competence and performance differ in developing children?
2. What are the major threads running through the stages of development of communication of children between the ages of 1 and 3?

3. Why is it important for parents and teachers to be aware of the role and characteristics played by the various language learning strategies?

REFERENCES

Armstrong, P.M. Unpublished research. Middletown, Ohio: Middletown City Schools, 1980.

Bates, E., & Johnston, J. *Pragmatics in normal and deficient child language*. Paper presented at the convention of the American Speech and Hearing Association, Chicago, 1977.

Bates, E., & Johnston, J. Paper presented to the Southwestern Ohio Speech and Hearing Association, Cincinnati, 1979.

Battin, R.R. Development of the auditory verbal mode of communication. *Seminars in Speech, Language and Hearing*, 1980, *1*(2), 99–106.

Bloom, L. *Language development: Form & function in emerging grammars*. Cambridge, Mass.: The MIT Press, 1970.

Bloom, L.; Hood, L.; & Lightbown, P. Imitation in language development: If, when and why. *Cognitive Psychology*, 1974, *6* 380–420.

Bloom, L. *Readings in language development*. New York: John Wiley and Sons, 1978.

Bloom, L., & Lahey, M. *Language development and language disorders*. New York: John Wiley & Sons, Inc., 1978.

Bowerman, M. Structural relationships in children's utterances: Syntactic or semantic. In T. Moore (Ed.), *Cognitive development and the acquisition of language*. New York: Academic Press, Inc., 1973.

Brown, R., & Bellugi, U. Three processes in the children's acquisition of syntax. *Harvard Educational Review*, 1964, *34*, 133–151.

Butterfield, E.C., & Siperstein, G.N. Influence of contingent auditory stimulation upon nonnutritional suckle. *Proceedings of Third Symposium on Oral Sensation and Perception: The Mouth of the Infant*. Springfield, Ill.: Charles C Thomas, Publisher, 1974.

Butterfield, E.C., & Siperstein, G.N. In J.G. deVilliers & P.A. deVilliers, Language acquisition. Cambridge, Mass.: Harvard University Press, 1978.

Chomsky, N. *Aspects of the theory of syntax*. Cambridge, Mass.: The MIT Press, 1965.

Clark, J.G. The effects of middle ear disease on early child development. *Seminars in Speech, Language and Hearing*, 1980, *1*(2), 149–157.

Dale, P.S. *Language development: Structure and function*. New York: Holt, Rinehart & Winston, Inc., 1976.

Delack, J.B. Aspects of infant speech development in the first year of life. *Canadian Journal of Linguistics*, 1976, (21), 17–37.

deVilliers, J.G., & deVilliers, P.A. A cross-sectional study of the acquisition of grammatical morphemes in child speech. *Journal of Psycholinguistic Research*, 1973, *2*, 267–278.

deVilliers, J.G., & deVilliers, P.A. *Language acquisition*. Cambridge, Mass.: Harvard University Press, 1978.

Eimas, P.D.; Siqueland, E.R.; Jusczyk, P.; & Vigorito, J. Speech perception in infants. *Science*, 1971, *171*, 303–306.

Eisenberg, R. The organization of auditory behavior. *Journal of Speech and Hearing Research*, 1970, *13*, 461–464.

Ginsburg, H., & Opper, S. *Piaget's theory of intellectual development.* Englewood Cliffs, N.J.: Prentice-Hall, Inc., 1969.

Greenfield, P.M., & Smith, J.H. *The structure of communication in early language development.* New York: Academic Press, Inc., 1976.

Hodson, B. *The assessment of phonological processes.* Danville, Ill.: The Interstate Printers & Publishers, Inc., 1980.

Hopper, R., & Naremore, R. *Children's speech.* New York: Harper & Row Publishers, Inc., 1973.

Hutt, S.J.; Hutt, C.; Leonard, H.G.; Benuth, H.V.; & Muntjewerff, W.J. Auditory responsivity in the human new born. *Nature,* 1968, *2,* 888–890.

Ingram, D. *Phonological disability in children.* New York: Elsevier, 1978.

Inhelder, B., & Chipman, H.H. *Piaget and his school: A reader in developmental psychology.* New York: Springer-Verlag, 1976.

Johnston, E.B. *Development of the communicative abilities test for young children.* Unpublished doctoral dissertation, University of Cincinnati, 1978.

Kaplan, E., & Kaplan, G. The prelinguistic child. In J. Eliot (Ed.), *Human development and cognitive processes.* New York: Holt, Rinehart & Winston, Inc., 1971.

Kirk, S., & McCarthy, J. *The Illinois test of psycholinguistic abilities* (Rev. Ed.). Urbana, Ill.: University of Illinois Press, 1968.

Kretschmer, R.R., & Kretschmer, L.W. *Language development and intervention with the hearing impaired.* Baltimore: University Park Press, 1978.

Lackner, J. A developmental study of language behavior in retarded children. *Neuropsychologia,* 1968, *6,* 301–320.

Leonard, L. What is deviant language? *Journal of Speech and Hearing Disorders,* 1972, *37,* 427–46.

Lewis, M.M. *Infant speech: A study of the beginnings of language.* New York: Humanities Press, 1951.

Lucas, E.V. *Semantic and pragmatic language disorders: Assessment and remediation.* Rockville, Md.: Aspen Systems Corporation, 1980.

Menyuk, P. The role of distinctive features in children's acquisition of phonology. *Journal of Speech and Hearing Research,* 1968, *11,* 138–146.

Morehead, D., & Ingram, D. The development of base syntax in normal and linguistically deviant children. *Journal of Speech and Hearing Research,* 1973, *16,* 330–352.

Muma, J.R. *Language handbook: Concepts, assessment, intervention.* Englewood Cliffs, N.J.: Prentice-Hall, Inc., 1978.

Nelson, K. Structure and strategy in learning to talk. *Child Development,* 1973, *1*(2), 38.

Oller, D.K. "Infant Vocalizations and Speech Sound Development," paper presented at the Ohio Speech, Language, and Hearing Association Convention, Cincinnati, 1981.

Oller, D.K.; Weiman, L.A.; Doyle, W.J.; & Ross, C. Child speech, babbling and phonological universals. *Papers and Reports on Child Language Development,* 1974, *8,* 33–41.

Oller, D.K.; Weiman, L.A.; Doyle, W.J.; & Ross, C. Infant babbling and speech. *Journal of Child Language,* 1976, *3*(1).

Piaget, J. *The origins of intelligence in children* [M. Cook, trans.], New York: W.W. Norton & Co. 1963.

Piaget, J. *The language and thought of the child* [M. Gabain, trans.], Cleveland and New York: The World Publishing Co., 1969(a).

Piaget, J. *The construction of reality in the child* [M. Cook, trans.], New York: Ballantine Books, 1974.

Piaget, J. *The essential Piaget.* Howard E. Gruber and Jacques Voneche (Eds.) New York: Basic Books, Inc., Publishers, 1977.

Protti, E.; Young, M.; & Byrne, P. The evaluation of a child with auditory perceptual deficiencies: An interdisciplinary approach. *Seminars in Speech, Language and Hearing,* 1980, *1*(2), 167–80.

Prutting, C., & Rees, N. *Pragmatics in language: Applications to the assessment and remediation of communicative behaviors.* Paper presented at the convention of the American Speech and Hearing Association, Chicago, 1977.

Sabatino, D. The construction & assessment of an experimental test of auditory perception. *Exceptional Children,* 1969, *35,* 729–739.

Sinclair, H. "Sensori-motor patterns as a condition for the acquisition of syntax" in R. Huxley and Ingram (Eds.) *Language Acquisition: Models and Methods.* New York: Academic Press, 1971.

Sinclair, H. The transition from sensorimotor behavior to symbolic activity. *Interchange,* 1970, *1*(3), 119–126.

Sinclair, H. Epistemology and the study in language. In B. Inhelder & H. Chipman (Eds.), *Piaget and his school.* New York: Springer-Verlag, 1976.

Singer, D.G., & Revenson, T.A. *A Piaget primer: How a child thinks.* New York: Plume, 1978.

Slobin, D. Cognitive prerequisites for the development of grammar. In C. Ferguson & D. Slobin (Eds.), *Studies of child language development.* New York: Holt, Rinehart & Winston, Inc., 1973.

Slobin, D., & Welsh, C. Elicited information as a research tool in developmental psycholinguistics. In C. Ferguson & D. Slobin (Eds.), *Studies in child language development.* New York: Holt, Rinehart & Winston, Inc., 1973.

Snow, C.E. Mothers speech to children learning language. *Child Development,* 1972, *43,* 459–565.

Snow, C.E. Paper presented to the Ohio Speech, Language and Hearing Association Convention, Cincinnati, 1981.

Snow, C.E., & Ferguson, C. (Eds.). *Talking to children: Language input and acquisition.* New York: Cambridge University Press, 1977.

Steinschneider, A.; Lipton, E.; & Richomod, J. Auditory sensitivity in the infant: Effect of intensity on cardiac and motor responsivity. *Child Development,* 1966, *37,* 233–252.

Stern, D.; Joffe, J.; Beebe, B.; & Bennett, S. Vocalizing in unison and in alternation: Two modes of communication within the mother-infant dyad. In D. Aaronson & R. Reiber (Eds.), Developmental psycholinguistic and communication disorders. *Annals of the New York Academy of Sciences,* 1975, 89–100.

Templin, M.C. Norms on a screening test of articulation for ages 3 through 8. *Journal of Speech & Hearing Disorders,* 1953, *18,* 323–331.

Templin, M.C. *Certain language skills in children.* Minneapolis: University of Minnesota Press, Institute of Child Welfare Monograph Series, No. 26, 1957.

Wadsworth, B.J. *Piaget's theory of cognitive development.* New York: David McKay Co., Inc., 1975.

Zimmerman, I.; Steiner, V.; & Evatt, R. *Preschool language scale.* Columbus, Ohio: The Charles E. Merrill Publishing Co. Pub. 1969.

Chapter 3

Diagnosing the Target Population

CHAPTER OBJECTIVES

After completing this chapter, readers will be able to:

1. Describe the differences between standardized and nonstandardized diagnostic instruments and techniques and the strengths and weaknesses of each.
2. Describe problems teachers or therapists often encounter in trying to diagnose children's difficulties with communicative language.
3. Describe the difference between screening and diagnostic tests and techniques.
4. Describe the population and the various types of handicapping conditions and their possible effect on children's language.

KEY IDEAS

1. A very necessary first step in treatment of children possessing language difficulties is diagnosis.
2. Diagnosis always must remain tentative and fluid while therapists or teachers search for more data.
3. Diagnosis is a continuing process but treatment of (or intervention with) children must begin as early as possible based upon the data at hand.
4. Many standardized and nonstandardized instruments exist for diagnosing language problems in children.
5. Teachers and therapists should be very familiar with a range of standardized and nonstandardized instruments and techniques.
6. Several possible disorders affect children's language. Language diagnosis is complicated by the fact that a number of severe disorders may have identical symptoms in the young.

THE NATURE OF DIAGNOSIS

It has been demonstrated that the development and integration of basic cognition and language can be expected to occur early in children's lives (Bloom & Lahey, 1978; Dale, 1976; Vygotsky, 1962) and normally become quite functional during the third year.

Children who fail to demonstrate this development in all aspects necessarily become the focus of attention. Research and practices stress the benefits of early diagnosis and early intervention for children at appropriate levels. This intervention is implemented in a variety of ways with varying degrees of success. The authors have met with substantial success using the preschool language nursery group setting in combination with brief but frequent individual sessions with a speech/language pathologist.

The language nursery format requires in-depth individual diagnosis of each child and a program of continuing testing and recordkeeping. Since the subjects dealt with here are the very young, a program such as this often constitutes parents' first attempt to identify what may be wrong. Any testing must be specific enough to help guide parents in this important first step without being so rigid that it fails to allow for the wide variations among children who will prove to be within the normal range. This testing must meet stringent requirements:

1. It must be thorough, covering a broad range of behaviors.
2. It must be continuous in order to provide the data needed for monitoring of the children's progress.
3. It must sample a variety of contexts and elicit the behaviors typical of the children while at the same time establishing the outer limits of their performance.
4. It must lend itself to the agency's recordkeeping system and to the essential elements of the parent counseling to be offered.

PROBLEMS IN DIAGNOSIS

While diagnostics must be done to provide an entry point for children who require assistance, there are several serious problems inherent in this process.

First, all diagnostic work is highly tentative and must be viewed simply as the establishment of a working diagnosis or hypothesis that must be kept current and must remain subject to revision or modification. Diagnostic results are subject to errors because of inadequacies of the instruments, the clinician, the children's responses, the setting, or any combinations of these. Specific diagnoses often conflict with others, illustrating the fallibility of test results per se, especially with the very young. If the results of a set of tests are reasonably cohesive and agree with the other known facts relating to a client, they can be formed into a working hypothesis upon which to base a first stage of intervention.

Second, the fact of making the diagnosis carries with it a tendency to label the children with the results, too often burdening them with the sum of the errors and incomplete notions that have been accumulated. The labeling of children is well known to be counterproductive because it limits the clinician's viewpoint and tends also to set circumscribed limits on the available opportunities offered. Even knowing this, the tendency to label the children according to diagnostic results still is strong. Once a diagnosis has been made and committed to paper, it often is viewed as possessing more validity than it may actually merit so it is more difficult to consider changes. This in turn often limits the program(s) available to the children.

In spite of these problems, diagnostic categories do serve some purpose in that they allow professionals to consider like children together and to abstract from their likeness and differences newer and more specific approaches to intervention. The optimum solution is for professionals to use the diagnostic categories to aid in the planning of therapy but not to consign individual children to specific diagnostic categories permanently.

The diagnostic phase of the program may be time consuming and frustrating for children, parents, and clinicians. Parents of a young child may have become concerned by deviant or delayed communication development and have sought help, or the referral may have been made by others who see the children such as teachers, medical personnel, or grandparents.

Regardless of who initiates the diagnostic evaluation, the amount of information known about young children may be little and unspecific. It often is difficult to gain the children's cooperation, requiring the skills and resources of more than one fully trained diagnostician. Children who do not respond to testing generally are perceived as incapable of response because of a lack of either language or knowledge.

Actually, neither of these notions may be true. Children may be unmotivated to answer. They may be unsure of how to interact with either the speaker or the context (Geffner, 1981) or there may be some higher motivation or personal reason that actually is served by not answering. Additional information is difficult to obtain and it often proves inconclusive and confounding.

The early diagnosis then merely succeeds in confirming the existence of a problem and more productive statements must be deferred until the teachers and clinicians have spent more time with the children in working situations. In this way, initial evaluation often leads to deferred diagnosis and to longer term diagnostic therapy. This continuing diagnosis can blend effectively into the therapy program.

A complete diagnostic evaluation has a fourfold purpose. It is conducted to determine:

1. the nature and symptoms of the problem
2. the etiology, or causes, contributing to the problem, if possible
3. the prognosis, the statement of what can be expected to be the outcome of the treatment of the problem
4. appropriate suggestions for intervention that can be provided to the professionals and/or parents.

THE DIAGNOSTIC BIND

Establishing a firm diagnosis for severely communicatively impaired children places clinicians in a real bind. This diagnostic bind comes about because, when children fail to display any communicative abilities at all, it is most difficult to say exactly why they do not talk. At this early level all disability categories may resemble each other and combinations of them also may exist. When children do not communicate, it may be quite impossible at first to be sure of whether they are mentally retarded, emotionally disturbed, neurologically impaired, or deaf, or some combination of these. Another major possibility, cultural/environmental deprivation, can be identified more often even though that factor can produce many of the same symptoms as the other categories.

At this point, diagnosis may take the form of relating specific behavioral indicators to major diagnostic categories and checking the hypotheses. For example, specific behaviors and responses could be expected of children with true peripheral deafness that would not be expected of those who are developmentally aphasic (Table 3-1). Diagnosis may become a matter of simply going through a process of elimination of one possibility at a time until an area (or, more often, a cluster of areas) is identified that cannot be eliminated. (It often is possible to tell what something is not before it can be determined what it is.) A tentative diagnosis, or working hypothesis, based on these areas may then be made and a trial period of intervention initiated. Obviously, carefully planned continuing diagnosis is essential at this juncture if any progress is to be made in understanding the problems. This tentative intervention phase is for the purpose of testing the hypothesis as well as gaining additional information. At the same time the intervention provides both therapy and further diagnostic information—a continuing but still diagnostic approach.

If the preliminary diagnosis is confirmed and the children progress, further therapy will be based on past successes while past inadequacies will be reexamined and modified. As the diagnosis is acted upon, added to, and modified, and as the children's successes attest to its accuracy, it acquires more stability until

Table 3-1 Characteristic Performance in Different Diagnosis Areas

Type of Disorder	History	Test Findings						
		Behavioral Symptomatology	Auditory Responses	Mental Capacity	Social Maturity	Motor Capacity	Language Functioning	Emotional Adjustment
Peripheral Deafness	Indicates alertness in general; often consistent response to loud sounds. Not bizarre or seriously retarded genetically.	Not bizarre. Compensatory use made of other sensory avenues. Integrated; environmental clues used well.	Consistent and integrated. Good listening behavior. Hearing used projectively. Scanning responses given.	Cluster is around average level. Little scatter. Integrated and consistent in performance on tests.	Good except for communication area. Average social quotient of approximately 90.	Good, but balance may be disturbed. No generalized uncoordination or retardation.	Good inner language. Good gesture. Voice used projectively. Behavior is symbolical.	Good responsiveness to people through vision. Good social perception and contact with environment.
Aphasia	Indicates some retardation in development. Confusion regarding hearing. Lack of shyness but not bizarre.	Disinhibited, hyperactive, responsiveness forced. Other sensory avenues not used in compensatory way.	Inconsistent, erratic, cannot listen. Disturbed in auditory perception. Hearing not used projectively.	Inconsistent, much scatter. Perceptual disturbances improve with structuring.	Retarded in all areas but especially in communication, socialization, and motor areas. Average social quotient about 75.	Slightly delayed in sitting and walking. Generalized uncoordination.	Poor inner language. Little or no use of gesture. Voice not used projectively. May use a word unexpectedly. May be echolalic.	Emotional expression lacks intensity. Tries to relate to people. Not oblivious or bizarre.
Psychic Deafness	Begins using speech, then stops. Many anxieties. Willful in rejection of environment. Withdrawn and in world of own.	Bizarre, no compensatory use of senses. Does not relate to people. Poor social perception. No projective use of hearing or voice and no gestures.	Seems to willfully reject sound, gives indirect responses. No projective use of hearing. Not disturbed in auditory perception. May show fear of sound.	Not perceptually disturbed. May do well on form-boards. Rejects test situation in total or in part. Behavior suggests good mental ability.	Deficient in all areas but notably in socialization. Average social quotient of about 80.	Stereotyped activity. Rigidity and random movements. Only slight retardation in sitting and walking.	Good inner language but uses it only for phantasy. No use of gesture. Voice not used projectively. May be mute.	Withdrawn in own world. Lacking in relationship to people. Stereotyped and bizarre.
Mental Deficiency	Retardation in all development.	Responsive but in low genetic and concrete manner. Not bizarre.	Responds directly or indirectly to tests that are suitable genetically. Uses hearing projectively.	Marked retardation in general.	Marked generalized retardation in all areas. Average social quotient of about 55.	Generalized retardation with incoordination. Marked delay in sitting and walking.	Language deficient but not seriously discrepant with mental age. Retarded in all phases of language development.	Passive, phlegmatic, infantile, deficient in animation.

Source: Reprinted from *Auditory Disorders in Children: A Manual for Differential Diagnosis* by Helmer R. Myklebust with permission of Grune & Stratton, Inc., © 1954.

ultimately it is relatively firm. However, it never should become so entrenched that the clinician fails to keep an open mind to new developments of all kinds. As time goes on, the format gradually becomes one of therapy, followed by evaluation, followed by more therapy and more evaluation, etc.

THE HIGH-RISK REGISTER

Major emphasis is being placed increasingly on early identification of young children's language problems so that intervention can begin as soon as possible. This has led to the establishment of high-risk registers—identification and tracking lists that identify babies who have sufficient predisposing factors in their lives to make them more likely to have certain problems. They are termed at risk for these problems. Their development then can be given specific monitoring and whatever assistance is indicated can be provided as early as possible.

For example, an infant at high risk for hearing problems would have one or more of the following factors: "History of hereditary childhood hearing impairment, rubella or other nonbacterial intrauterine fetal infection, defects of ear or nose or throat, birthweight less than 1,500 grams, bilirubin level greater than 20 mg/100 ml. serum" (Northern & Downs, 1972, p. 109; Northern & Lemme, 1982). Babies at high risk for hearing disorders then are monitored systematically for hearing problems as they develop and if any are noted, early intervention can be provided.

An infant at risk for child abuse might have a significant number of the following elements: parents who seem to trust no one and discourage social contact, parents who are isolated from friends and relatives, parents who are bothered by the baby's crying, parents who do not take care of the baby and find no pleasure in it, parents who see nothing positive about the baby, one parent who resents the time the other spends with the baby and is jealous of any affection shown toward it, parents who themselves were abused as children (Open the Door on Child Abuse and Neglect). Of these, the last element appears to be the one noted most. Monitoring of such children could lead in the direction of eliminating the entire self-perpetuating problem and ultimately provide advocacy for them.

STANDARDIZED AND NONSTANDARDIZED TESTS

The choice of standardized or nonstandardized measures must be made on the basis of the children to be tested, the information desired, and the materials available. At best, diagnosis is a two-stage process in which standardized tests may be used for appraisal and in-depth nonstandardized measures used to provide specific information and the broad diagnostic picture (Bloom & Lahey, 1978).

The history of diagnosis describes a course that has gone from the use of informal language techniques to batteries of highly structured formal tests and has returned to emphasis on the informal. The implementation of Public Law 94-142 (the Education for All Handicapped Children Act of 1975) has caused the number of children being tested to increase, justification for intervention programs to be written in detail, and costs to magnify, and has produced an expressed need for standardized tests that yield numbers and scores upon which to base planned intervention.

'The' Test: Yet To Come

In spite of numerous efforts to produce "the" test that would provide comprehensive information about children and their language, the available instruments still yield only scores of unrelated and poorly integrated elements, each providing one or more specific bits of unrelated data. Diagnosticians find that even after giving the standardized tests, they do not know everything they desire about the children and their language (Danwitz, 1981). The view of the children and the language becomes distorted even further when irrelevant, incomplete, and fragmented bits of partially standardized information are incorporated into the diagnostic statement; when remediation is based upon these results, it often does not prove effective.

At one extreme Irwin, Moore, and Rampp (1972) recommend highly structured procedures focused on an approach based entirely on the giving of a number (often very large) of standardized tests because they believe it fits into their communication model. This model includes isolated elements of cognitive processes, input (detection and perception of semantics and syntax), and output (semantic and syntactic).

More holistically oriented (i.e., focusing on the whole child) diagnosticians define these results as "characterized by the fragmentation and superficiality that result from focusing only on quantitative data obtained through administering batteries of unrelated tests" (Danwitz, 1981, p. 98).

At the other extreme, Muma (1978) rejects the use of standardized tests even at the appraisal level on the ground that they do not describe the children and their problems adequately. Berry (1980) does not include standardized tests in her treatments of diagnosis at all because she does not find value in isolating unrelated bits of syntactic, semantic, and/or phonological data without taking the entire realm of pragmatics into account. A number of experts insist that "oral" language must be evaluated in pragmatic terms, i.e., the children's use of language and the context in which it was generated (Bates, 1976; Lucas, 1980; Geffner, 1981; Gallagher & Prutting, 1983). Geffner notes that "tests do not typically identify the problems children have in comprehending or expressing their intentions and interactions in oral communication. . . ." (p. 7).

Bloom and Lahey (1978) recommend that standardized tests be used at the problem-finding level and nonstandardized measures then be utilized to explore the dimensions of any problems identified. This approach leans heavily on the use of nonstandardized measures.

"Since language is not a good age-related variable beyond the chronological age of 7 or 8 (except for some semantic skills) most of the content valid standardized measures are not designed for children older than 7 or 8" (Lucas, 1980, p. 117) and in fact do little more than isolate splinter skills not clearly related to verbal language. Even within this age range a number of other elements appear to affect language acquisition significantly.

Cognition and Referents

In normally developing children, language comprehension and expression generally are close together while "most children with language disorders or delays show a decreased level of complexity in production as compared to that for comprehension" (Lucas, 1980, p. 23). Until this relationship is fully understood, a problem will exist in interpreting any results that may be obtained.

Lucas notes that development of referents appears closely parallel to the construction of the cognitive system. If that is the case, the examination of semantic acquisition must be correlated with the acquisition of cognition. She also notes that children who generate the expected semantic and pragmatic relations build positive connections with the language family cultural group. However, those who do not generate these relationships will be seen, by their language family concept, as failing to do what was required of them. Lucas adds that this failure to use a variety of semantic (and, the authors feel, pragmatic) referents may be reflecting problems in the psychosocial aspects of development. All of these areas involve cognitive, psychological, social, and linguistic elements and are vitally important to the diagnosis of language disorders, yet none are incorporated into standardized testing systems.

Another group of factors to be evaluated in the use of standardized tests involves imitation, deferred imitation, elicited imitation, or produced language. Elicited imitation, in which children are assumed to reduce their imitation to correspond to their language comprehension, can provide meaningful information to the clinician under carefully controlled circumstances. However, meaningless rote imitation (echo behavior) provides no useful data about their language system. It generally is more useful to elicit generated language and to assess the effectiveness of this production (Geffner, 1981).

Much of the data used in expressive tests relies heavily on repetition of clinician utterances, often entirely out of context. This necessarily produces imitation that consequently represents questionable information. Everything professionals have discovered about imitation indicates that sampling children's imitated speech does not tell much about their language.

The problems suggested here, relating to actually performing the diagnosis, also extend to reporting the results of the sessions. Ways exist to measure and report children's language when it is developing normally or when it is delayed but in normal order. These are described in terms of level of language functioning compared to expected level. However, when the language is deviant, either in development or in use patterns, clinicians look for both adequate measures and a reliable mode of description. To report such deviant child language as a particular level of language functioning is to produce a strategic diagnostic error (Lucas, 1980). A more appropriate format for establishing, reporting, and using this type of data is needed to fill an existing gap in clinical/diagnostic operations.

Professionals generally fault the overuse of standardized tests because:

1. They provide only unrelated fragments of information (Danwitz, 1981).
2. They do not necessarily identify who has a problem and who does not (Muma, 1978).
3. They do not lead to appropriate remediation of form or function (Bloom & Lahey, 1978).
4. They fail to relate language to the other areas to which it is inseparably tied (Lucas, 1980).

The authors do not believe that the ultimate balance between standardized and nonstandardized measures has yet been struck but it probably is much closer to the latter than to the standardized tests, even very carefully chosen ones.

Many standardized language tests are available, each of which provides some information. Clearly, they do not all meet the established criteria to provide appropriate and sufficient information about children and their language. Since there are so many and they are so diverse, it is not possible to discuss them all. However, a few of the most commonly used tests are analyzed. It is hoped that individual clinicians will be able to use similar methods to evaluate available materials and make appropriate selections from the standardized tests to combine with appropriate nonstandardized measures.

Screening Tests

The purpose of screening is to identify as quickly as possible the individuals who need further testing. It is to be expected that a screening test will identify a number of individuals who will be shown by later diagnostic work to have normal communication. It is essential that in the screening, not only are a number of individuals identified but also that the appropriate ones are included.

Each screening test is established and normed to identify according to a specific criterion. It appears crucial to choose tests that are not based on imitation and that provide appropriate information. The tests also must be normed on a sample to which the group to be screened can be compared or the norms will only confound the study.

The Northwestern Syntax Screening Test (NSST)

This test (Lee, 1971) screens only syntax for children 3 to 8 years of age. It contains both expressive and receptive aspects that depend on the youngsters' ability to imitate and listen. It places high value on whether they can identify syntactic structure and imitate utterances of other persons, neither of which abilities have a proved relationship with expressive language.

In addition, the children must have other abilities before they can complete the task, e.g., visual perception, recognition, memory (for dealing with the picture), and the ability to analyze, store, and retrieve a sentence for the expressive portion. This is increasingly more difficult when the sentences are not natural ones for the youngsters to say or are pragmatically inappropriate for the context, i.e., some of the sentences begin with subject pronouns that would not normally be produced as isolated utterances (Johnston, 1978; Prutting, Gallagher, & Mulac, 1975).

Since it is known (Bloom, Hood, & Lightbown, 1978) that children do not imitate what they know well or what they do not know at all, clinicians must expect to find this test failing those at the top and bottom in any group and identifying those in the middle of the range by passing them. This does not appear to the authors to be especially useful screening information because it identifies not only those who need further testing but also those who have no problem while leaving out an undifferentiated middle group.

Stevens Oral Language Screening

This quick-scoring test (Stevens, 1977) relies entirely on children's ability to repeat sentences from an auditory model. While it reportedly does correlate highly with the *Carrow Elicited Language Inventory* (Carrow, 1974), it still is subject to the same problems found in any other imitative measure: those of not accurately sampling the propositional language. In addition, children often are asked to produce sentences that, while syntactically acceptable, are not pragmatically appropriate.

Kindergarten Language Screening Test (KLST)

This is a quickly given and quickly scored criterion-referenced screening test appropriate for average kindergarten children (Gauthier & Madison, 1978). Much of it is based on previously established norms for concept development, which have no proved relationship to the ability to generate language. In fact, it seems likely that many children would fail language items because they lacked the cognitive structures required. These cognitive receptive elements are followed by a section in which the children are asked to imitate a set of unrelated sentences out of any context. This syntactic requirement often is directly contrary to the children's sense of pragmatic appropriateness.

This test does have the very positive factor of a spontaneous language sample that then is related to age-appropriate syntactic criteria. This single element provides (in the authors' opinion) most of the useful information to be realized from this test.

Fluharty Preschool Speech and Language Screening Test

Designed by Fluharty (1978) for use with children age 2 through 6, this test samples vocabulary, articulation, and language performance. It is quickly given and scored and is one of the more promising of the standardized screening measures. The test is flexible enough that the children are not penalized for productions that are appropriate but do not exactly imitate what the examiner has said, and they are not asked to make pragmatically inappropriate utterances. The materials are interesting enough to hold the youngsters' interest throughout the test.

Communication Abilities Test—Screening (CAT-S)

This test by Johnston (1980) provides screening information in semantic, syntactic, pragmatic, and articulation areas, with added information about concept development. The test is quickly given and scored. Armstrong (1980) shows it to correlate highly with the Fluharty at the .001 level of confidence. Since it employs the alternative story model developed for its companion diagnostic instrument, the *Communication Abilities Test* (CAT) (infra), it does not depend solely on imitation with most children. Consequently it does not have the same areas of weakness. Of course, clinicians will find youngsters in any group who respond only at an imitative level; when that occurs, this test has the same problems as any other imitative instrument.

Astute clinicians should examine the variety of screening measures available and their nature, background, and purposes for screening, and choose the most appropriate measures. They should adapt and modify these instruments, adding whatever is necessary until they meet personal screening needs.

STANDARDIZED DIAGNOSTIC TESTS

The most important strengths for clinicians to possess in giving standardized tests are: (1) the ability to administer them appropriately, (2) the ability to choose appropriate measures, (3) the ability to score them accurately, and (4) the ability to interpret them. These factors can be learned best by studying the tests and practicing their administration and scoring. Clinicians must have a critical attitude that assures a wide choice of tests and indicates when results have been invalidated by some extraneous happening. They also must have keen observational skills and a clear knowledge of what constitutes normal language behavior in order to make use of other diagnostic information that may come to light during the sessions.

'Comparison Shopping' for Tests

There are many diagnostic tests, standardized on various populations and with varying degrees of reliability and validity. To choose wisely, clinicians must test and compare their children (it could almost be called "comparison shopping") only to populations that are truly comparable to the norming population lest the test be invalidated by the use of the norms.

For example, the *Northwestern Syntax Screening Test* (Lee, 1971) is normed on upper and upper middle class Midwestern children. To use it and its norms to score a poor Mexican child from a border city would be a flagrant misapplication. The sample also must be compatible with the children being tested if the use of the norms is to be appropriate. It must have validity, it must test what it purports to test, and it must have reliability; it must work the same way across trained examiners and achieve repeatable results across groups of children. It must measure children's language in pragmatics, semantics, syntax, and/or phonology if it is to be really informative.

Tests abound that examine a combination of elements but they have virtually no commonality in the areas sampled. All omit some necessary elements in pragmatics, semantics, syntax, and/or phonology and all introduce elements of confusion by including behaviors that are not clearly a part of the production of language. When receptive language is sampled, it is not in an orderly and sequential manner. It is virtually impossible to relate salient features of language reception with correlates in the expressive portions of the same tests.

There are literally hundreds of standardized tests on the market, each furnishing a specific discrete bit of information and each based on a different rationale and norming population. While it is not feasible to attempt to describe them all here, the following are representative of the range of standardized tests available.

Preschool Language Scale (PLS)

This test by Zimmerman & Steiner (1979) yields a receptive and an expressive score. The test is age rated for children between 1½ and 7 years. There are four questions per level, which its authors present as being in sequential order. It produces minimal syntactic information and does not describe the parameters of the children's ability to generate language.

While it yields communication data, this test does not evaluate semantic, syntactic, or pragmatic elements in any systematic way. Instead, the PLS extracts bits of behavior from a number of areas and aligns them in roughly developmental order. The structures elicited from the children do not constitute a comprehensive or organized taxonomy of language acquisition from any specific aspect (Johnston, 1978). According to Johnston, "The scale fails to differentiate between cognition and language and the derived scores are too general to provide a basis for therapy" (p. 11).

Utah Test of Language Development

This test (Mecham, Jones, & Jex, 1972) purports to test expressive and receptive verbal language skills between the ages of 2 and 15 and ranges from five to nine items per level. Despite the fact that language knowledge is cumulative and the children amass a large amount of information in the first few years, the test is divided into levels of only one year at younger ages, two years at older ages, and a final level of three to five years.

Test items involve mainly reception, identification, imitation, rote memory tasks, and some drawing and copying. None of the component areas of semantics, syntax, pragmatics, or phonology are examined. According to Johnston (1978) "scores are derived . . . by observing a series of behaviors which may or may not be related to the child's linguistic capacity, but . . . which are expressed as language age equivalents" (p. 12).

Although this test claims to measure expressive and receptive language, items are lumped together at the various age levels and no such specific elements are identified in the scoring. It appears to the authors that the test allows for comparison of a set of observed behaviors but reveals little or nothing of the children's particular ability to generate new and original sentences.

The Receptive Expressive Emergent Language Scale (REEL)

This observational scale (Bzoch & League, 1971) relies on parent report and is appropriate for children up to 36 months old. The scale rates expressive and receptive language development. Its premise is that language deviant children can best be identified very young before the visible aspects become obscured by various compensations, adaptations, and the learning of splinter skills. This basis appears to be valid. Patterns that emerge relate to basic communication.

This is a scale of communicative development but not a diagnostic tool. It does not differentiate pragmatic, semantic, or syntactic information but does identify some specific phonological elements. The expressive language it scores between 2 years and 3 years is significantly less than the semantic and syntactic development noted by Bloom and Lahey (1978) or pragmatic development cited by Bates (1976) and Bates and Johnston (1979) to be present in normally developing children. This differential causes the norms on the REEL to be suspect.

According to Johnston (1978), this scale differentiates only between the receptive and expressive scores of a particular child and makes only the grossest discriminations among children. It is considerably more sensitive from the infant level to 2½ years and its usefulness lessens as children grow older.

Sequenced Inventory of Communication Development (SICD)

Attempts to sequence children's expressive and receptive communication development between 4 and 48 months provide the main structural framework for this test (Hedrick, Prather, & Tobin, 1975). It is based on the assumption that communication develops in a sequential order that can be observed and delineated. It samples both early language and early pragmatics.

The resulting long taxonomy lists somewhat fragmented language behaviors (Johnston, 1978), rather than the cohesive communication analysis that the authors believe is necessary, and the elicited behaviors never are correlated to the children's spontaneous language. Since much reliance is placed on imitation, the attendant problems (Bloom, Hood, & Lightbown, 1974) implied by the imitative tasks are of concern.

Test of Language Development (TOLD)

This broad range test (Newcomer & Hammill, 1977) purports to test phonology, semantics, and syntax but actually the elements it measures differ significantly from the general definitions of these terms. Chapter 1 of this book discussed the nature of semantics (the meaning), syntax (the grammar), phonology (the sounds), and pragmatics (the tool use) as seen by leading child language researchers. Yet when the TOLD deals with phonology, it refers to the ability to hear and articulate certain speech sounds but does not identify the rules.

In the TOLD, semantics simply means children's ability to define and recognize pictures of vocabulary words with no focus on semantic relationships; syntax is represented by the ability to imitate sentences and/or identify pictures. It does not deal with pragmatics at all with no focus on grammar or morphology. It then becomes a test simply of recognition of language and picture stimulus, auditory discrimination between words, and articulation and imitation of utterances that are unrelated to content. Some of the sentences are too illogical and pragmatically inappropriate to expect children to produce them.

Scoring is inflexible, often penalizing the children for producing something that would be completely appropriate. In scoring the sentences, one error makes the entire sentence wrong, with the result that it is possible to say the sentences correctly except for the omission of the initial determiners and yet receive a seriously depressed language score (the same, in fact, as children who omitted all the verbs would receive) that shows nothing of the language strengths they possess. If poorly scored, the results of this test can confound the final diagnostic statement.

The Illinois Test of Psycholinguistic Abilities (ITPA)

This test (Kirk, McCarthy, & Kirk, 1968) is one of the most widely used and at the same time most controversial tests in the language area. It was conceived to sample specific component abilities in the language realm through a set of subtests of psycholinguistic abilities such as visual association, auditory association, or visual memory. This test has its ardent supporters and an equally vocal group of detractors. Linguistic theory in the early 1980s tends to minimize its usefulness as a test of language ability.

Many of the problems related to the use of the ITPA center on four areas, according to Bloom & Lahey (1978):

1. The test does not differentiate between children who do and do not have language problems.
2. Specific intervention planned on ITPA results does not necessarily remediate language disorders.
3. Subtests cannot be proved to be tapping the psycholinguistic skills they claim to relate to.
4. There is no statistical proof that the psycholinguistic skills identified by the ITPA are indeed necessary subcomponents of language.

It also should be noted that the test does not identify problems in pragmatics, semantics, syntax, or phonology. Indeed, it is the authors' experience that while many children who fail to achieve the expected scores on the ITPA have adequate expressive language, many who do earn such scores do not have acceptable expressive language. It further appears that therapy based on these results is largely irrelevant to language improvement.

Carrow Elicited Language Inventory (CELI)

This entirely imitative syntactic test (Carrow, 1974) is limited by the constraints concerning what children do and do not imitate. Scoring is strict and children are penalized for any paraphrasing or grammatical ellipsis they produce. In some instances they are asked to generate sentences that are unnatural, illogical, or pragmatically inappropriate.

For example, the sentence, "The dog is under the house," as an isolated utterance, is no more likely than "A dog is under a house." Yet only the first of these two utterances receives credit. In another instance, children are asked to produce the illogical "The dog is in the tree." Since the test does not sample pragmatics, semantics, or phonology and reflects only imitated syntax, insertion of these scores into a diagnostic battery must be done with caution.

Environmental Language Inventory (ELI)

This inventory (McDonald and Nichols, 1974) is one of the more promising language tests to use with young children. Based on early 1970s' semantic-syntactic notions, this test provides an assessment of early semantic expressive language following the Schlesinger (1971) model.

The ELI is limited to semantic-grammatical information and does not go higher than the three- to four-word level. Consequently, it is most useful with the very young or the mentally retarded. While the test contains a level of imitative responses, it also provides for the collection and semantic analysis of a spontaneous language sample. It does not, however, identify syntactic structures that may appear to be emerging already. While it does allow clinicians to account for utterances that cannot be interpreted and provides a place for the phonological marker, it makes no further assessment of phonological development.

Communication Abilities Test for Young Children (CAT)

This unpublished test (Johnston, 1978) appropriate for ages 3 through 8 years, 11 months, functions like a criterion-referenced test while at the same time establishing a set of developmental norms in pragmatics, semantics, and syntax. It does not test phonology.

It uses an alternative story format to increase the likelihood that specific structures will be produced but reduce the likelihood that the children will imitate the clinicians. The scoring is flexible and care is taken to ensure that the youngsters are not penalized for producing an appropriate utterance other than the desired one. All scoring is within a pragmatically appropriate context.

The test presupposes that the clinicians have a substantial language background. Its results enable them to compare a particular child with the composite score achieved by normal ones who took the test and determine how this one child differs in any area from these norms.

CLINICIAN OBSERVATIONS

Observation necessarily plays a major part in the evaluation of young children's language. The importance to clinicians of understanding normal child development in all areas cannot be overemphasized. Their knowledge of developmental scales enables them to make appropriate developmental observations. It is just such observations that furnish the framework within which the results of specific standardized tests may be most useful—if they are used at all.

In addition to observations used to relate to the various developmental scales, clinicians may rely heavily on their ability to describe development in specific areas, enabling them to present detailed profiles of particular children. The profiles can be incorporated into the diagnostic pattern.

Finally, thorough knowledge of the developmental scales also enables clinicians to project future developments and make the most of all available information in planning for the children's therapy.

NONSTANDARDIZED MEASURES

Probably the most useful nonstandardized or informal evaluation measures available to speech language clinicians are the variety of analysis models. Each of these is standardized to some extent in the way it is administered but the children's spontaneous language sample is used in each instance as the material to be scored.

Developmental Sentence Types (DST)

This measure (Lee, 1966) was constructed to identify sentence types being used by young children. It classifies types of sentence fragments on a syntactic basis only and does not score the results. Unfortunately, it does not take into account the fact that many sentence fragments actually are pragmatically acceptable and are rather complex utterances, representing the youngsters' ability to delete redundancy. Consequently, if this measure alone is used, the children may receive no credit for their appropriate utterances and are penalized for the very elements that signal language strength.

Developmental Sentence Scoring (DSS)

This method of scoring (Lee & Canter, 1971) is widely used to provide syntactic information only. For their purposes, Lee and Canter define a sentence as an utterance containing a subject and a verb, again penalizing children for their more complex and appropriate fragments. The youngsters are scored according to the number and complexity of form classes found in their utterances but this does not include all form classes in the scoring, e.g., adverb, adjective, or preposition. This makes it possible for some children to have complex language that receives little credit. This addition of the single point for a grammatical sentence does not correct the diagnostic error thus produced.

Since this is strictly a syntactic measure, does not score all types of sentences equally, and does not give children credit for their pragmatically appropriate conversational language, the authors believe its use must be monitored carefully. Its main strength probably involves its use as a test-retest measure to determine progress.

Language Assessment, Remediation, and Screening Procedure (LARSP)

This measure (Crystal, Fletcher, & Garman, 1976) is based on the notion of the primacy of syntax. It provides for a syntactic focus on grammatical analysis, count of structures, evaluation of grammatical patterns, and statement of remedial goals. It leads to statements of remedial procedures while completely ignoring semantics, pragmatics, and phonology.

Kretschmer Spontaneous Language Analysis

The individual spontaneous language analysis model (Kretschmer & Kretschmer, 1978) is exceptional in that it incorporates in-depth analysis of semantics, syntax, and pragmatics into a thorough formula for identifying communication strengths and weaknesses. While it is presented as a technique for analyzing the language of deaf children, it also is highly effective in evaluating others whenever a complete comprehensive statement is needed.

Mean Length of Utterance (MLU)

This measure (Brown, 1973) provides a formula for finding syntactic complexity by measuring the mean length of utterance in morphemes. It provides a valid measure of language complexity so long as the utterances are no higher than Stage 4 (four to five morphemes) because at this level in children's development, each additional morpheme does indeed index additional complexity. According to deVilliers & deVilliers (1973), the mean length of utterances (in morphemes) (MLU) is a better prognosticator for the acquisition of Brown's 14 earliest-developing morphemes than is chronological age and can be used effectively to analyze this development. Certainly these are below the Stage 4 limit and represent a valid use of the MLU.

However, beyond Brown's Stage 4, an increased MLU does not necessarily indicate increased complexity (Brown, 1973). After this point, complexity elements such as T/blocking (which deletes redundancy), T/substitution (which substitutes a pronoun for a noun phrase), etc., actually may reduce MLU while increasing complexity.

For example, the sentence "The boy ran and the girl ran and the boy jumped and the girl jumped" (MLU = 17 morphemes) has less complexity than the possible "They ran and jumped" (MLU = 6 morphemes). This measure often is used inappropriately as a measure of complexity for children with higher MLU than Stage 4 (Muma, 1978), both to gauge progress and to provide research baseline language data, probably resulting in faulty baselines for numerous language studies.

Communication Analysis Model

The model (Johnston, Johnson, & Weinrich, 1978) discussed in detail here and used in describing the language of children in the preschool language nursery was based on an early Kretschmer model as it was taught in 1975. It has evolved to its 1983 form as the authors of this book have modified it since to meet the needs of their University Speech, Language, and Hearing Clinic. This in-depth analysis of propositional speech/language encompasses pragmatics, semantics, and syntax and assesses both strengths and weaknesses in each. From this, a summary is produced and therapy targets can be established or ordered. This is a normalized way of producing nonstandardized information.

The pragmatic portions of this analysis record the youngsters' successes and failures in using pragmatics, as described by Bates and Johnston (1979) and Bloom and Lahey (1978). They answer the questions: "Do the children use language appropriately?" "Is it an effective tool for them?" "Do they use appropriate register, topicalization, and grammar forms to signal pragmatic information?" etc.

The semantic portions of the analysis show successes and failures in semantic relationships, as semantics is presented by Chafe (1970). They answer the question: "Can the children produce all necessary semantic relationships and use them to make their language specific enough to say exactly what they want to say?"

The syntactic portions report successes and failures in using correct syntax, modified from Chomsky (1965). They answer the questions: "Have the children internalized the grammar rules of the language family in which they live?" "Do they produce the basic sentence patterns of the language?" "Do they produce elaborated nodes—sentence elaborations at the deep structure level such as embedded adjectives, relative clauses, etc.?" "Do they produce all transformations—surface structure level actions done to the sentence, such as deleting redundancy, moving elements, etc.?"

All these analysis data then are summarized, making it possible to relate the results to the diagnostic statement in terms of specific strengths and weaknesses and to choose from them specific targets to be worked on.

To make an individual communication analysis, clinicians first obtain an appropriate sample. This can best be gained from several diverse settings in which the children can be expected to produce their most natural language. Clinicians engage the youngsters in conversation and note both the actual utterances and the semantic intent. It is important that the children be comfortable in the settings, that a variety of stimulus materials be used, and that the language samples analyzed are truly typical of the clients.

The clinicians then make syntactic trees of the linguistic content, diagram forms that show the grammatical organization of the sentences, and analyze the actual utterances in terms of the semantic intent. This analysis usually furnishes the most realistic information about what the children are doing with language production. It can be incorporated easily into the observational format, where it furnishes needed specific information. The analysis probably will not be useful in making any statement about etiology—the cause of the problem.

In instances where children do not use a syntactic, semantic, or pragmatic element in the language sample, the clinicians can only state that it was not used, not that the youngsters were unable to use it. To answer that question, the authors recommend talking to the children again to see whether it is possible to elicit and record the desired element.

When the analysis of individual sentences is complete, a summary of the entire analysis is prepared and from it patterns are identified, implications are noted, and topics/targets for intervention can be chosen.

Obviously, this analysis model (or others that could be used) does not yield a developmental score. It will be necessary for the clinicians to evaluate the pattern of strengths and weaknesses (as shown in the analysis) in terms of age and other significant factors.

Cognitive Functioning

The focus of this program is communication and the majority of diagnostic treatment is involved with its various aspects. However, if children are to be grouped effectively, some determination of their cognitive functioning must be made. Those studied here are very young and usually have not had any need for formal psychological/psychiatric assessment. In the event that such an evaluation is indicated, specific children should be referred to a qualified psychiatrist, psychologist, or psychometrist. The authors do not believe the training of either speech clinicians or teachers equips them to attempt this task.

The cognitive observations that must be made for assembling children in sensorimotor or preoperational groups can be done by teachers/clinicians using any number of less formal means. Less highly structured observational scales to accomplish this purpose are compatible with the diagnostic protocol suggested and with the theoretical base of the program.

The Program Evaluation Measure (PEM) developed by the Early Admissions Program of the Baltimore public school system is such an observational tool, covering a variety of cognitive, social, visual, auditory, and motor skills. Based on nine objectives, the program assesses children monthly through the preoperational period and provides both diagnostic information and guidelines for planning therapy.

Diagnostic Procedures

As clinicians will find, there are numerous problems inherent in the diagnosis of young children. The first of these is the choice of appropriate measures from among the wide variety of diagnostic materials available. This can be determined according to the specific nature of the children and their particular weaknesses and strengths, the type of information needed, and the time and materials available. It is important to match the subjects, the needed information, and the materials as closely as possible. A diagnostic protocol (Exhibit 3-1) that organizes a sampling of all parameters of the problem and allows a testable hypothesis to be made in problem areas would include a variety of materials and tests.

If a complete diagnosis is accomplished and the clinicians have standardized test results, in-depth analysis results, some amount of observational data, and information from parents and teachers, this all can be drawn together into a cohesive and informative diagnostic report and the conclusions used as a base for planning further intervention (Exhibit 3-2).

THE DIAGNOSTIC POPULATION

Since the focus of this book is a language nursery program for severely impaired preschoolers, the diagnostic process identifies a wide variety of children. The younger they are, the less firm the diagnosis is likely to be and the more dependent the professionals tend to be on the use of continuing diagnosis and evaluation to provide program and direction.

Diagnosis most often is tentative when the infant or young child enters the language nursery. In fact, since a variety of specific diagnostic categories all have highly similar presenting symptoms, and since all possible combinations also may be expected, the diagnosis may remain tentative for an extended period or may never be established absolutely. Since children are grouped not on the basis of diagnosis or age but on cognitive developmental level, the group remains constant, with a variety of children in each unit, each able to learn from the others.

The authors do not think this lack of specific diagnosis hinders the therapy in any way. In fact, the consistent use of continuing diagnosis and willingness to consider changes are vital signs that in fact should enhance the therapy. The basic differential diagnosis (the diagnostic bind) involves children who are hearing impaired, emotionally disturbed, neurologically damaged, or mentally retarded. To this group are added other children who present with environmental impoverishment, severe speech problems, etc. The resulting group is varied and provides a forum for vital and compelling activities.

The discussion that follows is intended to present only a brief description of each type of children as they present for diagnosis. Specific technical information must be acquired about each child if appropriate intervention is to be planned.

Exhibit 3-1 Format for the Preschool Diagnostic

History:

Complaint:

Cognitive Development:

Articulation Test (Including Stimulability):

Any Standardized Language Tests:

Language Sample (Analyzed):

Oral-Peripheral Examination:

Hearing Test (Including Impedance Test):

Other Tests:

Informal Observations:

Summary:

Recommendations:

Hearing Disorders

Hearing impaired children at times may be easier to identify than the others in the diagnostic bind because hearing often can be better objectified and consequently easier to identify and isolate than other possible problems. Children with hearing-related problems also have language problems because of the lack of auditory stimulation and in fact may not have adequate learning in any of the areas of language development.

Exhibit 3-2 Sample Diagnostic Report

Name:	Ira McBain	Date:	10-9-82
Age:	3 yrs., 6 mo.	Birthdate:	4-12-79
Parents:	John & Mary McBain	File No.:	3777
Address:	202 Heart Circle, Sparks, Nev.	Diagnostician:	S. Sharp
Phone:	DI 3-7293	Referral Source:	Dr. Aymes

History: History to date is unremarkable except for lack of communicative development. This child achieved the motor milestones at appropriate ages and is in good health. The speech and language delay exhibited also occurs in several other family members.

Complaint: The child is not developing speech and language. The frustration he feels seems to be causing behavior problems.

Cognitive Function: Observations of cognitive development indicate that the child is functioning at the preoperational level. Nonverbal cognitive functioning is age appropriate.

Articulation: The Goldman-Fristoe Test of Articulation was attempted. Child appears to recognize most items (as demonstrated by gestures) but was virtually unable to produce the words. The standard utterances were /dʌ/ga/æ/ with variations of these. The child was not stimulable for any sounds.

Language: The receptive portion of the Preschool Language Scale was administered and indicated receptive skills at or above age level (3 yrs., 6 mo.) while expressive scores were depressed (1 yr., 6 mo.).

Language Analysis: The child did not produce enough language for formal analysis. It is noted here that normal prosody is consistently present and the few sounds produced are used as syllable markers.

Oral Peripheral Examination: Results were unremarkable. Structures are present, symmetrical, and functional.

Hearing: Puretone hearing was within normal limits. Impedance audiometry indicated normal middle ear function.

Other Testing: Informal evaluation for oral apraxia indicated this to be a problem area.

Observations: This child accompanied the examiner willingly and was generally cooperative. However, when the focus of the evaluation was on movement of the articulators, he became upset and ceased to try. The child appeared fearful and discouraged but did seem to understand everything.

Summary: Results of testing indicate that this client has severe multiple articulation problems, which possibly have an apraxic base. There is a significant language delay of undetermined dimensions. The child demonstrated adequate comprehension and motivation.

Recommendations:
  1. Language nursery group four days per week, with daily individual therapy for 15 to 20 minutes.
  2. Complete diagnostic testing for oral apraxia.
  3. Mother's attendance at parent group is required.

This lack of language development tends to accompany a general delay and distortion of cognitive development. Speech development also may be delayed. Socioemotional problems may overlie the basic problem, further complicating intervention patterns. The lack of auditory stimulation and language development takes a toll in other areas of learning and development, causing an array of educational problems (Northern & Lemme, 1982). The earliest possible diagnosis and intervention are essential if the children are to gain maximum benefits from it. Even with the earliest and most comprehensive intervention, the need being addressed may last a lifetime.

Hearing-related problems often are differentiated on the basis of degree (severity) of hearing loss or on the basis of type (location) of the dysfunction.

Hearing disorders in young children may be the result of prenatal or natal accident or disease or postnatal accidents, diseases, or fevers, or of genetic transmission. In general, anything that damages middle or inner ear function can produce a hearing loss, as can damage to the outer ear (such as atresia, congenital malformation of the ear) or a foreign object stuck in the ear.

Hearing acuity—the ability to hear the auditory signal—is tested by professional audiologists. They are skilled in threshold testing, determining how loud each sound frequency must be for the children to hear it (in comparison to the established norms); impedance testing, which determines middle ear function; and numerous more specialized examinations. Their work in coordination with that of medical specialists leads to the diagnosis of hearing disorders (Northern & Lemme, 1982). Once the hearing loss has been established, speech pathologists determine the amount and nature of speech and language delay. It then is the responsibility of special educators, working with speech therapists, to plan the necessary intervention.

Degree of Hearing Loss

The determination of whether children are deaf or hearing impaired (and, if impaired, how much) is directly related to planned intervention, prognosis, and development in all areas (Kretschmer & Kretschmer, 1978).

If children are deaf, they can be expected to show cognitive delay as well as semantic, syntactic, phonological, and pragmatic language problems. They may have difficulties relating to other people and, when very young, may lack language and be so frustrated at this inability to communicate with others linguistically or pragmatically that they essentially quit trying and give up in despair.

These children may show many frustrations by behavior that is far from appropriate. Communication problems, at their most severe with the deaf, also exist to varying degrees with children who have varying amounts of hearing loss. As might be expected, those with the least amount of hearing loss usually reflect the best overall prognosis (Northern & Lemme, 1982).

Type of Hearing Loss

Children with hearing loss can be divided on the basis of where the problem occurs. Sensorineural losses, caused by some problem with the sensation to the inner ear and/or pathways to the brain, present specific types of educational challenges. These children tend to have problems hearing specific frequencies and levels and may hear with distortion even when the signal is received. Problems range from mild to severe, depending on the amount of loss and their other residual problems and abilities. The children may suffer from tinnitus, sensation of sound in the head, or recruitment, in which a slight increase in sound presented creates disproportionate increases in sound received, without being able to explain their confusion and frustration to anyone.

Those with conductive hearing loss fail to hear because of some breakdown in the process that transduces the sound waves from the environment through the outer ear and middle ear to the fluid in the sensitive inner ear.

While there are a number of other conditions that would result in conductive hearing problems, it appears that the majority are related to the presence of otitis media (middle ear disease), which often causes fluid to fill the middle ear and thus prevents the sound from being conducted and preventing the reception of auditory signals.

There is no proved relationship between otitis media and language/learning disabilities. There are children who have had middle ear disease yet show no problems. But numerous others have such a history and are severely impaired. Research in the early 1980s, although inconclusive, did point to a causative relationship between chronic otitis media and some type of language problem or learning disability (Aram & Nation, 1982).

It is felt that the presence of recurring otitis media either during the primary language development time before the age of 3 or continuing over any long period places children at high risk for language or learning problems.

While the actual degree of hearing loss during otitis media might be mild to moderate, its occurrence during the prime language learning years can be catastrophic. The sequence of events frequently is that the children eventually recover from the otitis media and have normal hearing but a serious residual language and learning disability remains. This gap in language reception, or the distorted auditory signals experienced, yields a faulty base upon which to build later development. Subtle language disabilities that persist into the school years may well contribute to learning problems at this level.

Early intervention would seem crucial for children with this kind of history and they often are found among the language impaired in the Piagetian Language Nursery, not because they have other problems but, because of fluctuating hearing or auditory distortion, they have not had the auditory stimulation necessary to learn the language. While some children's problems remain severe for extended periods, the authors have found that some do very well in the language nursery due to their specific combination of characteristics and abilities. They progress rapidly, and go on to regular nursery programs in record time.

Children with a hearing loss also may be identified on the basis of whether the problem is central or peripheral in nature. Those with a peripheral problem with the function of the ears display the symptoms generally associated with hearing loss because they are not hearing the signals, which causes them to fall behind developmentally. Both conductive and sensorineural hearing losses fall into this category. The uneven development they build on this faulty base probably cannot help but become distorted.

Those with a central problem in associating auditory impulses with their meaning at the brain level have difficulty orienting and organizing the auditory message and attaching meaning to it for later recall and use. This auditory processing ability will become crucial at a later date when they proceed to the learning model at school.

There is little general agreement about the importance of the auditory processing skills to language development or therapy. Professionals tend to minimize their role as meaningful language targets. They are finding that specific training in these areas does not generalize to other areas or necessarily result in corrected language (Aram & Nation, 1982; Bloom & Lahey, 1978).

Since the problems related to central hearing disorder are more closely allied with those of neurological dysfunctions, the authors include them in the discussion in the following section.

Neurological Disorders

These congenital disorders range from mild to severe and affect a wide range of central nervous system functions. They generally result from prenatal or natal damage or genetic transmission. Their symptoms and causology are so similar to that of central hearing impairment that such children often are interchangeably diagnosed and there is great overlap in therapy recommendations (Aram & Nation, 1982). It may be, in fact, that such terms as developmental aphasia, severe learning disorder, central deafness, and idiopathic language disorder, in which the etiology is not known, are used to describe the same population of children.

All possible degrees and combinations of symptoms appear to be possible, causing an unlimited variety of specific problems. The most common ones in the Piagetian Language Nursery are developmental aphasia and developmental apraxia.

Developmental Aphasia

Aphasia, absence of speech and language, and dysphasia, impairment of speech and language, result from central nervous system damage. The terms refer to both children and adults who share a common etiology. Here, however, the similarity begins to diminish. Adults with acquired aphasia, who have suffered a stroke, have lost all or some of their ability to use symbolic language but at one time they did have language functions. Children with developmental aphasia never had the advantage of a developed language system so they have nothing to fall back on, no base to build from. Because of this, Weiss & Lillywhite (1981) believe the problems of the adult aphasic are likely to be far less complicated than those of developmentally aphasic youngsters.

Children can sustain damage to the central nervous system before, during, or immediately after birth that results in congenital malfunction of the mechanisms for learning language and speech. According to Weiss & Lillywhite (1981), it has been estimated that some 4 percent of all communication disorders are aphasic in nature. Many of these children (the less severe ones) are among the 20 percent of youngsters with severe learning disabilities. In a treatise on this subject, Weiss and Lillywhite state:

> Childhood or developmental aphasia is extensive and severe enough to present a serious problem to parents, educators and many others dealing with children. Speech/language pathologists can be sure of having a sizable number of children with developmental aphasia among their caseloads in almost any situation. (p. 182)

Aphasic children's problem is largely one of perceiving, processing, and transmitting language symbols. They are inefficient operators of the language code, if they can operate it at all. This is an associative disorder: aphasics cannot associate sounds with their sources or meanings, and when language does begin it is based on the distorted and never understood bits and pieces received. (Even the "motherese" heard as an infant probably was never at a level that sense could be made of it.) The symbols acquired resemble the faulty ones learned previously and are a poor foundation for further learning. (These symptoms seem identical to those identified for central deafness.)

Although the problem essentially is associative and linguistic, aphasic youngsters often have secondary neuromuscular problems, resulting in articulation, resonation, and phonation difficulties, and may make abnormal responses to auditory signals (Weiss & Lillywhite, 1981). They also are likely to present with a history of severe language delay and to have generated some amount of emotionally overlaid problems.

This is to be expected when clinicians consider the rage and frustration, the confusion and hurt that must be felt by children who have intelligence, ideas, and a desire to communicate and whose efforts, no matter how monumental, are doomed to failure. The natural compulsion to strike out against such an unfair fate cannot always be resisted, so they develop behavior problems, further confounding personal and family adjustments.

Frequently these are the children thought to have idiopathic language disorders, problems where the cause is not identified, who are taken to the speech/language therapist by frustrated parents who have nowhere else to turn. It is hoped that such children will be taken in as early as possible. It is the authors' belief that the type of interaction provided in the language nursery is highly appropriate as young as 2 years of age. There the children can be provided with intervention and encouragement before there is time to become extremely frightened or hurt by failure or build an elaborate defense of bizarre behaviors and before the emergence of very real emotional problems.

Developmental Apraxia

In the speech/language area, the term apraxia implies lack of voluntary control of the speech musculature. Dyspraxia refers to impairment of voluntary control of this musculature. This problem also is caused by damage to the central nervous system and results in problems in the voluntary control of musculature that normally functions satisfactorily on an involuntary basis. This disorder often is seen in combination with developmental aphasia and cerebral palsy but also appears as the single physical manifestation of unseen damage.

Children with developmental apraxia usually have normal intelligence and can hear and comprehend speech appropriately. While their articulators work well at times, their volitional control over speech production is not adequate and articulate speech may not be possible, Weiss and Lillywhite report. These youngsters' speech sounds are characterized by repetitions and/or substitutions of sounds, most errors occurring in place, rather than in manner, of articulation (Weiss & Lillywhite, 1981) and by a lack of organization (Darley, Aranson, & Brown, 1975). Weiss and Lillywhite estimate that about 10 percent of persons with articulation problems have some amount of apraxia.

According to Aram and Nation (1982), apraxic children are likely to be boys. They also are likely to be physically clumsy—unable to stand on one foot, hop, or skip. They may have mixed cerebral dominance and difficulty with eye-hand coordination. Aram and Nation, eminent speech pathologists, quote Eisenson as describing these children as equally inept with either hand. (See Exhibit 3-3 for a summary description of developmentally apraxic children.)

Usually when youngsters with developmental apraxia require language nursery placement for intervention, the dysfunction is associated with some other problem such as aphasia or cerebral palsy. Occasionally, however, children placed in the nursery present mainly a phonological/articulation disorder (which often turns out to be primarily apraxic) or simply developmental apraxia severe enough to have caused the referral. They often are outgoing, communicative—and totally unin-

Exhibit 3-3 Summary Description of Apraxic Children

In addition to their phonetic, phonemic, and prosodic problems, developmentally apraxic children:

1. are unlikely to have a history of normal babbling as infants
2. are unlikely to have normal expressive vocabularies
3. show much use of gestures to convey intended messages, along with reliance on onomatopoeic sounds
4. show virtually no use of verb forms
5. demonstrate many difficulties with words denoting spatial relationships (prepositions)
6. demonstrate high incidence of anomia, occasionally using a wrong but related word or obviously searching for a word
7. encounter delay in the onset of speech, both single-word and two-word utterances
8. have comprehension of syntax and semantics commensurate with mental age but have increased trouble with longer sentences
9. encounter difficulty with semantic and syntactic formulation of language
10. are likely to have problems with reading, writing, and spelling when they enter school.

Source: Constructed from *Child Language Disorders* by D.M. Aram and J.E. Nation published by The C.V. Mosby Company, 1982, pp. 159–160.

telligible. Most often their developmental apraxia is felt to be the visible sign, with some accompanying problems to be diagnosed later. The authors have found these children enjoy and benefit from their nursery experience but also require specific intervention for their articulation disorder.

Cerebral Palsy

Cerebral palsies are complexes that result from damage to various parts of the brain, occur between conception and 2 years of age or so (most between conception and 1 month), and appear in various forms or combinations of sensorimotor, perceptual, behavioral and speech disorders. (Mysak, 1982, p. 403)

These neurologically caused disorders produced by damage to the brain affect between one and six of every 1,000 births (Mysak, 1982). It is a diverse disorder that affects motor behavior and, through it, speech. It also often affects cognitive and linguistic functions and carries a number of associated sensory problems. Children diagnosed as cerebral palsied often also demonstrate both aphasia and apraxia.

There are five basic types of cerebral palsy: spasticity, athetosis, ataxia, tremors, and rigidity. All usually are accompanied by learning, language, and motor speech problems and often by hearing and vision distortions. As would be expected of a disorder so diverse, the child often also has social and emotional problems.

Cerebral palsied children face a long training period if they are to make the most of their assets and minimize the effects of the dysfunction. This specialized remediation work is the province of a team of specialists: the pediatrician, who coordinates the efforts; the physical therapist, who works on posture and walking; the occupational therapist, who works on small muscle and self-help skills; the speech/language therapist, who works on all aspects of communication; the orthopedist, who provides and fits braces and other aids; the special education teacher, who adapts educational approaches; and any other specialists needed.

Young cerebral palsied children may be very slow to develop language because they have had few experiences and a very difficult time getting things together to produce the language. Intensive stimulation and feedback are required for them to do well. This can be supplied in the language nursery, where they have a number of models and where there is appropriate activity. This placement does not take the place of the comprehensive cerebral palsy treatment training program but, under controlled circumstances (with careful coordination of all professionals involved), the nursery makes an ideal first group experience incorporated into the overall program.

Mental Retardation

This term is intended to refer to individuals who for a number of reasons do not have the mental ability required to function independently in their social context. They have less than the ability needed to become independent thinkers and, because of this, require assistance in most or all areas of development. Great care must be used diagnostically to avoid including children in this classification who fail to function at the expected levels for various other reasons, i.e., deprivation, cultural differences, sensory disability or distortion, emotional disturbances, etc.

Mental retardation results from an uncountable number and combination of factors including heredity, developmental disorder, disease, accident or brain damage, and chromosomal fault. It has been estimated (Lillywhite & Bradley, 1969; Weiss & Lillywhite, 1981) that there are 5 million to 6 million children in the United States who have mental scores below 70 IQ points. These children have more vision, hearing, and orthopedic problems than their peers and require more prostheses, therapy, and specialized schooling. According to Lillywhite and Bradley (1969) the retarded sustain two to three times as much conductive hearing loss because of middle ear infection as do their normal peers. It is logical to project that this further delays their language development, which already may be going very slowly.

This population ranges from slow learners, who can be expected with training to live less complex but satisfying and generally independent lives in society, to the trainable persons, who can be guided to learn basic self-help skills and function under supervision, to, finally, the custodial persons, with varying degrees of self-awareness, who must be cared for.

The language nursery may be the ideal placement for mentally retarded children because they can interact there in a language-rich environment to receive the added help needed to develop language. It is important to remember that the mentally retarded are expected to achieve only up to their mental (not chronological) age. If they have a chronological age of 6, a mental age of 3, and language at the 3-year-old level, they would not be considered to have a language problem and should not be pushed to achieve beyond that mental age.

The authors have found it important to control the number of retarded children who are enrolled in any particular group to preserve its normal nature. In general, they believe any group of five, six, or more children can include one retarded child without affecting the cognitive functioning of the unit.

All group members benefit when this is done. They learn that they can share and can help and be helped in various ways by every other child present. The mentally retarded benefit because they have the model of the normal children to learn behavior patterns from and to learn language with. Mixed group composition provides benefits for all members because of their interaction with each other. When children of all types learn to grow together and to share their lives, the entire society benefits. Clinicians should continue to provide each child in the group with the language stimulation needed and give each the appropriate feedback.

Down's Syndrome

In the mentally retarded population, the Down's syndrome group is probably the earliest identified and the most widely recognizable. Medical science has studied the causes and physical factors related to all the various chromosomal errors that are possible. Of these, Down's syndrome represents the most children and the largest group, occurring in approximately one in every 600 to 700 births (Murphy, 1978). Down's children can be classified as:

- Trisomy 21, the most common, in which there is simply an extra #21 chromosome in each surviving cell
- Translocation, in which the extra #21 chromosome is attached to another chromosome (this is the type most likely to be transmitted genetically)
- Mosaicism, in which the chromosome error is produced early in the cell division but not with the first cell; cells succeeding from this faulty one contain an additional #21 chromosome while others will be normal (Pueschel, 1978).

While the syndrome has many possible physical characteristics, no single child has them all. Each has an individual cluster of symptoms (and, in fact, is much more an individual human being than a carrier of a syndrome). They have their own personalities, capabilities, and responses, just as any other children. It is known that early intervention is crucial to the ultimate training of these children but little actually is known about the specific nature of such training.

For years, the standard approach to Down's children was to wait until they were 4 or 5 years old and then begin training, which usually was only partially successful. However, the authors have had extremely positive experiences with very young Down's children in therapy by providing wide-ranging stimulation and an abundance of positive feedback and by keeping them busy in an effort to build curiosity and a notion of self as a mover in the world.

This implies assistive intervention through the parents as soon after the child is born as possible, with the earliest feasible inclusion in a specific group interaction. The authors have found that one Down's child can be included in each language nursery group of five or six normal children, to the benefit of all. This is an ideal placement for Down's children, who benefit most from being with normal young-sters, who then serve as role models.

It should be noted that Down's children generally are loving, gentle, and cooperative and a delight to have in any group. They may bring more of personal value to every member of the group, child, or teacher/clinician than any other one child enrolled. The authors are grateful to the Down's children in their lives for the enrichment they have added.

Emotional Disturbances

This general category covers a wide variety of psychological/emotional prob-lems and an untold number of degrees and combinations. They can be divided into three broad categories: psychosis, autism, and schizophrenia (Weiss & Lillywhite, 1981). They report that psychotic children rarely have true commu-nication problems but are so severely involved psychologically that they must be treated by psychiatrists or psychologists. Such children are unlikely to be enrolled in the preschool nursery. However, if they are entered in the nursery, it is essential that the speech/language pathologist work with and under the guidance of the psychological specialist.

Autism

Kanner (1973), who first identified autism, lists five symptoms:

1. inability to relate themselves to others in normal ways
2. obsessive desire to maintain sameness
3. failure to use language purposefully

4. fascination and dexterity in manipulating objects
5. good cognitive potential.

This condition is fairly rare, occurring in about five children in 10,000 according to the National Society for Autistic Children (Morgan, 1981) but it constitutes one of the major areas of concern to anyone who works with the emotionally disturbed. While little is known about this disorder, it apparently is congenital, and research may be beginning to identify organic or chemical causes for it (Morgan, 1981). "It is quite rare for the symptoms to emerge after 30 months of age." (Morgan, 1981, p. 13)

Children affected by this disorder are described as ritualistic, compulsive, and unable to relate to other people in a normal way, and appear to be at the mercy of their senses. They are characterized by extreme delay in language acquisition. Some never do so, and those who do often produce only bizarre and disordered utterances. Some have rather normal sounding utterances but are unable to use them in pragmatically acceptable and appropriate ways. They may be extremely echolalic and may never learn to use pronouns appropriately, adding even more confusion to their verbal output.

The diagnosis of autistic children, which is difficult, is the province of psychological specialists. Intervention is likely to be slow and ineffective. Because language disorders are a major component, speech/language clinicians are essential members of the team working with virtually all aspects of autistic children's development.

Schizophrenia

Apparently related to autism, schizophrenia is equally difficult to diagnose. Unlike autistic children, schizophrenics probably are not born that way, although investigation into this possibility is reported in the *New York Times,* June 7, 1983. While autism was defined originally as an early variant of schizophrenia, the two now are usually regarded as separate entities, although autism in preschoolers may progress into schizophrenia in school children. Morgan (1981) and Rimland (1964) illustrate the differences in onset and development between the two (Table 3-2).

This disorder probably has a specific onset and there are periods when the children seem normal. They probably are withdrawn, have difficulty relating to people, and may have hallucinations or delusions of persecution. Schizophrenic children's speech and language often are both delayed and deviant. There may be both articulation disorders and phonological problems as well.

These youngsters may have severe problems and require extensive intervention at the same time they are in need of psychological help. As was the case with the autistic or psychotic children, intervention with the schizophrenics must be coordinated with and follow the lead of the psychological specialist.

Table 3-2 Differences in Onset and Development of Autism and Schizophrenia

Autism	Schizophrenia
Very early onset, birth to 30 months	Initial period of normalcy with definite period of onset
Steady developmental course	Unsteady course, with relapses and remissions
Good physical health and development	Sickly, with developmental problems
Aloof, does not cuddle or interact with others	Clings as infant; responses confused and anxious
Little or no meaningful language, much echolalia	Bizarre language but not totally uncommunicative; much confusion in language formulation
Apparently no hallucinations or delusions	Periodic hallucinations and delusions of persecution
Mostly boys	About equal distribution between boys and girls

Source: Constructed from *Infantile Autism* by B. Rimland, published by Appleton-Century-Crofts, Inc., 1964, and from *The Unreachable Child: An Introduction to Early Childhood Autism* by S.B. Morgan, published by the Memphis State University Press, 1981.

Trauma (Including Abuse)

A number of other language disorders are based on emotional problems. These also may bring numerous speech/language problems requiring creative clinicians to work with psychological and other professionals to achieve the needed outcome. As Morgan (1981) notes, ". . . traumatic events occurring early in a child's life have caused language and speech not to develop, to stop after starting, or to be late developing, often with substantial disorders of various kinds" (p. 189).

Since children differ widely in their ability to adapt to their lives, what is traumatic for one youngster may not be a problem for another. Such things as a death of a loved one, a broken home, child abuse, new baby, sibling rivalry, extreme illness, etc., all have the potential to cause trauma. The results depend on the age and stage of development of the youngsters when the trauma occurred; results may range from elective mutism through psychotic reactions or behavior problems to stuttering.

Children can be permanently damaged by a variety of abuses. According to Weiss & Lillywhite (1981), the most common and most frequently overlooked is verbal abuse. Because of its close relationship with the emergence of the communicative process, this form has extreme potential for destroying children's fragile, emerging communication system.

It is quite possible that youngsters with emotional disorders would be in need of intervention at an early age. The language nursery could be an ideal solution, for there they have not only intensive language stimulation but also interactions with other children. It should be noted that, as with the mentally retarded, the small language group can absorb only one emotionally disturbed child at a time without changing its nature. The authors have periodically had very successful groups that contained one emotionally and/or one mentally retarded child with five or six normal ones.

Speech Problems

While they never would be a majority of any preschool language group, children with significant speech problems also are candidates for the language nursery. Cleft palate children, in addition to their basic speech problems, are likely to have hearing and language problems (McWilliams, 1982):

> For many [cleft palate children] the language disorder is a true form of disordered development and will require management of the type recommended for young children with language disabilities. The fact that the child has a cleft . . . may complicate language therapy but it will not change it. (p. 363)

After palate repair has been made, these children appear to benefit greatly from group language activities and varied stimulation of the language nursery program.

Similarly, children with phonological, fluency, or voice problems may benefit from the group activity and the language input and feedback, as well as the encouragement they receive from the Piagetian approach. In addition to the group activities, they need extensive individual attention to the remediation of their speech problems.

Idioglossia (in Twins)

Occasionally twins (or triplets) will develop a particularly strong idioglossia that lasts beyond the time when it should have turned to regular language.

According to Nicolosi, Harryman, and Kresheck (1980), idioglossia is:

> Any unique speech code invented by an individual which differs markedly from normal language standards . . . Type of jargon often used by

twins for communication between each other to the exclusion of others. (p. 101)

The twins may not appear able or anxious to develop the normal expected language. Their efforts to produce English result in language that is both delayed and highly deviant in semantics, syntax, and phonology. Pragmatics ordinarily is unaffected by idioglossia.

These children may require intensive assistance to ready themselves for public school. Ideally, they should be scheduled into two different sessions of the language nursery. This would give each the advantage of being in an appropriate language group and still separated from the twin. This separation appears necessary if each is to be motivated to communicate with others in the language of the culture and to build adequate language skills.

This may present insurmountable scheduling problems and clinicians must explore creative methods of scheduling to meet the needs of these children as fully as possible. For example, in the authors' situation it has been necessary to schedule both children into the same nursery group but schedule the individual therapy each received in such a way that they were separated for most of each session.

Environmental Differences

Children from environmentally impoverished or culturally different homes have done what they were expected to do and learned the language they were exposed to, and they do not have language problems. However, they may be scheduled into the language nursery program for added stimulation and to help them build vocabulary and a repertoire of culturally appropriate behaviors. The language nursery can help them organize themselves cognitively, linguistically, and socially.

Frequently they do very well in this setting, enjoying the interactions, learning quickly, responding normally to stimulus, and adding an extra dimension to the combined group experiences. The cultural exchange is beneficial for children and teachers/clinicians and may be especially rewarding to the parent group. This type of language nursery placement seldom is a long-term arrangement and the children soon are on their way to regular nursery and kindergarten.

Echolalia

While not a diagnostic category in the same way as the preceding ones, echolalia is a difficult language dysfunction. Children who are echolalic repeat what they just heard without visible signs of comprehension or processing, presenting special problems. This complicates the language intervention program and makes certain therapy formats less effective than others.

The language nursery setting seems counterproductive for echolalic children. This type of child is found most often among mentally retarded or autistic groups. Their inclusion in any group program based on language experiences, modeling, and expansion should be evaluated carefully. If they are scheduled into the nursery program, alternative means of eliciting and responding to language should be explored. It is likely that a much higher ratio of individual therapy to group activity would be beneficial.

The authors do not believe, because of the nature of the group language experience and the extensive modeling component, that the language nursery is appropriate for echolalic children.

The Group Approach

This discussion has covered types of children who might enhance the language nursery while benefiting from being enrolled in it, as well as one type that probably would not benefit. The authors' experience has been that so long as cognitive level and interest can be held relatively constant (except for mentally retarded children), groups can be formed from among those children who need such remediation. The group should be a blend of types so that the strengths and weaknesses of each child can help meet the needs of the others. This diversity adds to the group and provides strength and stability.

The authors' division of children into a sensorimotor group and a preoperational group provides continuity so they can move from one to the next with the attendant appropriate modifications in activities and emphasis. However, once formed, groups should remain as stable as possible, with promotion from sensorimotor to preoperational coming at the end of logical time segments or achievement levels.

After the groups have been carefully established, the goals chosen, and the children assimilated, the clinicians/teachers turn to the task of providing appropriate therapeutic activity.

SUMMARY

Diagnosis is a necessary first step in working with children who possess language delay or deviancy, although teachers or therapists always must maintain open minds in collecting data for the diagnosis and consciously endeavor to keep that step an open-ended process.

Many instruments and techniques, both standardized and nonstandardized, exist to help professionals determine an entry point to begin intervention. Careful study of the therapists' particular situation is necessary to guide selection from the many tests available. Much work in recent years has been devoted to identifying as early as possible the factors and conditions that place children at risk in developing the language of the family and social group.

Testing, whether for screening or diagnostic purposes, requires the use of a variety of instruments and techniques. Efforts to prepare testing materials have resulted in many diverse instruments and techniques, several of which have been evaluated here. It appears that a number of the tests measure skills other than language, i.e., articulation, vocabulary, or ability to imitate. Visual association and visual memory, for example, are not language abilities although they are important to an individual's functioning.

Several tests that do in fact evaluate children's language systems in pragmatics, semantics, syntax, and phonology were described and suggestions made for use in specific situations.

Various types of disorders and handicapping conditions were described and some ideas offered for benefits to be expected from placement in the language nursery.

DISCUSSION QUESTIONS

1. How do standardized and nonstandardized instruments for diagnosis differ in form and function?
2. How should teachers or therapists view diagnosis?
3. What seem to be the common factors that teachers or therapists should look for in the diagnostic population?
4. When does diagnosis end and intervention begin?

REFERENCES

Aram, D.M., & Nation, J.E. *Child language disorders*. St. Louis: The C.V. Mosby Company, 1982.

Armstrong, P.M. *A comparison of the Fluharty preschool speech and language screening test and the communication abilities test—screening*. Unpublished research, 1980. Available from P.M. Armstrong.

Bates, E. *Language in context: The acquisition of pragmatics*. New York: Academic Press, Inc., 1976.

Bates, E., & Johnston, J. Workshop presented at the Southwestern Ohio Speech and Hearing Association, Cincinnati, January 1979.

Berry, M.F. *Teaching linguistically handicapped children*. Englewood Cliffs, N.J.: Prentice-Hall, Inc., 1980.

Bloom, L.; Hood, L.; & Lightbown, P. Imitation in language development: If, when and why. *Cognitive Psychology*, 1974, 6, 380–420.

Bloom, L., & Lahey, M. *Language development and language disorders*. New York: John Wiley & Sons, Inc., 1978.

Brown, R. *A first language: The early stages*. Cambridge, Mass.: Harvard University Press, 1973.

Bzoch, K., & League, R. *The receptive expressive emergent language scale (REEL)*. Gainesville, Fla.: Tree of Life Press, 1971.

Carrow, E. *Carrow elicited language inventory*. Austin, Texas: Learning Concepts, Inc., 1974.

Chafe, W.L. *Meaning and the structure of language*. Chicago: The University of Chicago Press, 1970.

Chomsky, N. *Aspects of the theory of syntax*. Cambridge, Mass.: The MIT Press, 1965.

Crystal, D.; Fletcher, P.; & Garmen, M. *The grammatical analysis of language disability: A procedure for assessment and remediation*. New York: Elsevier North-Holland Publishing Company, 1976.

Dale, P.S. *Language development: Structure and function* (2nd Ed.). New York: Holt, Rinehart & Winston, Inc., 1976.

Danwitz, S.M.W. Formal versus informal assessment: Fragmentation versus holism. *Topics in Language Disorders*, 1981, *1*(3).

Darley, F.; Aranson, A.; & Brown, A. *Motor speech disorders*. Philadelphia: W.B. Saunders Company, 1975.

deVilliers, J.G., & deVilliers, P.A. A cross-sectional study of the acquisition of grammatical morphemes in child speech. *Journal of Psycholinguistic Research*, 1973, *2*(3).

Fluharty, N.B. *Fluharty preschool speech and language screening test*. Boston: Teaching Resources Corporation, 1978.

Gallagher, T.M., & Prutting, C.A. *Pragmatic assessment and intervention issues in language*. San Diego: College Hill Press, Inc., 1983.

Gauthier, S.V., & Madison, C.L. *Kindergarten language screening test*. Tigard, Ore.: C.C. Publications, Inc., 1978.

Geffner, D.S. Assessment of language disorders: Linguistic and cognitive functions. *Topics in Language Disorders*, 1981, *1*(3).

Goldman, R., & Fristoe, M. *Goldman-Fristoe test of articulation*. Circle Pines, Minn.: American Guidance Service, Inc., 1969.

Hedrick, D.; Prather, E.; & Tobin, A. *Sequenced inventory of communicative development* (SICD). Seattle: University of Washington Press, 1975.

Irwin, J.; Moore, J.; & Rampp, D. Nonmedical diagnosis and evaluation. In J. Irwin & M. Marge (Eds.), *Principles of childhood language disabilities*. New York: Appleton-Century-Crofts, Inc., 1972.

Johnston, E.B. *Development of the communicative abilities test for young children*. Unpublished doctoral dissertation, University of Cincinnati, 1978.

Johnston, E.B. *Communication abilities test—Screening*. Unpublished research, 1980. (Available from E.B. Johnston, 20 Bachelor Hall, Miami University, Oxford, Ohio.)

Johnston, E.B. *Communicative abilities test for young children*. Unpublished research, 1980.

Johnston, E.B.; Johnson, A.R.; & Weinrich, B.D. *Language through experience: A model for therapy*. Unpublished manuscript, 1978.

Kanner, L. *Childhood psychosis: Initial studies and new insights*. New York: H.V. Winston & Sons, 1973.

Kirk, S.; McCarthy, J.; & Kirk, W. *The Illinois test of psycholinguistic abilities* (Rev. Ed.). Urbana, Ill.: The University of Illinois Press, 1968.

Kretschmer, R.R., & Kretschmer, L.W. *Language development and intervention with the hearing impaired*. Baltimore: University Park Press, 1978.

Lee, L. Developmental sentence types. *Journal of Speech and Hearing Disorders*, 1966, *31* 311–330.

Lee, L. *The Northwestern syntax screening test*. Evanston, Ill.: Northwestern University Press, 1971.

Lee, L., & Canter, S. Developmental sentence scoring. *Journal of Speech and Hearing Disorders*, 1971, *36*, 315–341.

Lillywhite, H.S., & Bradley, D. *Communication problems in mental retardation*. New York: Harper & Row Publishers, Inc., 1969.

Lucas, E.V. *Semantic and pragmatic language disorders: Assessment and remediation*. Rockville, Md.: Aspen Systems Corporation, 1980.

McDonald, J., & Nichols, M. *Environmental language inventory* (ELI). Columbus, Ohio: Ohio State University Press, 1974.

McWilliams, B.J. Cleft palate. In G.H. Shames & E.H. Wiig, (Eds.), *Human communication disorders: An introduction*. Columbus, Ohio: The Charles E. Merrill Publishing Co., Inc., 1982.

Mecham, M.; Jones, D.; & Jex, L. *Utah test of language development*. Salt Lake City: Communication Research Associates, 1972.

Morgan, S.B. *The unreachable child: An introduction to early childhood autism*. Memphis: Memphis State University Press, 1981.

Muma, J.R. *Language handbook: Concepts, assessment, intervention*. Englewood Cliffs, N.J.: Prentice-Hall, Inc., 1978.

Murphy, A. A child with Down's syndrome is born. In S.M. Pueschel (Ed.), *Down's syndrome: Growing and learning*. Kansas City, Kan.: Sheed, Andrews & McMeel, Inc., 1978.

Myklebust, H.R. *Auditory disorders in children: A manual for differential diagnosis*. New York: Grune & Stratton, Inc., 1954.

Mysak, E.D. Cerebral palsy. In G.H. Shames & E.H. Wiig (Eds.), *Human communication disorders: An introduction*. Columbus, Ohio: The Charles E. Merrill Publishing Co., Inc., 1982.

Newcomer, P.H., & Hammill, D.D. *The test of language development*. Austin, Texas: Empire Press, 1977.

New York Times, June 7, 1983, Section C-2.

Nicolosi, L.; Harryman, E.; & Kresheck, J. *Terminology of communication disorders: Speech, language, hearing*. Baltimore: The Williams & Wilkins Co., 1980.

Northern, J.L., & Downs, M.P. *Hearing in children*. Baltimore: The Williams & Wilkins Co., 1974.

Northern, J.L., & Lemme, M. Hearing and auditory disorders. In G.H. Shames & E.H. Wiig (Eds.), *Human communication disorders: An introduction*. Columbus, Ohio: The Charles E. Merrill Publishing Co., Inc., 1982.

Open the door on child abuse and neglect, Prevention and Reporting Kit. Columbus, Ohio: Ohio Department of Public Welfare, Children's Protective Services (pamphlet).

Piaget, J. *The essential Piaget,* H. Gruber and J. Voneche (Eds.) New York: Basic Books, Inc., Publishers, 1977.

P.L. 94-142, *The Education for All Handicapped Children Act of 1975,* 20 U.S.C. 1401, 1411. Washington, D.C.: Government Printing Office, 1975.

Program evaluation measure (PEM). Baltimore: Baltimore City Public Schools, Office of Pupil and Program Monitoring and Appraisal.

Prutting, C.; Gallagher, T.; & Mulac, A. The expressive portion of the NSST compared to a spontaneous language sample. *Journal of Speech and Hearing Disorders,* 1975, *40,* 40–48.

Pueschel, S.M. The cause of Down's syndrome. In S.M. Pueschel (Ed.), *Down's syndrome: Growing and learning*. Kansas City, Kan.: Sheed, Andrews & McMeel, Inc., 1978.

Rimland, B. *Infantile autism*. New York: Appleton-Century-Crofts, Inc., 1964.

Schlesinger, I.M. Production of utterances and language acquisition. In D.I. Slobin (Ed.), *The ontogenesis of grammar*. New York: Academic Press, Inc., 1971.

Stevens, M.I. *Stevens oral language screening test*. Peninsula, Ohio: Interim Publishers, 1977.

Weiss, C.E., & Lillywhite, H.S. *Communicative disorders: Prevention and early intervention.* St. Louis: The C.V. Mosby Company, 1981.

Vygotsky, L.S. *Thought and language.* Cambridge, Mass.: The MIT Press, 1962.

Zimmerman, I., & Steiner, V. *Preschool language scale.* Columbus, Ohio: The Charles E. Merrill Publishing Co., Inc., 1979.

Chapter 4

The Curriculum

CHAPTER OBJECTIVES

After completing this chapter, readers will be able to:

1. Describe the ways curriculum for the nursery school implements the theory of Piaget.
2. Explain, at a beginning level, how the nursery school brings together child development, language development, and child management theory to facilitate each youngster's growth.
3. Explain the differences between experience and programmed therapy and when each would be used by the teacher/therapist.
4. Explain some criteria for developing goals for children: social, cognitive, language, and motor.
5. Develop a specific lesson plan designed to accomplish a specific social, cognitive, language, or motor goal.

KEY IDEAS

1. Children's total development must be the concern of the therapists and teachers in the language nursery.
2. A diverse nursery school program will facilitate children's development in all ways and is better than teaching them to perform a specific task.
3. Therapists/teachers, in designing the language nursery program, must pay considerable attention to sequencing specific goals carefully to foster optimum growth for each child.
4. Children acquire important knowledge in the cognitive, language, social, and motor areas as they are guided through play, refreshment, and cleanup activities in the nursery.

THE PIAGETIAN SCHOOL

After the initial diagnosis has been completed and a compatible group of children has been selected, the real business of planning the curriculum of the language nursery program begins. This actually involves four types of activity:

1. planning the overall curriculum
2. choosing individual goals
3. determining specific intervention techniques for specific children
4. planning appropriate activities for the parent group (to be discussed in Chapter 9)

Piagetian theories of the development of reality and language (1977) provide teachers with a way of looking at child development and integrating it into the preschool format (Kamii & DeVries, 1977). These theories form a skeleton structure into which elements of preschool education and language development are incorporated. The interactionist views of Piaget emphasize what is internal to each child and use indirect methods of encouraging their development of operativity. A fundamental in Piaget's theories, operativity refers to the basic structure of intelligence, specifically understanding, reasoning, thinking, and ideas (Kamii & DeVries, 1977; Piaget, 1977).

The proposed class or group program is specific in its approach and builds logically upon Piagetian presuppositions. Teachers and clinicians must keep in mind the key notions that:

1. Children pass through stages of development. They are not expected to be miniature adults but are expected to think in ways characteristic for their ages. The same stimulus (and feedback) does not function in the same way on children at ages of 1 month or 1, 3, 7, or 12 years (Kamii & DeVries, 1977).
2. Language and play, like cognition, develop over time. Children are expected to progress through a sequence of levels of language, play, and cognition, doing what is appropriate at each level.
3. The interaction between the clinician and the children should enhance their progress as they construct their own passage through the sequence.
4. Children should be encouraged to exercise their mental operations and to predict the outcome of activities.
5. Teachers are expected to ask questions that will encourage the children to expand their cognitive processes. This can best be done by encouraging creativity and innovation in play, stimulating the youngsters to seek new and novel ways of using materials and reacting to situations.

Play is crucial to children's development, and the younger they are, the more important it is. According to Kamii & DeVries, the play process is the instrument by which schemata develop. As the youngsters use their biological (and sensory) processes, exercising and stretching them to their limits, the schemata develop by differentiation and coordination.

Structural Base for Teachers

The Piagetian format the authors have devised provides a structure base for the teachers. They question, guide, and encourage the children to manipulate, learn to predict, and construct information. The youngsters must rely on their own initiative and intelligence in actually manipulating their environment. Thus, very young children can begin to succeed. Isolated exercises to improve specific sensory skills usually are of little value. What the children need is to engage their own senses and entire intelligence in constructing a personal reality. "Spontaneous play should be the primary context in which teachers encourage the use of intelligence and initiative" (Kamii & DeVries, 1977, p. 372).

Children construct knowledge in three areas:

1. Sensorimotor knowledge is constructed as they interact with their physical environment. Its beginnings must precede other development.
2. Socioemotional knowledge is constructed as children interact with others. Social knowledge depends in part on logicomathematical knowledge.
3. Logicomathematical knowledge is built as the children reflect on their observations of physical phenomena (Kamii & DeVries, 1977). It is not taught specifically, but children are encouraged to develop it in an orderly fashion. Once constructed, logicomathematical knowledge furnishes the base for further physical knowledge—a way of thinking that, once learned, will not be forgotten.

To test progress through the various developmental stages, a set of Piagetian tasks is used to sample the levels at which the children are functioning. These tasks could be taught in school but their predictive value would be diminished. If children were directly taught conservation of liquid, for example, they might get much less of the necessary feedback from the environment and have less actual experience with the notion. The resulting learning probably would be merely a splinter skill and not the organized construction that would fit into the overall structure.

According to Kamii and DeVries (1977):

> It is true that one can directly teach children to perform better on Piagetian tasks. However, such teaching promotes social conformity,

rather than reflecting abstraction . . . [It] Usually results in the "passing on" of correct answers to the child's genuine way of thinking. More important, however, a child who learns to give the "right answer" is likely to become unsure of his own ability to figure things out. (p. 385)

Educators who hold a more programmed educational philosophical view tend to plan for the teaching of specific skills in their schools. According to Kamii and DeVries (1977, p. 369), "Cognitive development is not a matter of improving cognitive skills as one would program a computer or build an information processing machine." If the school program is aimed at isolating and programming in specific cognitive skills, the end result almost surely will be no more than a collection of fragments, unrelated to each other or to reality.

These two concepts (Piagetian and programmed) represent divergent educational approaches. Educators may feel required to consider both and choose between a main focus on education for content (the teaching of specific skills) and education for process (encouraging the construction process so children are active in building their education). True Piagetian teachers can be expected to focus on the construction of a process model, which will necessarily incorporate content.

Cognition Also a Key Element

While the focus of this program is specifically language, teachers and clinicians must plan the setting carefully so all opportunities for cognitive development are exploited for the full benefit of each child. The curriculum generally is derived from Piagetian theory, basic child development, and a language development curriculum and adapted by daily living activities. To quote Kamii & DeVries (1977), again, the teacher's intent is to focus on the cognitive realm:

1. Teach in the context of the child's play.
2. Encourage and accept the child's wrong answers.
3. Figure out what the child is thinking about and teach according to the three kinds of knowledge.
4. Teach to content as well as to process. (pp. 383–384)

Teachers and clinicians will learn to consider each child and each activity. They must know what children are interested in and what level of thinking they have achieved. It is necessary to accept the youngsters' current thinking and work from that foundation. The professionals choose experiences with which children can interact in play and that illustrate the specified targets.

As the children experience the problem or project, the teachers stimulate thinking by open-ended comments and questions such as, "I wonder what will happen if . . . ," "I project that . . . ," "I wonder why that happened?" etc. In addition, appropriate feedback and encouragement must be given so children will know when they are on the right track and will find satisfaction in the activity and feel good about themselves. It is important that they never be given the idea that the problems must be answered only or at all in the way the adult has chosen. If reaching the "approved adult conclusion" becomes the primary goal, the youngsters' creativity is diminished and their thinking becomes restricted.

It becomes the task of teachers or clinicians to construct interesting problems and activities and to pose questions that help make the children aware of interrelationships within them. Ideally, the learning situation should be both challenging and enjoyable so the children see no separation between work and play.

THE GENERAL CURRICULUM

While staff members and aides differ from setting to setting, the curriculum chosen can be adapted easily to the particular personnel and facilities available. When planning for severely language impaired children, the authors have found that more adults are needed to ensure that each youngster receives the appropriate amount of assistance. The curriculum should include a balanced combination of language activities arranged to move fluently from individual to group interactions (Table 4-1).

Careful planning of language activities and use of free playtime provides the clinician with the opportunity to encourage the children in the development of the cognitive and language goals chosen (see Tables 4-2 and 4-3).

The language nursery program appears to function best when it meets at least two hours a day, no less than four days a week. The authors favor the curriculum discussed next.

Opening Exercises

This time is devoted to roll call and discussing the weather, day, date, etc. The children gather in a group and begin the day by responding to the roll-call question, "Who is here today?" by either "I am here today. Johnny is here today," or some variation, while placing the appropriate pictures of themselves on a chart. The class roll and the calendar are represented by flannel boards upon which children can place photographs as well as felt shapes representing the weather (clouds, sun, rain, etc.), day, and date. (In this program, pictures are taken of each child by instant print cameras. These pictures have the advantage of being readily identifiable by each child, no matter how young or inexperienced.)

This is followed by a discussion of the season and the weather. Weather permitting, children are taken outside to do this so they can relate physically to the description of weather conditions. They then return to the room to place the

Table 4-1 Sample Daily Lesson Plan for a Group

Activity	Implementation	Equipment
Opening Exercises:	roll call; day/weather	flannel board and felt pieces
Group Language Experiences:	making paper bag puppets	small brown bags, crayons, glue, bits of felt, etc.
Free Play:	children's choice	toys in the nursery
Cleanup:	children put toys away	Song: "Picking Up Toys"
Snack Time:	children sit around table	cookies and fruit juice
Story Time:	children read silently for a few minutes; clinician then reads one story, with flannel board.	stories from bookshelf, "Little Red Riding Hood"
Music Time:	rhythm band, marching time	piano, records, instruments
McGinnis Circle:	children sit in circle and take turns responding to clinician	McGinnis cards, objects; marshmallow rewards
Cleanup:	children put toys away	Song: "Picking Up Toys"

appropriate pictures on the felt calendar. If the weather is bad, the children go to the outside doors and discuss what they see. For some children this marks the first time they have directly discussed a particular attribute and then removed themselves to some distance and related it to some activity (as in discussing the rain and walking back to the room to represent it on the flannel board).

Group Language Experience

For very young children, group experiences must be extremely simple, basic, and closely related to their daily lives, e.g., stacking blocks, playing with clay, washing dishes, etc. For older preschoolers, the group language experiences can be more complex: crafts, cooking, or elementary science experiments. The group experience is a continuing activity chosen by the clinician to stimulate specific language.

The children take part in the activity and are stimulated to produce the appropriate language. They benefit from joining in this interaction with other children and the adults. They are given numerous opportunities to hear appropriate language as it is related to facts and to receive the models, prompts, and feedback that let them know how well they are producing the target language.

Table 4-2 Examples of Goals Being Reached by Sensorimotor Activities

Language Nursery Activities	Ego Boundary	Social Awareness Responses	Object Constancy	Coordinated space	Temporality	Causality	Symbolic Play	Imper./Ques.	Gesture Language	Prosody	Phonology	Chaining	Holistic	Subject-Verb Dichotomy	Hearing Listening
Manipulation of Toys in Free Play	X		X	X		X	X								
Block Building			X	X		X	X								
Painting			X	X											
Role Play	X	X	X	X	X	X	X	X	X	X	X	X	X	X	X X
Stories		X	X	X	X		X	X	X	X	X	X	X	X	X X
Singing/Playing Instruments		X	X	X		X									X X
Movement				X											
Sand/Water Play			X	X	X		X								
Large Muscle Equipment			X	X											
Table Games (puzzles, bead stringing, etc.)			X	X											
Language Experiences		X	X	X	X	X		X	X	X	X	X	X	X	X X
Interactive Stories															
McGinnis Associative Therapy		X	X	X				X			X	X	X	X	X X
General Operation within the Group Setting	X	X	X												X X

Source: Cognitive portion adapted from "Piaget for Early Education" by Constance Kamii and Rheta DeVries in *The Preschool in Action: Exploring Early Childhood Programs* (2nd ed.), M.C. Parker and R.K. Parker (Eds.), published by Allyn & Bacon, Inc., Boston. Copyright © 1977, by permission of Allyn & Bacon, Inc. Language portion from *The Piagetian Preschool: A Model for Language Remediation*, paper presented by E.B. Johnston and D.C. Hutchinson to the American Speech and Hearing Association, Detroit, 1980, by permission of the authors.

Table 4-3 Example of Goals Being Reached by Preoperational Activities

Language Nursery Curriculum in Terms of a Piagetian Framework — Cognitive Goals

Preoperational Period — Language Goals

Language Nursery Activities	Classification	Seriation	Number	Physical Knowledge	Spatial Reasoning	Temporal Reasoning	Social Knowledge	Index	Symbol	Sign	Pragmatics -Appro. to Situation & Listener -Initiate Conversation -Topicalize -Ask/Answer Questions	Semantics (Developmental Progression)	Syntax (Developmental Progression)	Phonology (Developmental Progression)	Hearing Listening
Manipulation of Toys in Free Play	X	X	X	X	X	X	X	X	X						
Block Building	X		X	X	X	X			X						
Painting				X					X						
Role Playing						X	X	X	X	X	X	X	X	X	X
Stories				X		X	X		X	X	X	X	X	X	X
Singing/Playing Instruments			X	X		X		X	X	X					X
Movement															
Sand/Water Play					X					X					
Large Muscle Equipment				X	X			X							
Table Games (puzzles, bead stringing, etc.)	X	X					X	X	X	X					
Problem-Solving Activities	X			X		X	X	X	X	X					
Language Experiences							X		X	X	X	X	X	X	X
Interactive Stories							X		X	X	X	X	X	X	X
McGinnis Associative Therapy							X	X	X	X	X		X	X	X

Source: Cognitive portion adapted from "Piaget for Early Education," by Constance Kamii and Rheta DeVries in The Preschool in Action: Exploring Early Childhood Programs (2nd ed.), M.C. Parker and R.K. Parker (Eds.), published by Allyn & Bacon, Inc., Boston. Copyright © 1977, by permission of Allyn & Bacon, Inc. Language portion from The Piagetian Preschool: A Model for Language Remediation, paper presented by E.B. Johnston and D.C. Hutchinson to the American Speech and Hearing Association, Detroit, 1980, by permission of the authors.

They often have their first experiences at cooperating with others and find great pleasure in the way language relates to what is going on. The authors find that this soon becomes the most valued and valuable language development time in the entire program.

Free Play

Certainly one of the most important and productive parts of the daily curriculum is that spent in free play. During this time, each child is allowed to choose activities and to express personal ideas.

While teachers/clinicians are expected to take every available opportunity to strengthen cognitive development, this particular time is most valuable. They use the Piagetian model of questioning to stimulate children to construct cognitive operations. For example, the clinician during play time with a child might use questions like, "I wonder why that happened?", "What do you think would happen if . . .?", "How can we make . . .?", and "Tell me what happened," always keeping in mind that questions must be at the child's level of operation and must stimulate them to think. They follow the youngsters' lead in choice of toys, activities, and type of dialogue. They accept the children's ideas and through them build cognitive and linguistic levels. They model and give the needed feedback and encourage the children to keep trying. The adults often find themselves interacting with several children in the same activity at the same time. They must take care to respond at each child's level of language and cognitive functioning.

It is important to realize that adults often have strong preconceived notions about how children will play. It sometimes appears that the direction, "You may play with anything you wish," seems to spur adults on to even more preconceived notions of how things should be. This must be resisted strongly. Care must be taken that this time neither be abridged by more adult planned activity nor be directed by the adults.

Refreshment Time

This occurs in the middle of each session. It is a time when children sit around the table and have selected refreshments. Children take turns helping make snacks, distribute napkins and cups, and clean up afterward. These tasks provide opportunities for learning one-to-one correspondence, sequence of operations, turn taking, following directions, social consideration, etc.

Children are given the first snack and serving of a drink. (Since adults do not hold the drinks for them and do not want to spend more than the minimum amount of time cleaning up, and since they do not nag, the servings are notably small.) It is infinitely better to provide seconds and even thirds and fourths of one-ounce servings than to spend interminable time cleaning up.

This first bit of refreshment is "on the house" whether or not the children ask for it. Thereafter, they have to make some appropriate effort to request anything more. Refreshment time is ideal for encouraging children in social graces, e.g., saying "please" and "thank you" and being considerate of each other.

Story Time

After refreshment time each day, the children are encouraged to sit in a circle on their mats on the floor and look at the pages of a book that they personally have chosen from the shelf. The authors believe that this is the way children learn to respect books and to expect them to be a source of pleasure. In part they learn to read and to value reading by doing so and seeing others do so. They acquire respect for the power of books by watching adult models in their lives.

Children are encouraged to look at their books and comment on the pictures. The younger the group, the more closely this story time resembles the story minute, but all children go through the exercise each day. (They are not allowed to wander off and find something to play with during that period.) Following this brief encounter between the child and the book, one of the adults chooses a short story and reads or tells it to the group. This is often done with the aid of a flannel board, acting out the story, etc.

It has been the authors' experience over the years that many of the children who have graduated from this program have gone on to become highly successful readers, often reading several grades above their age level. While some children initially resist story time, they soon become enthusiastic "readers."

McGinnis Therapy

This is the only programmed technique routinely employed in the language nursery curriculum. Loosely patterned on the earliest level of the association method (McGinnis, 1963), it helps children learn to sit in a semicircular group, respond to requests by clinicians, and return to their seats. They are called one by one to stand in front of the teacher, who asks them to select a toy and name it or to produce language related to it (depending on the individual child's language ability). They are shown a card upon which the name of the object is written in cursive and the relationship between sound and symbol is emphasized (pointed to). Following an acceptable attempt, they are given a food reward (generally a popular cereal) and asked to return to their seats. There are a number of other features and levels in the McGinnis method that are not used in the language nursery.

As children become able to respond to the format, they are encouraged to trade places with the teacher so they also can learn to operate in the "teacher" role. As soon as the teacher or clinician feels that the children have mastered this format, have learned to attend, respond, and return to their seats, the technique is terminated. The authors have found that the 2-year-old group has responded well to this brief segment of highly structured time and has benefited greatly from it. This technique seldom is continued into the preoperational level, the time being used for more challenging work.

Music Time

Music is a powerful teaching medium, especially with young children. Part of each day's curriculum is devoted to music in some form. Children take part in a rhythm band, performing on instruments along with either the record player or the piano.

Songs with a clear, steady rhythm are chosen and children enjoy and benefit from the opportunity to hear and respond to the music. Easy songs, especially those involving finger and hand motions, are fun and the children enjoy learning to incorporate melody, rhythm, lyric, and hand games into a relaxed situation. They often begin to "sing" a few key words meaningfully as soon as they can produce the words and often before they have other linguistic uses for them. Marching and rhythmic games also help them learn to incorporate physical activity into a meaningful format.

Learning to play an instrument in the rhythm band gives children a feeling of accomplishment. They learn that they can join a group and produce music, and they learn to think of themselves as agents or doers of things. The physical activity in rhythm may be especially important to the continuing language therapy because of the high correlation between motor ability and language development (Perkins & Perkins, 1977).

Individual Language Therapy

Very young nursery school children (the 2-year-olds) do not always appear ready for individual language therapy but the older (age 3 and above) preschoolers always are also scheduled into short daily individual language therapy sessions administered by a clinician from their own nursery session. This keeps their interactions centered in a specific group of teachers and supervisors and prevents the confusion that may come when they are served by a number of professionals simultaneously. These sessions are planned with each particular child's needs in mind and are correlated carefully with the other group activities.

Specific methods, chosen according to the nature of the children's problems, are incorporated into the individual sessions (see the section on Specific Language Intervention later in this chapter).

Individual therapy may be a combination of a number of techniques or it may be a single one. Any combination of programmed techniques may be used and sometimes is. However, these are not really consistent with the developmental philosophy of the Piagetian Language Nursery. More compatible techniques such as experience therapy and interactive therapy are the methods of choice.

In the experience technique, the clinician chooses an activity and models the target language while performing the activity with the children. They are encouraged to practice the target language and are given appropriate prompts and feedback. The relationship is carefully maintained between the language and what is true in the environment. It is most effective for children through the age of 6 or 7.

After children have gotten a little old for experience therapy, they often enjoy and benefit from interactive therapy, as described by Lee, Koenigshnecht, and Mulhern of Northwestern (1975). This method also uses modeled experiences, prompts, and feedback but in a somewhat more abstract manner. Stories containing a number of targets are presented and illustrated on flannel boards. This format is less structured than experience therapy and is an excellent way of providing carryover practice for middle-grade children. The format also is enjoyed by preschoolers who are ready to work on a number of targets at one time and who can operate comfortably in the somewhat more abstract context.

Cleanup Time

This important activity takes place several times during the session, notably after free play, before snacks, and before going home. It is an important part of the curriculum for two reasons:

1. It is necessary to keep the play/work area orderly. A chaotic array of toys and clutter actually deters and hampers the planned productive activity.
2. Children benefit from learning to cooperate in the cleanup, categorize and put away toys, take responsibility in the context, etc.

The clinicians do not always find this an easy activity to introduce but the children do fall into the spirit of it, especially when they learn to sing a specific song about "Picking Up the Toys" and when it is played while they work. In this way the work becomes a game of sorts. As children learn to do this necessary task without undue pressure, they learn to take more pride in their school and the way it looks to others.

CONDUCTING THE NURSERY PROGRAM

The planned curriculum must be kept moving and lively. A quick pace maintains the children's interest in day-to-day activity. The conduct of the class sets the tone for pupil interaction. If teachers keep their voices calm and quiet, the children reflect this more controlled atmosphere in their emerging communication. If teachers do not yell, threaten, or continually repeat requests, children learn to listen the first time and do not have a model of yelling and threatening to follow.

This also improves the overall tone of the group interaction. If the adults speak with the same consideration and politeness they would use with a valued guest in their homes, the children respond in a like manner most of the time. This is not to say that every child, and every teacher, for that matter, does not have less controlled moments. It only suggests that these be held to a minimum.

It is important to plan the curriculum to take advantage of the special holidays that punctuate the year. No celebration should be elaborate, nor should parties last any longer than a few minutes. Children add to their temporal map as they mark the passage of Halloween, Thanksgiving, Christmas, Hanukkah, St. Valentine's Day, Easter, Memorial Day, and Independence Day, as these are important in their community. The opportunity can be taken to teach children about their heritage at these times, thus enriching them socially and culturally.

It also appears to the authors that some of the material and time available can be designed to introduce the children to good music, literature, and art. They can learn to enjoy and appreciate some of the more lasting productions at their own age and level. In the same vein, if the group contains children of other cultural backgrounds, they all can benefit from introductions to the divergent cultural heritages: the Americans because they learn something new and the others because they see that others value the beauties of their culture.

For example, Kim Yen, age 3½, was delighted to bring a Korean book to school to show the group. He was thrilled when the teacher chose his book to read aloud. Although he lacked the language to express it, he was proud of his book and happy that others admired his culture. The other children benefited from seeing the book and from the growing knowledge that beauty exists in all the cultures of the world.

PROGRAMMED AND EXPERIENCE THERAPY

The choice of therapy model must be made individually for each child. The authors believe that a wide variety of therapies will be indicated for members of the group. Clinicians who have looked discriminately at the needs of their patients find themselves working with the entire range of techniques.

The programmed methods of therapy are not really compatible with the Piagetian philosophy because they stem from widely different philosophies about learning. Nevertheless, there are occasions when programmed methods are most efficient. They are quick ways to start the children responding appropriately and also to improve learning behavior so they are freer to learn.

In the authors' view, the major deficiencies of these methods are:

1. their failure to work on development of pragmatics, semantics, syntax, and phonology
2. their tendency to train the children in rote imitation of unrelated fragments of language
3. the fact that the language they produce is not really generated and not necessarily founded in truth and reality
4. the lack of generalization from the target structures to other structures.

There is something essential about experience in the learning of language. The experience technique is compatible with the Piagetian philosophy because it is consistent with the learning model recommended. This method is efficient in that it:

1. allows clinicians to target pragmatics, semantics, syntax and phonology
2. trains the children to see the essential relationship between language and reality
3. helps the children develop operating rules so they will have the capacity to generate new and novel sentences
4. generalizes from the target structure in a natural manner to all other structures used with it
5. is done in the format in which the children naturally learn language so it is not subject to extinction from cessation of therapy.

The following two studies speak directly to the potential for improvement and generation to other structures that are possible from experience therapy.

Research with the Experience Model

Menyuk (1971) reports a carefully controlled study by Kolstóva, a Russian linguist, in which two matched groups of 20-month-old children were given the identical amount of language stimulation. One group was given only the direct model: "This is a doll. Tell me doll. Say doll." Members of the other group did everything with the doll. They bathed it, fed it, changed it, and spanked it. At the completion of the input, each child was taken individually into a room filled with toys and asked to find all the dolls. Those who had received only the identification model were able to find only the one doll they trained with while those who had experienced the doll were able to find every doll in the room.

A series of comparison studies was made of two groups, one undergoing normal development and the other interactive therapy, which operates on an experiential base (Lee, Koenschnicht, & Mulhern, 1975). At the conclusion of the study, all the children in both groups had learned the target structures. While they still had language problems, members of the experience group exceeded the normal group in rate of acquisition and also generalized to a wide variety of other structures, all of which they used generatively.

Examination of the research, experience with the therapy over time, and philosophical choice of model all point to the experience model as the method of choice in the Piagetian preschool nursery setting, for a number of reasons:

1. It is the most natural way to learn language.
2. It innately relates language to meaning.
3. It focuses on generated language rather than rote imitation.
4. It produces language that generalizes via experience to new structures.
5. It is embedded so well in the children that at the termination of therapy, structures learned by experience do not fade out.
6. It allows for simultaneous advances in pragmatics, semantics, syntax, and phonology.

CHOOSING INDIVIDUAL GOALS

Once the working diagnosis has been made, the results (see Exhibit 3-3 in Chapter 3) are scrutinized carefully and areas where the children's development lags behind their cognitive functioning are identified (see Table 4-4 for profile chart) and specific ways of meeting these needs are built into the nursery plan. The intent is to bring all other areas of their functioning up to the cognitive level, then systematically elevate the level of the whole (Figure 4-1).

Cognitive Goals

The cognitive function having been assessed, specific materials and interactions are chosen to give the youngsters the opportunity to construct the next cognitive level. This is done by providing appropriate materials, with meaningful modeling and feedback, but mainly by the use of the Piagetian questioning mode (discussed earlier in this chapter).

For Ira, the child in Exhibit 3-3, cognitive goals might include activities for symbolic formation and for encouraging early classification skills.

Language Goals

Communication goals are set for each child to bring the language to the expected level. The goals are pragmatic, semantic, syntactic, and/or phonological, as

Table 4-4 Profile of Child's Development

KEY: + Most items passed
± About half passed
− Few items passed

Child's Name _____ Age _____
Is the child's voice normal? _____ Is the child's fluency normal? _____
Is the child cooperative? _____ Does the child have any health problems? _____

Directions: Circle the symbol that applies in each case and draw profile.

Age	Speech	Receptive Language	Expressive Language	Cognition	Gross Motor	Fine Motor	Self-Help	Social
6 yrs.	+ ± −	+ ± −	+ ± −	+ ± −	+ ± −	+ ± −	+ ± −	+ ± −
5½	+ ± −	+ ± −	+ ± −	+ ± −	+ ± −	+ ± −	+ ± −	+ ± −
5	+ ± −	+ ± −	+ ± −	+ ± −	+ ± −	+ ± −	+ ± −	+ ± −
4½	+ ± −	+ ± −	+ ± −	+ ± −	+ ± −	+ ± −	+ ± −	+ ± −
4	+ ± −	+ ± −	+ ± −	+ ± −	+ ± −	+ ± −	+ ± −	+ ± −
3½	+ ± −	+ ± −	+ ± −	+ ± −	+ ± −	+ ± −	+ ± −	+ ± −
3	+ ± −	+ ± −	+ ± −	+ ± −	+ ± −	+ ± −	+ ± −	+ ± −
2½	+ ± −	+ ± −	+ ± −	+ ± −	+ ± −	+ ± −	+ ± −	+ ± −
2	+ ± −	+ ± −	+ ± −	+ ± −	+ ± −	+ ± −	+ ± −	+ ± −
1½	+ ± −	+ ± −	+ ± −	+ ± −	+ ± −	+ ± −	+ ± −	+ ± −
1	+ ± −	+ ± −	+ ± −	+ ± −	+ ± −	+ ± −	+ ± −	+ ± −

Source: Reprinted from *The Piagetian Preschool: A Model for Language Remediation,* paper presented by Elizabeth B. Johnston and Dianne C. Hutchinson to the American Speech and Hearing Association, Detroit, 1980, by permission of the authors.

Figure 4-1 Overall Therapy Model

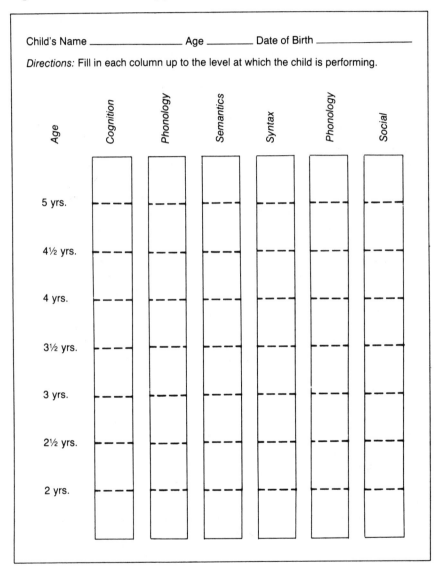

Child's Name _____ Age _____ Date of Birth _____

Directions: Fill in each column up to the level at which the child is performing.

appropriate. For Ira, the boy in Exhibit 3-3, the earliest and most necessary pragmatic goals would appear to be eye contact and verbal turn taking. Semantic goals involve meaningful vocabulary and learning to use the agent-action-patient relationship.

While clinicians must model the correct syntax and articulation at all times, they should refrain from focusing on these elements at this time to avoid overloading the children's systems. Syntactic goals therefore are deferred until a broader semantic-pragmatic base has been established and then would begin with Kernels 1 and 2, the easiest direct action sentences in the language and the use of modality.

The correct production of the sounds also is deferred until an appropriate base has been established. Initially the children should be encouraged to make the voice-voiceless distinction and to expand this to the other phonemic distinctions that, if they were normal, would have been established during the first year of life.

These targets should be designed to bring the entire system into a developmental order. When the children's development reaches an appropriate even level across systems, the entire set is worked on simultaneously, advancing the language in a systematic way (Figure 4-1). (In this it would appear that the clinician, first, is minimizing the deviancy of the language and, second, remediating the delay.) The main emphasis begins and remains firmly on cognition.

Language is taught in appropriate context and the children are encouraged to construct it. If they have specific problems that cause the language disorder, these should be considered and the special intervention indicated should be provided. For example, a hearing impaired child would have special activities designed to minimize the effects of the hearing loss and a cerebral palsied child might have specific head control, breathing, and/or phonation practice.

For Ira, the boy in Exhibit 3-3, special activities designed to remediate the oral apraxia should be planned. The child is taken systematically through a series of oral exercises, often of a rhythmic nature, ultimately working on the oral apraxia.

Social Goals

These objectives are chosen to help the children learn to interact appropriately for their ages. This training can best be implemented by the examples and expectations set by the teachers, therapists, and aides. It has been the authors' experience that when adults provide a good example, with quietly spoken, polite language and consideration for others, this atmosphere can prevail even in a preschool setting.

Since the aim of the program is to encourage the children to become not only autonomous and self-confident but also cooperative and considerate, a minimum of adult rules is imposed and children are encouraged to work out their own problems insofar as possible. A quiet order is advised in which each child can be encouraged to achieve the socioemotional goals established. It seems at this level that the less competitive the interactions are, the more considerate and cooperative the children are.

For Ira, it seems likely that his goals in this area also relate to the pragmatic objectives of eye contact and turn taking. In addition, he has the social goal of learning to interact with others in the setting, at least one at a time. Since there are some emerging behavior problems and the child's self-esteem is very low, the teacher can strive to build a warm relationship to help him establish trust and become less discouraged. He must come to expect that some good can come his way and begin to build some self-confidence and self-esteem. Ira should be encouraged to learn to share by the example of the clinicians. The authors do not believe children learn to share by external force but rather by being shared with and feeling that there is equity in their world.

For example, Jason, barely 3, willingly shares his toys because others in his world have always shared with him. He perceives the world as a fair place in which people are happy to share what they have with little brothers and others. After helping his mother make a cherry pie, Jay unfortunately fell asleep before the pie was cut. Early morning found him knocking on her door, confident that "his pie" was waiting for him. As he expected, his pie had been covered with wrap and placed in the refrigerator. His confidence in home justice was confirmed and his own ability to deal generously with others strengthened.

Motor Goals

For many children who have goals in the other areas, motor development should present no problem. They are not assigned specific remedial goals but are encouraged to continue developing their motor skills. Other children may need physical practice to enhance their motor development. Consultation with occupational and/or physical therapists or body management specialists is highly recommended for this intervention. Goals may well be set that develop a number of motor abilities in hierarchical order. Since motor development correlates more highly with language development than any other area (Perkins & Perkins, 1977), attention to motor development is a necessity.

Ira probably would have the motor goal of developing and smoothing motor movements that are regarded as awkward, especially those prerequisite to other motor development. This could be expected to be related to the finding of oral apraxia. After consultation, this can be implemented through specific games, exercises, activities, and practice.

SPECIFIC LANGUAGE INTERVENTION

So far, the Piagetian format, the overall conduct of the sessions, and the general curriculum have been discussed. Goals have been established for each of the children in social, cognitive, language, and perhaps motor areas. Children who are mature enough to respond in individual therapy have time in their schedules for it. Since there are a number of children in the nursery group, some are sure to have widely different overriding problems. It is necessary that clinicians or teachers not only establish meaningful goals and group activities but also be aware of the specific needs signaled by each child's special problems. These special needs must be met during both group and individual times by teacher/clinician interactions with the particular child. The professional must understand what the disability means to the child and how intervention relates to all aspects of the program.

Children who have one specific disorder may well have a cluster of other problems, i.e., delayed cognitive development (often resulting from the major problem), social development delay, motor dysfunctions, hearing difficulties, and psychological or behavioral disorders. They also may have some degree of mental retardation, whether or not this is related to the major problem. This combination must be considered in the overall planning and remediation built into the therapy program.

It is important to remember that intervention must consist of the combination of group and individual activities most appropriate for each child. It must contain a carefully balanced combination of intervention for the primary disorder and elements designed to alleviate the secondary problems. It must be remembered that no language exists in a vacuum. Pragmatic goals specific to each child must be established and can act as a framework or superstructure within which other knowledge can be constructed.

An important element in implementing intervention with children is the establishment of the social framework that can support the developing communication. This requires the clinician to understand the youngsters' social context and problems, be able to plan appropriate practice sessions, and give the children the opportunity to learn how to communicate effectively within it. While research continues in all areas, the following represents current understanding.

Hearing Disorders

In planning remediation for the hearing impaired (see the diagnostic discussion in Chapter 3), group and individual therapy become highly important. In general, the earlier any problem with hearing is identified, the better off the children will be. As soon as the problem is identified, work can begin at minimizing its effects. If any medical/surgical intervention is indicated, it must be done at the earliest logical time. If a hearing aid is warranted, it must be provided as early as possible so the children will have all the advantages of sound as they learn about their world.

Moderate Sensorineural Loss

Children with moderate peripheral sensorineural hearing loss can be incorporated into a group more easily than the more severely impaired. It is to be hoped that they are wearing an appropriate hearing aid and are ready to begin to learn language.

Care must be taken to provide comprehensive social experiences so children learn in social situations that previously may have been confusing to them. The teachers must monitor the cognitive development of every child, being sure the foundations being put down form a solid base for later learning. These children may need a great deal of initial encouragement to keep on trying but this should become less of a problem as success meets their efforts. Individual therapy must incorporate speech, voice, articulation, and language into overall learning experiences (Northern & Lemme, 1982). Experience-based therapy has proved to be a powerful tool in working with the hearing impaired (Kretschmer & Kretschmer, 1978; Streng, Kretschmer, & Kretschmer, 1978) and one that helps children relate the reality of the cognitive world with appropriate linguistic expression.

Conductive Loss

Children with conductive hearing losses (probably caused by recurrent otitis media) may be among the majority of those who have hearing disorders but may be the least understood. While it is quite possible that *hearing may be normal* at the time of the diagnosis, the residual effects of several bouts with otitis media may have resulted in an incomplete and distorted auditory background with which to learn (Zinkus & Gottlieb, 1978). The most obvious result of this is failure to develop language but the underlying problems of cognitive distortion, social delay, lack of self-confidence, and discouragement also are factors.

If the destructive nature of middle ear infection has not been understood, the children may have the problems of the more severely hearing impaired and/or the perceptual problems of learning disabled (LD) youngsters (Zinkus & Gottleib, 1978), including a reduced prognosis for achieving normal function. In such cases, therapy might more closely resemble that for sensorineural loss.

If the middle ear disease has been identified and understood, parents will have been informed of potential problems and ways of minimizing them. If the necessary adaptations are made, i.e., surgical or medical treatment, etc., these children should be able to progress in a rather normal developmental order even though delayed, with therapy if and when indicated. If their learning situation is uncomplicated by other problems, they could be expected to become essentially normal in many areas, with good prognosis for full habilitation.

Profound Hearing Loss or Deafness

Children with profound peripheral hearing loss or peripheral deafness are more handicapped than those discussed earlier. They are likely to have many other problems that accompany deafness and produce deviant learning patterns, emotional overlays, etc.

Very young deaf children probably lack communication and may become so frustrated that extreme behavior problems develop, as noted earlier. They may or may not have been identified as hearing impaired and a hearing aid fitted. Their prognosis often is highly questionable.

It is an unfortunate fact that many young deaf and severely hearing impaired children are unidentified. When mothers try their natural "motherese" on them, the youngsters do not hear and so do not respond. Mothers become discouraged and quit, with the result that children who need auditory stimulation the most may receive the least. Even if the deafness has been identified, parents still may be struggling for acceptance and unable to give maximum stimulation. The result is that profoundly hearing impaired/deaf children may spend the most important years of life (from a language development standpoint) with no language at all—language to facilitate cognitive development or to provide a way to interact with the world.

Believing that some form of communication is essential to the well-being of all people, the authors recommend doing whatever is necessary to establish it. It may be necessary initially to teach some basic signs, accompanied by voice. If the children have the potential to become oral, the signs must always be accompanied by voice and a vocal effort required of them. Oral communication is more universal and if children have any potential for learning it, no effort should be spared in teaching it.

It must be remembered, however, that those who cannot learn oral language still need to communicate (Northern & Lemme, 1982) and should be taught either in a total communication program or in sign language. "Signed Exact English" (Gustason, Pfetzing, & Zawolkow, 1980) appears to be the most versatile for children who will be signing to hearing people. Since it follows the English order, it is easier for hearing people to learn and the children will have more individuals with whom they can converse. Those who will communicate mainly with the deaf community may be better off to learn their language, usually American Sign Language (Northern & Lemme, 1982; Rickehof, 1978).

Careful attention must be given to providing appropriate social and cognitive experiences and to being sure the communicative foundation the children build is solid. Emotional overlays and frustrations must be dealt with realistically. Since the youngsters receive little or no auditory feedback, their motor skills—lacking environmental feedback—also may be deviant and adaptive measures must be instituted. Language and speech both are critical to deaf children's optimum development but this can be expected to be long-term intervention. Experience therapy has proved to be effective with deaf children (Kretschmer & Kretschmer, 1978; Streng, Kretschmer, & Kretschmer, 1978) but they also may need some more highly structured training as well. The use of the *Fokes Sentence Builder* (Fokes, 1976a) is warranted sometimes, as are a number of other methods (for a complete discussion see Kretschmer & Kretschmer, 1978). Individual therapy must be aimed at speech, voice, and language. The prognosis may remain guarded, and the children may continue to need a great deal of direct instruction and encouragement.

Because of the nature and importance of hearing to learning, special consideration always must be given to cognitive development. Unless there is a very good deaf education program in the public school, it seems likely that these children will need to obtain at least part of their education in a special school or class for the hearing impaired. Considerations of mainstreaming probably should be deferred until they no longer need the specialized help often available in special programs.

Educating deaf children is an exacting and time-consuming process requiring a high degree of specialized training. If the public school is unable to deliver this training, the youngsters probably would be better off to obtain their initial education in a school or class for the deaf. After certain progress has been achieved, they may return to public school to be mainstreamed.

The preschool language nursery is not a deaf program and by itself is not sufficient for the deaf or profoundly hearing impaired. When these children are enrolled in this program, the preschool teachers and clinicians conscientiously consult with the audiologists and specialized educators of the deaf who are responsible for them. As an initial supportive program, the language nursery with intensive individual therapy has been very effective.

Neurological Disorders

The common denominator in this area is central nervous system dysfunction. In addition to developmental aphasia, apraxia, and cerebral palsy, children with central hearing problems and severe learning disabilities must be brought under this rather large umbrella, where they are considered with the developmental aphasia category. Treatment for neurological disorders primarily involves dealing with the residual effects of damage so as to minimize weaknesses and maximize strengths and thus to improve the quality of life.

Developmental Aphasia

Young aphasic children may be either primarily receptive (including those with a central hearing problem) or primarily expressive, or a combination (which also may include those with severe learning disabilities). These children may well be delayed cognitively because when language is absent, cognition, while possible, is much more cumbersome and time consuming to develop. There may be an accompanying motor handicap related to central nervous system damage and there are likely to be social development problems stemming from the lack of language. With all of this, it is almost a certainty that the children also will suffer from behavioral and psychological problems.

Regardless of the cluster of related problems, the main issues to be addressed for the receptive aphasic are learning to hear, identify, associate, store, retrieve, and use auditory signals. Specifically, these children must learn to obtain meaning from incoming auditory signals and use it to form responses as the information is incorporated into daily experience. Since using the incoming signal is a problem, many children understand more easily and respond more readily when the clinicians and teachers use a reduced rate and simplified prosodic pattern.

For young children, the self-talk and parallel talk techniques discussed in Chapter 3 are useful as they emphasize the association of sounds to referents. The primary level of McGinnis association therapy is well equipped to provide practice in responding to verbal requests, helping the youngsters focus on language specifics. Any time spent in rhythmic activities or in the playing of sound games also has direct benefits for aphasics. Activities that focus on vocabulary building or early reading readiness are highly beneficial to both receptive and expressive aphasic children and will have lasting benefits as they go on to school.

The salient feature in training young expressive aphasics is that of being able to plan and produce the appropriate response. This, of course, is based on success with the receptive area. The methods most pertinent are those that provide modeling, practice, and feedback in making simple and appropriate responses. When needed, prompts must be chosen carefully to give maximum information. Here again, the primary level of McGinnis association therapy is effective in providing practice.

Experience therapy, either group or individual, is perhaps the single most effective technique because of its specific structure and feedback and because it is designed to help children relate language to referent. For example, the experience may involve making peanut butter sandwiches. The children perform the physical activity while the appropriate language is being elicited, and come to understand the essential relationship between language and the physical world.

If prompts are required, they can be chosen to give exactly as much information as needed to elicit the appropriate response. The clinician then can offer rewarding feedback to confirm that appropriateness. As the children develop, selected elements designed to train for the oncoming school process may be appropriate (Barry, 1961).

As might be expected, children with receptive/expressive combination aphasia require a carefully chosen combination of methods, probably organized along developmental sequential lines.

Developmental Apraxia

Apraxic children often appear to have speech productions related to the remainder of their apraxic (motoric) problems so therapy may be part of a general overall program. Since apraxia is a production disorder, it has not been the authors' experience that these children suffered significant cognitive or social delay. Of course, they must make adaptations in these areas, and they usually are able to do so with assistance.

The essential component of therapy for young apraxics is training and practice in volitional control of the speech musculature. They need general practice in large and small motor movements that can be focused gradually on specific speech musculature. This often is done through imitation of movement patterns, gradually moving from large muscle to small muscle to articulatory and to the eventual production of the stream of articulated speech.

There must be an extensive articulation component (often using nonsense) in which the children learn to make the consonant-vowel (CV) patterns of the language (Aram & Nation, 1982). Forms of music and rhythm to which motor actions are performed often are helpful in making this practice both effective and pleasant, as are any rhythmic or singing games. Group singing and choral reading also furnish apraxic children with successful experiences and are very encouraging.

If the apraxia is pervasive, specific work in general body management may be the primary recommendation. One very successful and well-organized approach to working with verbal apraxic children is presented by Weidner and Square (1980). They report that therapy begins at the syllable level and focuses on easy movement sequences, initially constructed around sounds already in the children's repertoire. They emphasize a slow rate, even stress, and careful monitoring. The therapy progresses in a controlled manner and in all phases stresses the learning of sequences of movement.

Since apraxia often accompanies either aphasia or cerebral palsy, the therapeutic intervention designed often consists of a combination of intervention techniques and emphasis.

Cerebral Palsy

A well-balanced and total approach to treatment and training for children with this all-encompassing problem is needed. As noted in Chapter 3, these youngsters need the entire coordinated team approach to deal with the likely combinations of cognitive, social, motor, and psychological effects, in addition to communication.

If the communication needs are being mediated through the language nursery, it is essential to coordinate these with the rest of the program. The important features are likely to be the motor-speech and linguistic developments that occur earliest, i.e., feeding (sucking, chewing, swallowing, which are so important to later speech), head control, and breathing (and, with it, phonation).

The cerebral palsy probably has resulted in a lack of prerequisite experiences— a major factor contributing to the language problem. During the same time the children are beginning to establish motor control, opportunity can be provided to ensure the prerequisites for the development of language (Bloom & Lahey, 1978; Finnie, 1975).

The children must have linguistic experience (must hear the language spoken), nonlinguistic experience (must have the experiences of doing things and going places), and sensorimotor knowledge (in the Piagetian sense discussed in Chapter 1) if language is to develop normally. All of these are the province of the language nursery.

In the opinion of the authors, no better method can be suggested to meet this need than carefully planned language experiences. Care must be taken not only to provide language input but also to give the children needed physical experience even if it is necessary to manipulate their limbs. It is important that clinicians have a general understanding of treatment methods (Bobath, 1967; Phelps, 1940; Rood, 1954).

As the children become more capable in these early developmental areas, therapy may turn more to speech, to coordinating the use of the speech musculature, and language production. The specific methods for therapy presented by Cass (1951); Hoskell, Burnett, and Taylor (1977); and Mysak (1980) are among the most promising for work with preschool children. If a more specific articulation method is needed, the McDonald *Sensorimotor Therapy* (1964) is widely used. In any instance, speech therapy must not be conducted in a vacuum but must be maintained as part of the total team approach insofar as possible.

It is important to be aware of the likelihood that cerebral palsied children also may have elements of mental retardation, aphasia, apraxia, and vision/hearing loss that also must be dealt with.

Mental Retardation

With children whose major problem is lack of intellectual ability to achieve up to socially expected levels, the primary professional is the special educator. It is strongly recommended that speech clinicians and special education professionals coordinate their efforts when planning a curriculum for such youngsters. Although children should not be expected to achieve language above their mental age, any communication development that is below that mental age can be worked on using any combination of therapies that have been found to be effective.

Operant means (therapy using stimulus response and a tangible reward) often are used with the mentally retarded and certainly have their place in this area. However, it does appear that these methods often train the children only to parrot words, not to communicate meaning. It is the opinion of the author-clinicians that operant methods provide successes in eliciting specific imitated utterances and in building noun vocabulary. These do not, however, generalize to the production of new and novel sentences. They do nothing to enhance the use of semantics or pragmatics, both areas that are likely to be deviant and/or delayed. They have no relationship to cognitive development.

Experience therapy, on the other hand can be planned to work effectively on all aspects of language (semantic, syntactic, and pragmatic) and to augment cognitive development. It provides organized practice in all areas of language in a frame that can be planned to teach new cognitive information as well.

The *Fokes Sentence Builder* (1976a) is a semiprogrammed technique that is helpful in combination with either of the major language therapy approaches. The McGinnis (1963) association therapy primary level has proved effective with the majority of retarded children it has been tried on in the language nursery, helping them learn to respond to requests and act within a format. Both *Precision Articulation Therapy* (Mowrer, 1977) and *Phonemic Contrasting Articulation Therapy* (Fokes, 1976b) also have proved appropriate with this population once the mental age has reached a level high enough to begin to modify the sound system—an approximate mental age of 4½ years.

Down's Syndrome

All factors in the preceding section also apply to Down's children. Far too little research has been done to identify the best ways of working with this population or to establish reasonable expectations. A good description of what is known about this type of child is provided by Pueschel (1978).

The authors have had a number of Down's children enrolled in various speech and language programs and have seen most of them make exceptional gains. Whether the format followed was responsible for these gains, or some other factors, is uncertain. Nevertheless, the following guidelines, generated by the authors, appear beneficial and are employed whenever Down's children are to be seen for therapy or incorporated into the language nursery:

1. Children should begin preexperience language stimulation as early as possible (self-talk, parallel talk, etc.).
2. Language experiences must be modeled consistently by both parents and teachers.
3. Cognitive stimulation must be well planned and extensive.
4. Children must be discouraged from mimicking or echoing (discussed later in this chapter).
5. Phonemic contrasting articulation therapy must be built into early sound learning.
6. Adults must be accepting and positive about children to help them build a good self-concept.
7. Independence must be encouraged, no matter how messy.
8. Children must be kept busy to build curiosity and a desire for activity.

9. Movement patterns and music should be incorporated into therapy as often as possible.
10. Clinicians must learn to measure with a spoon, not with a bucket.

Therapy with the mentally retarded moves slowly but if handled with gentleness and care can become a rewarding and productive experience.

Emotional Disturbance

Children with emotional problems may find their way into language therapy because of their lack of purposeful communication. Their problems often are complicated by their failure to use hearing, their apparent mental abilities, etc. They exhibit unusual behavior that also must be dealt with. Their prognosis for improvement tends to be poor. Regardless of the apparent components of the accompanying cluster, the major problem must be seen as psychological. Whatever is done by speech/language/hearing specialists must be in cooperation with a psychological professional, who heads the team. Psychological and language intervention both are essential and generally are mutually dependent on each other, requiring both coordination and cooperation.

Autism

The essential features of language therapy with autistic children appear to be (1) to encourage them to interact with others and (2) to make their utterances appropriate. This often includes breaking up an echolalic quality of speech. This requires creativity by clinicians. It is likely that clinicians' work to improve their relationship to the children will require more in interpersonal skill and professional insight than in technique.

If there is a significant degree of echolalia, all forms of therapy that depend on modeling or imitation appear to be contraindicated. This includes both operant conditioning and experience therapy, although some modifications of each might resolve the issue. The clinicians must design a format that will elicit a response without modeling it first and the children must be given instant feedback when their answer is acceptable. Such an interaction also must be clearly related to "truth" or "fact." This is difficult but it can be done and it can effect change (discussed later in this chapter). As the children become more verbal, they tend to become less echolalic.

A significant group of autistic children function relatively better than the others but demonstrate extreme pragmatic problems. Even though their prognosis is not high, it is better than for the others. Thus, pragmatic-like therapy probably is the best model because it is a combination of experience therapy and role playing, with very explicit reinforcers. Care must be exercised to prevent the reappearance of echolalia when clinicians turn to the experience format.

Schizophrenia

Language therapy for schizophrenics, like that for other emotionally disturbed children, must be guided by the psychological specialist. The speech-language clinician's role, however, is extremely important in overall habilitation. These children's language is likely to be both deviant and delayed and their articulation distorted. The most common speech and language approaches in this type of work are behavioral or programmed. While these teach planned utterances, it is rare for children to use them in an appropriate and generative manner.

Schizophrenics often have semantic problems and extreme pragmatic distortions that must be dealt with if they are to express meaning. This further confounds the therapy program. The authors' experiences with individual language therapy and with children with the diagnosis of schizophrenia lead them to prefer a combination of modeling, role playing, and carefully chosen social reinforcement, within an experience frame.

Puppets are nonthreatening and schizophrenic children often find satisfaction in using them in various ways. Clinicians or teachers must use their interpersonal time with these youngsters to build a warm relationship based on truth, trust, and mutual respect.

Abuse

In this case, as the others in this category, the major responsibility is on the psychological professional. Children who suffer physical, verbal, or other abuse can and often do develop many kinds of speech and language problems. These range from total failure to develop language, to voice and fluency problems, to elective mutism. For these children, the speech-language pathologist has three roles:

1. to establish a therapeutic relationship to help the youngsters build a better self-image
2. to help parents find a nonabusive way to interact verbally with the children; if the abuse is physical, the clinician must take part in the required reporting and intervention sequence
3. to work through therapy to remediate the language, articulation, voice, or fluency problems.

Much of this can be done through the use of speech and language therapy as indicated for the problem. Extensive use can be made of role playing, puppetry, and free play (under the guidance of a consulting psychologist).

It is imperative to work with key professionals in alleviating this problem and to be aware of the professional responsibility to report all cases of physical abuse, etc., to the proper authorities.

SPEECH PROBLEMS

For this group, the speech-language clinician is the primary professional. The clinician's responsibility is to evaluate, plan, and remediate problems of language, articulation, voice, stuttering, etc. When these exist in the preschool population enrolled in the language nursery, the methods used with older children must be adapted. Care must be exercised to ensure that no speech therapy be too intensive or threatening to the children or put them under too much pressure.

The authors also believe the speech therapy must be presented primarily in a playful format. The same goals can be maintained but simply are presented in a format that is pleasant for the children.

Throughout this chapter, a number of language therapy models have been discussed (Experience, Fokes, Interactive, McGinnis, and Operant). Each can accomplish specific things and, wisely used, can be effective in combination with the others. Therapy must be planned to remediate the areas of pragmatics, semantics, syntax, and phonology and to enable the children to generate new and original sentences to transmit information.

Those with articulation problems who would be enrolled in the nursery probably also have other dysfunctions that require attention. For articulation, however, adaptations can be made in a variety of techniques such as *Precision Articulation Therapy* and *Phonemic Contrasting Articulation Therapy*. The nursery activities then can be used as carryover for the speech therapy while other aspects of the curriculum are being taught.

Voice and stuttering problems are rare in the nursery population. Both are likely to respond well to low-pressure modeling of desired behavior and to gain much from interaction with others. These children benefit from a positive experience and feedback and from being placed in a situation where they will not fail. The choice of specific methods of therapy in these cases is entirely dependent upon the individual child and problem.

Youngsters with cleft palates have multiple problems. For this reason, they require a combination of language, articulation, and voice therapy designed to meet their specific individual needs. This therapy should be coordinated with the surgery schedule and must incorporate all communication elements on the most advantageous time schedule for the children. It has been the experience of nursery personnel that cleft palate children gain much from interaction with others in the group.

Idioglossia (in Twins)

When idioglossia is to be replaced with English, the speech-language clinician has a twofold task: (1) to encourage the development of language, best done by experience therapy and interactive therapy, with a great deal of modeling; (2) to teach the children to produce the phonology, phonetics, and inflectional patterns of English.

This implies that the idioglossic language of twins is a language in its own right. Operating on this principle, the clinician must analyze what is to be replaced, identify what is wrong with it, and plan how to modify the productions. These children should be seen in therapy separately and can benefit from as much time as possible in the nursery without the twin so that each might be able to interact more with the other children in English.

Therapy sessions must be planned to present the same material to each twin so each will have the same potential to produce the desired speech and language. If they make something in therapy or if they go somewhere, each child should have the same experience separately. This greatly enhances the potential for them to use English and talk about these experiences or play with the materials.

The end result of all this is to make sure that both children are provided with the same tools, using the same methods but separate lessons, thereby increasing the possibility that the structures can be used at home as carryover material. When the twins go on to kindergarten it is essential that they be in different classrooms, even though this may have been impossible in the nursery.

The choice of language and articulation methods must be dictated by the needs of both children. It probably will be necessary to pattern English prosody during all sessions. A great deal of positive reinforcement of all kinds is necessary to keep twins encouraged enough to persevere in trying to produce a different language when they already have one that works between them.

Echolalia

This very difficult problem is found in the language of children who are mainly autistic and/or schizophrenic. It also is a secondary problem in mental retardation and developmental aphasia and occasionally in children with other combinations of difficulties. The problem of echoing what has been said by another is not amenable to any therapy that relies on imitation or modeling. Unfortunately, this means that operant and experience models are contraindicated.

It is possible to break up the echolalic pattern by putting the children in a situation in which a specific response is elicited without verbal modeling. When the answer is produced, the clinician immediately gives appropriate feedback. Gradually over time, this can help the children learn to generate nonecholalic responses.

The authors have found it helpful to keep the verbal input to the children slow in rate and simple in complexity to give them an advantage in processing it. This helps them learn to generate nonecholalic responses. The authors also note that as the volume of purposeful language used increases, echolalia appears to decrease.

For example, the clinician may place the child in a situation requiring expression of a choice (for something that is genuinely wanted) that has not been directly modeled by the clinician. The child is thus effectively prevented from rote imitation. As soon as the child generates any meaningful nonechoed utterance, the clinician reinforces the response: (To a hungry child) "See this sandwich and this cookie that were in the box? Which one do you want?" When the child finally generates any part of "I want cookie" (or sandwich), the clinician immediately reinforces the response and at the same time interrupts the youngster to prevent the utterance from becoming echolalic. Once the echolalic pattern begins to break up, it is easier to elicit a few meaningful responses to build upon, but the first few times will be frustrating to both clinician and child.

Nonoral Communication

For most of the children seen in the nursery program, the goal is the attainment of standard spoken language. However, occasionally children may be enrolled who require adaptive measures if they are to communicate. These nonoral communication systems are basically of two types: manual language (gestural) and adaptive (board or electronic systems).

Manual Systems

Manual or gesture systems ordinarily are used by those who have full use of hands and arms. Sign languages are used most often by the deaf although recent years have seen an increase in their use with the emotionally disturbed and mentally retarded as well. The three best-known sign languages are:

1. *Amerind* (Skelly, 1979) based on the sign languages of the American Indians. This system basically is more gesture and personal sign than the two others. It is chosen in many situations where its user will not have the use of the specific endings, etc., of English.
2. *American Sign Language* (Rickehof, 1978) is considered the standard language of most deaf communities. It is a language in its own right. It appears to be the system of choice for individuals whose main communications are with the deaf community.
3. *Signed Exact English* (Gustason, Pfetzing, & Zawolkow, 1980) is relatively new. It represents a full translation of English and has the potential for excellent representation. It is typically more widely used when its users will be signing to hearing adults because it follows English rules and endings and consequently is much easier for hearing persons to master.

Accompanying these systems is the manual alphabet, the system by which anything can be spelled out with the fingers. While it is much too slow ever to operate as the main system for anyone, it serves a very important function in all systems. Through it, anything can be produced if it is needed to augment another system.

Adaptive and Electronic Boards

For those who lack the ability to sign, a variety of board communication systems have been devised. Since individual differences in this area are so great, the adaptations on these boards are unlimited (Silverman, 1980).

Many communication boards are arrays of pictures, words, or symbols to which the individual points in sequence to communicate. If pointing is not feasible, an alternative is the use of an electronic signal (a pointer or light) that shows the board identification of the chosen element.

Finally there are electronic boards where the individual types on a keyboard and the communication appears as a visual display. Some few exist in which the words are typed in and an electronic voice produces a verbal message (Silverman, 1980).

Regardless of the many intriguing possibilities, speech remains unquestionably the most practical and satisfactory medium. For this reason only, handicapped individuals who cannot communicate by voice can be expected to use nonoral communication means. Nevertheless, these systems provide one of the essentials of life for speechless individuals.

Environmental Problems

Since children with environmental problems are in the nursery for added stimulation to enrich their development, they are not considered to have language problems. Ordinarily they might be enrolled in individual therapy, if they are in therapy at all. The focus then probably would be on articulation. They could be expected to learn a great deal in all areas from the nursery experience.

Children from foreign language backgrounds, enrolled in the language nursery, might not have language problems per se but might benefit from a little specific speech therapy to help them adapt to the English language of their new country. Methods for this would have to be chosen specifically for the individual child and problem.

The authors' experience has been that these children benefited greatly from the language nursery and required only a minimum of assistive articulation therapy. They also benefited from the increased stimulation of group activities to fill in cultural gaps. Individual therapy is unlikely to be necessary in the nursery format. Certainly music, rhythm, and story times play a large part in their school experience.

Therapy for the Group

The therapy planned and offered to children in the language nursery obviously is of two kinds: individual and group. Individual therapy always is designed to do things one child can do best alone such as specialized areas of speech or language requiring specific practice or intervention related to a major disorder. Group therapy on the other hand incorporates a suitable number and combination of children and provides experiences that are meaningful to all. To this end, the clinician plans for and conducts the group for the benefit of all members.

Children who start the nursery as rather isolated little parallel players soon become more tolerant of each other, ultimately becoming friends. At that point their group therapy activities acquire a new strength of meaning as each child puts more into the group and also gets more from it.

SUMMARY

Curriculum planning for the language nursery requires consideration of four areas: overall planning, choosing individual goals, determining intervention techniques for specific children, and organizing the parent group (this last discussed in detail in Chapter 8). Piagetian cognitive theory provides the organizing principles around which the language activities are grouped, so the children gain in knowledge as well as language.

Teachers' questions stimulate thinking, so the youngsters are encouraged to work out problems and solutions personally. All school activities—opening exercises, free play time, refreshment time, and story and music time—are excellent sources of language and intellectual development, as are group and individual language sessions.

Children diagnosed as needing language therapy have individual programs designed for them. These usually consist of experience therapy or interactive therapy. Occasionally elements of programmed therapy, such as the McGinnis approach, are used when they seem warranted.

Experience and interactive therapy are seen as more compatible with the developmental philosophy as they are more efficient in targeting the language areas—pragmatics, semantics, syntax, and phonology. Studies comparing interactive with operant therapy consistently show more generalization in the groups treated with experience therapy.

Experience therapy is considered best because it is a natural way to learn language, relates language to meaning, focuses on generated language rather than rote imitation, is more generalizable, is longer lasting, and allows more even growth in language systems. Some specific suggestions and examples related to various handicapping conditions were offered.

DISCUSSION QUESTIONS

1. How do the Piagetian theories of cognitive development and Adlerian child management theory organize the language nursery school?
2. What are the differences between programmed (operant) and experience or interactive therapy in the ways in which they treat language deficiencies or deviancies?
3. How can the Piagetian Language Nursery help children who are deaf or hard of hearing?
4. What are the common elements among the various neurological disorders?
5. What are the various types of disorders to be considered in curriculum planning for the language nursery school?

REFERENCES

Aram, D.M., & Nation, J.E. *Child language disorders*. St. Louis: The C.V. Mosby Company, 1982.

Barry, H. *The young aphasic child: Evaluation and training*. Washington, D.C.: Alexander Graham Bell Association for The Deaf, Inc., 1961.

Bloom, L., & Lahey, M. *Language development and language disorders*. New York: John Wiley & Sons, Inc., 1978.

Bobath, K., & Bobath, B. The neurodevelopmental treatment of cerebral palsy. *Journal of the American Physical Therapy Association*, 1967, *47*, 1039, 1041.

Cass, M.T. *Speech habilitation in cerebral palsy*. New York: Columbia University Press, 1951.

Fay, W.H., & Schuler, A.L. (Eds.). *Emerging language in autistic children*. Baltimore: University Park Press, 1979.

Finnie, N. *Handling the young cerebral palsied child at home*. New York: E.P. Dutton & Co., Inc., 1975.

Fokes, J. *Fokes sentence builder*. Boston: Teaching Resources Corporation, 1976. (a)

Fokes, J. *Working with the sound system of children with multiple articulation problems: Phonemic contrasting*. Unpublished, Ohio University, 1976. (b)

Gustason, G.; Pfetzing, D.; & Zawolkow, E. *Signing exact English*. Los Alamitos, Calif.: Modern Signs Press, 1980.

Haskell, S.H.; Barrett, E.K.; & Taylor, H. *The education of motor and neurologically handicapped children*. New York: John Wiley & Sons, Inc., 1977.

Johnston, E.B., & Hutchinson, D.C. Paper presented to the American Speech and Hearing Association, Detroit, 1980.

Kamii, C., & DeVries, R. Piaget for Early Education. In M.C. Day & R.K. Parker (Eds.), *The preschool in action: Exploring early childhood programs* (2nd ed.). Boston: Allyn & Bacon Inc., 1977.

Kretschmer, R.R., & Kretschmer, L.W. *Language development and intervention with the hearing impaired*. Baltimore: University Park Press, 1978.

Lee, L.; Koenigshnecht, R.; & Mulhern, S. *Interactive language development teaching*. Evanston, Ill.: Northwestern University Press, 1975.

McDonald, E. *Articulation testing and treatment: A sensory-motor approach.* Pittsburgh: Stanwix House, Inc., 1964.

McGinnis, M.A. *Aphasic children: Identification and education by the association method.* Washington, D.C.: The Alexander Graham Bell Association for the Deaf, Inc., 1963.

Menyuk, P. *The acquisition and development of language.* Englewood Cliffs, N.J.: Prentice-Hall, Inc., 1971.

Mowrer, D.E. *Methods of modifying speech behavior.* Columbus, Ohio: The Charles E. Merrill Publishing Co., Inc., 1977.

Mysak, E.D. *Neurospeech therapy for the cerebral palsied: A neuroevolutional approach.* New York: Teachers College Press, 1980.

Northern, J.L., & Lemme, M. Hearing and auditory disorders. In G.H. Shames, & E.H. Wiig (Eds.), *Human communication disorders: An introduction.* Columbus, Ohio: The Charles E. Merrill Publishing Co., Inc., 1982.

Perkins, W.H. *Speech pathology: An applied behavioral science* (2nd ed.). St. Louis: The C.V. Mosby Company, 1977.

Phelps, W.M. The treatment of cerebral palsies. *Journal of Bone Joint Surgery,* 1940, *22,* 1004–1013.

Piaget, J. In H.E. Gruber & J. Vonèche (Eds. and trans.), *The essential Piaget.* New York: Basic Books, Inc., 1977.

Pueschel, S.M. The cause of Down's syndrome. In S.M. Pueschel (Ed.), *Down's syndrome: Growing and learning.* Kansas City, Kan.: Sheed, Andrews & McMeel, Inc., 1978.

Rickehof, L.L. *The joy of signing.* Springfield, Mo.: Gospel Publishing House, 1978.

Rood, M.S. Neurophysiological reactions as a basis for physical therapy. *Physical Therapy Review,* 1954, *34,* 444–448.

Silverman, F.H. *Communication for the speechless.* Englewood Cliffs, N.J.: Prentice-Hall, Inc., 1980.

Skelly, M. *Amerind gestural code: Based on universal American Indian Hand Talk.* New York: Elsevier, 1979.

Streng, A.H.; Kretschmer, R.R.; & Kretschmer, L.W. *Language learning and deafness: Theory, application and classroom management.* New York: Grune & Stratton, Inc., 1978.

Weidner, W.E., & Square, P.A. *Developmental apraxia program.* Paper presented to the Southwestern Ohio Speech and Hearing Association, Cincinnati, April 1980.

Zinkus, P.W., & Gottlieb, M.I. Chronic otitis media and auditory processing deficits: A preventable learning disability. *Ohio Journal of Speech and Hearing,* 1978, *13*(2), 9.

Chapter 5

The School, the Child, and the Law

CHAPTER OBJECTIVES

After completing this chapter, readers should be able to:

1. Explain the operation of Public Law 94-142, the Education for All Handicapped Children Act of 1975.
2. Explain what is meant by "mainstreaming" and "least restrictive environment."
3. Explain the importance and problems involved with the Individualized Education Program.
4. Describe adaptations of the language nursery to meet some provisions of P.L. 94-142.

KEY IDEAS

1. The federal government has established a minimum set of requirements for education of special children in public schools. Several of those provisions are pertinent to language nursery programs.
2. The provisions of Public Law 94-142 have forced educators to plan more carefully for each child and to follow each plan meticulously.
3. Implementation of the provisions of this act have resulted in formation of an important working relationship between educators, various special services, and parents.

PUBLIC EDUCATION AND THE HANDICAPPED

The American public education system, with its goal of providing an education for all members of society, has generated many new and innovative ideas in the last two centuries. While it has not always met its goal, it keeps expanding and improving its efforts.

The school system has aimed to educate normally developing children to take their place in society but it has not been so comprehensive or so consistent in its efforts for the handicapped. For many years, children who were not deemed able to benefit from public education were excluded from school, sent to private or agency schools (ranging from very good to very poor), or given partial training on an individual basis.

The result was a hit-or-miss education, subject to the effects of numerous outside influences—a system in which 25 percent of all handicapped children received no education at all and 50 percent an inadequate one (Tremblay & Vanaman, 1979, p. 21).

In an effort to eliminate countless abuses and improve the outlook for this population, Congress in 1975 passed the Education for All Handicapped Children Act (Public Law 94-142).

THE NATURE OF THE LAW

This wide-ranging law was adopted after lesser attempts in 1968, 1970, 1973, and 1974 to deal with the many ramifications of this problem. The 1975 law, and its implementing regulations promulgated in August 1977, resulted in a comprehensive act with considerable federal funding to states that developed acceptable plans for educating their handicapped children. The 1977 regulations made compliance with P.L. 94-142 mandatory for any program that received federal financial assistance. It was hoped that this funding scheme would achieve the desired results from the states without resorting to direct federal interference with their educational systems (Tremblay & Vanaman, 1979).

The following acts and regulations, complemented by other legislation, are at the core of the new emphasis on education for the handicapped:

1. The Rehabilitation Act of 1973 (P.L. 93-112).
2. Educational Amendments to the Vocational Education Act of 1968 (P.L. 90-576).
3. The Education for All Handicapped Children Act of 1975 (P.L. 94-142) and its implementing regulations (August 23, 1977).
4. The Section 504 Regulations (May 4, 1977) of the Rehabilitation Act of 1973 (P.L. 93-112).

Each state has completed an acceptable act to comply with federal law. The state acts vary considerably in this compliance but the general effect is that, to some degree, the requirements of P.L. 94-142 (see Exhibit 5-1) are being met everywhere.

Exhibit 5-1 P.L. 94-142: Requirements for Each Eligible State

---

Under the Education for all Handicapped Children Act of 1975 (P.L. 94-142), states that accept federal funds for any part of their program must:

1. Adopt a state plan that assures all handicapped children the right to a free, appropriate public education.

2. Develop an effective "search and serve" program, i.e., to locate and identify all handicapped children not being served (child find).

3. Establish a priority in the use of received funds for two groups, those (1) not receiving any education and (2) the most severely handicapped who are receiving an inadequate education.

4. Establish a procedure to ensure an Individualized Education Program (IEP) for each handicapped child. The IEP guarantee generally is regarded as the law's major development.

5. Provide full tuition grants for private education where public facilities are inadequate for an appropriate special education and assure that the private schools providing these programs meet standards applicable to state and local schools.

6. Use tests that are nondiscriminatory both in selection and in manner of administration. The tests must be in the primary language of the child and no one test or procedure can be used as the sole determinant of a child's program.

7. Provide a system of due process safeguards that are incorporated into the state plan, including prior notice of all actions affecting the identification or placement of a child; the right to a free, independent assessment of the child's abilities; access to school records; and the opportunity for an impartial due process hearing.

Source: Adapted from "The Constitutional and Statutory Right of Handicapped Children to a Free, Appropriate Public Education" by J.D. Tremblay and J.D. Vanaman, in *Human Advocacy and P.L. 94-142: The Educator's Roles,* Leo F. Buscaglia and Eddie H. Williams, (Eds.), published by Charles B. Slack, Inc., Thorofare, N.J. Copyright © 1979, by permission of Leo F. Buscaglia.

COMPLIANCE WITH THE LAW

The intent of this law clearly is to ensure legal compliance with its principle and spirit. The major requirements are imposed on the public school systems of the country, which by now have adopted plans for meeting the specific objectives (See Exhibit 5-2). To avoid duplication of effort and needless expenditures, school personnel are expected to become acquainted with and work cooperatively with all other agencies that serve the same population of children.

Exhibit 5-2 P.L. 94-142: Major Expectations of Educators and Parents

Under the Education for All Handicapped Children Act of 1975 (P.L. 94-142), participating schools are required to:

1. develop a practical and useful Individualized Education Program (IEP) for each individual with exceptional needs.

2. establish a system for joint development of the IEP and the preceding individual pupil assessment.

3. make maximum use of a broad variety of fiscal and personnel resources so as to provide a free, appropriate public education for each individual with exceptional needs.

4. identify and serve all handicapped individuals of school age.

5. complete an information system capable of informing the parents of exceptional children of the process and steps necessary to full understanding and exercise of procedural due process rights.

6. complete a mechanism that directly addresses the principle of the least restrictive environment in each child's IEP.

7. develop a written school philosophy and procedure so that maximum interaction takes place between handicapped and nonhandicapped students housed in the building.

8. develop an assessment process with accompanying specific procedure(s) assuring proper assessment and placement for limited-English speaking and non-English-speaking children and those with nontypical cultural backgrounds.

9. work out agreements so that the necessary related services described in IEPs can be funded through appropriate agencies.

Source: Adapted from "The Problems and Pitfalls in Implementing P.L. 94-142" by Leslie Brinegar, in *Human Advocacy and P.L. 94-142: The Educator's Role,* Leo F. Buscaglia and Eddie H. Williams (Eds.), published by Charles B. Slack, Inc., Thorofare, N.J. Copyright © 1979, by permission of Leo F. Buscaglia.

Mainstreaming

In uninformed circles, P.L. 94-142 is equated only with an inaccurate view of mainstreaming the handicapped, when in actuality that word does not appear in the act or the regulations. This notion evolved from the concept of attempting to normalize the lives of the handicapped. The act provides for these individuals to be placed in the mainstream of public education, the regular school classes in their home district, assuming this is their least restrictive environment. Obviously this would cost a school district less than other means of providing the required education, and school officials often see this as *the* option.

The act declares (Sec. 612(5)(B)) that to be eligible to receive federal funds, states must establish:

> procedures to assure that, to the maximum extent *appropriate*, handicapped children, including children in public or private institutions or other care facilities, are educated with children who are not handicapped, and that special classes, separate schooling, or other removal of handicapped children from the regular educational environment occurs *only* when the nature or severity of the handicap is such that education in regular classes with the use of supplementary aids and services cannot be achieved satisfactorily . . . (emphasis added)

The act (Sec. 614(a)(1)(C)(iv)) also requires that states establish a goal of providing full educational opportunities to all handicapped children, including:

> (iv) to the maximum extent practicable and consistent with the provisions of section 612(5)(B), the provision of special services to enable such children to participate in regular educational programs.

In the implementing regulations issued August 23, 1977, (revisions—not affecting these portions—were published by the successor Department of Health and Human Services as of July 1, 1981, including changing the numbering of all clauses) the government said in Sec. 300.552(3)(d) that each state and local public agency must ensure that:

> In selecting the least restrictive environment, consideration is given to any potential harmful effect on the child or on the quality of services which he or she needs.

In its comment on this section, the department noted that "the section also requires each agency to have various alternative placements available . . ." It then quotes the government's analyses of the regulations under Section 504 of the Rehabilitation Act that also are pertinent to this section:

> It should be stressed that, where a handicapped child is so disruptive in a regular classroom that the education of other students is significantly impaired, the needs of the handicapped child cannot be met in that environment. Therefore regular placement would not be appropriate to his or her needs . . .

Thus, it is clear that mainstreaming not only is not mandatory in all cases but that alternatives are assured when the children's conduct disrupts the regular classroom.

Advocates of mainstreaming advance three main reasons for it, apparently based more on their philosophical rationale and beliefs than on empirical research (Buscaglia & Williams, 1979). As one writer puts it:

1. Handicapped children do a better job of achieving both academically and socially when their isolation ends.
2. A regular school setting does a better job than a segregated setting in helping handicapped children adjust to and cope emotionally with the "real" world when they grow up.
3. Exposure to handicapped children will help normal children enlarge their world by better understanding individual differences in people: it will also help to diminish the stereotyping of the handicapped. (Brenton, 1974)

Research actually yields mixed results that defy a firm conclusion (Buscaglia & Williams, 1979). It is likely that each premise listed above is true of some children and contexts and not true of others. Since special education, by definition, involves special children, there are few commonalities upon which to base such broad assumptions.

It often is assumed that the least restrictive environment is mainstreaming in the regular classroom. For children for whom this is true, mainstreaming is a powerful advantage and they can be expected to prosper. When this is not true, mainstreaming may fail, preventing them from reaching their potential. For example, a deaf child actually may need the specialized facilities of the state deaf school to make maximum gains. Even well-intentioned mainstreaming could fail to serve the child, distort the educational endeavor, and predispose the youngster to failure. If the mainstreaming is deferred until the child has made the maximum gains from the self-enclosed setting, it may turn out to be a powerful educational advantage.

The Least Restrictive Environment

The term least restrictive environment is not synonymous with the mainstreaming concept, although it is desirable that the two co-occur. For certain children, the two concepts result in the same placement but this must not always be assumed to be the case.

The least restrictive environment is an individual placement concept. It is to be determined for each child on the basis of particular diagnostic results, personal factors, and needs. It represents the placement that provides the child the most positive opportunity to learn and grow and places the least restriction on that progress.

All things considered, it is the single most advantageous placement possible. When this placement also mainstreams children in their own school, the two most important concepts of the legislation are brought into phase. It becomes incumbent on professionals to understand each special student's needs and aptitudes and the potential of each placement option available to meet these needs.

Due Process

The provisions on this element of the law have as their purpose: (1) keeping parents informed about actions the school wishes to take regarding their child's testing, placement, and education, and (2) keeping parents informed of their rights and the appropriate means of exercising them. The law makes parents and schools partners in the education of the child.

Due process legislation underscores the principle of nonexclusion by setting up time limits for the completion of the various stages it mandates in the placement and training of special children. It sets up guidelines covering testing, placement, program planning, and periodic review. It also makes the parents aware of the school files and their right to inspect them and of ways in which they can have input into the records. Specifically, they may participate in the development of the Individualized Education Program (IEP) and can approve or reject proposed school placements.

INDIVIDUALIZED EDUCATION PROGRAM (IEP)

This innovative element requires school personnel—a team composed of the professionals involved—to write a comprehensive plan for the delivery of services to each special education child. Careful guidelines have been established for the IEP, regulating its writing, and requiring it to be accepted by the school and the parents (Allen, 1980). It is mandated to contain everything that is necessary for the most appropriate education program. Once accepted, it must be implemented.

The intent of the law seems to be that "Whatever the cost or the current availability of the program or service, if written into the IEP, the service must be provided" (Brinegar, 1979, p. 30). This program is implemented by those who planned it. It should then be the single most appropriate plan available since it was developed by the people who want it to succeed.

PERIODIC REVIEW

In schools, the review of the IEP takes place at the end of the time frame for which the plan was written. It is intended to represent a candid appraisal of the implementation of the IEP. The child is reevaluated in certain areas and progress noted. Specific elements on the IEP are considered and determination is made as to which ones worked well and should be continued, worked well and no longer are needed, and did not work as planned and why they did not. From this, further recommendations are made and plans for implementing them are incorporated into the new IEP.

As was the case with the placement conference and the IEP conference, parent input and approval are required.

REFERRALS

When dealing with handicapped children, the assistance of other professionals often becomes necessary. This means that from time to time during diagnostics and therapy, referrals will be made to such professionals as psychological or medical specialists or others. It is implied that the teacher or clinician who makes the referral will take the responsibility for guiding this multistep process.

The parents must be informed of the need for the referral and assisted in the way to make it. Contact should be maintained between the referral source and the receiving agency to keep communication channels open. The reports and recommendations from the receiving agency must be interpreted and acted upon.

At least some school districts interpret the law to say that any firm recommendation for referral actually made by the school district also must be paid for by the district. This implied cost to the schools could have the effect of reducing the number of referrals. Certainly, no teacher wants to make unnecessary referrals but no referral that actually is needed should be left unmade.

PROBLEMS IN IMPLEMENTATION

It would be remarkable if legislation so all-encompassing could be implemented without the emergence of a number of problems, and unfortunately that is not true here. As might be expected, both proponents and opponents of various aspects tend to approach their arguments with more energy and emotion than fact. Surely no one would fault the nobility of the spirit of the law (Buscaglia & Williams, 1979) but it has generated a new set of abuses. There is a dearth of research data concerning such aspects as mainstreaming, a gap that will be filled as more research is completed, so a decision as to the worth of that controversial law must wait until the evidence is completed.

As they explore its ramifications, school administrators complain of the cost, and teachers and support personnel of the time-consuming red tape. Both types of complaints have led to successful adaptations in some districts, to abuses in others.

Some problems with implementation may always exist:

- There will be times when established educational principles are at variance with what parents see as their right to input into the education of the child and these due process proceedings can lead to the courts.

- There will be times when the mainstreaming sought by either the parents or the schools will not be to the best advantage of the child.
- There will be times when even though ''Congress has accepted the notion that all children can benefit from a public education '' (Tremblay & Vanaman, 1979, p. 24), the child will not in fact benefit.
- There will be groups that cry ''foul'' that a disproportionate percentage of public education money is spent on the population with the least potential while the gifted children, whose education comes under special education in many states, actually receive little of these funds even though they also have unmet needs.

There are and will continue to be failures in the system because of error or misjudgment on the part of either the parents or the schools.

The underlying financial problems have not been solved. Implementation of P.L. 94-142 obviously will become increasingly more expensive if maintained to the act's performance standards, yet the government actually has underwritten only a fraction of this cost (Tremblay & Vanaman, 1979) with full realization that state and local funds also would have to be appropriated.

It is surely true that these guidelines for special education also would be effective if adopted for regular classrooms. It is only reasonable that parents of normally developing children would want these advantages for their progeny. It probably is true also that there is not sufficient money in the entire system to finance such a move.

As often is the case with new legislation, this law must be allowed time to ''cure.'' It is to be hoped that, as time goes on, arguments over it will be resolved, litigation will diminish, and implementation will become smoother and more efficient—all to the educational benefit of handicapped and normal children everywhere.

PRESCHOOL IMPLEMENTATION AND ADAPTATION

P.L. 94-142 is binding on all state and local agencies that receive federal funding or support. Obviously, this covers many of the agencies that serve the preschool population and is extended even further whenever public funds become involved in the delivery of private services.

Since the intent of P.L. 94-142 is to better serve the handicapped (Streng, Kretschmer, & Kretschmer, 1978), preschool children's interests also are being addressed. Voluntary compliance by preschools in the private sector benefits their own population by implementing a number of innovative guidelines. One benefit is that handicapped children in preschools can receive a thorough assessment of ''gross motor skills; fine motor skills; preacademic skills; self-help skills; music, art, and story skills; social and play skills; and receptive and expressive language skills'' (Allen, 1980, p. 76).

THE PIAGETIAN LANGUAGE NURSERY

The program for the handicapped in the Piagetian Language Nursery is purely communication oriented. Nevertheless, the guidelines written for a more complete educational setting have been adopted for use there.

Individual Goals

In this language nursery program, the IEP translates to an individualized set of therapy goals. The information is taken from the diagnostic workup (see Exhibit 3-3 in Chapter 3) and formulated into Individual Therapy Goals (Exhibit 5-3) for the child in this specialized setting. These individual goals, first discussed in Chapter 4, involve cognition, social development, linguistic development, and motor development. This information then is kept on file for use in making daily lesson plans designed to result in the realization of the child's goals.

Daily Group Plan

Once the Individualized Therapy Goals have been established for each child, they can be incorporated into a daily lesson plan for the group (Exhibit 5-4). Additional plans are drawn for children who also have individual therapy sessions. The coordinating plans must be carefully drawn by the clinician, who works in both settings, to avoid any confusion or duplication of effort.

The planner of the individual therapy time must take a number of factors into account:

- the activities of the child's day in the group setting
- the child's cognitive, language, social, and motor goals
- the requirements set by the child's specific problem(s).

These form the content of the individual therapy session and must be planned so the activities in the nursery group fit into this overall plan and can be used as carryover activities for the individual emphasis (Exhibit 5-5). The individual emphasis also must be planned to enhance the child's ability to function in the group.

At its conclusion, the individual session must be evaluated and filed with the other lesson plans as a part of the accumulated data needed to write the final reports.

Exhibit 5-3 Individual Therapy Goals

Name: Ira McBain*   Birthdate: 4-12-79   Term: Fall, 1982

Session: A.M. (Sensorimotor)   Clinician: E. Johnston

Summary of Diagnostic Statement: Tentative diagnosis of developmental expressive aphasia with developmental apraxia.

Summary of Latest Recommendations: Language nursery, with individual therapy daily (20 min.). Mother in parent group.

Status at Beginning of Term: One-word utterances, age-appropriate receptive ability, vocabulary about 10 words, frustration.

Goals

Cognitive: Symbolic formation, classification of toys by type of play, i.e., dolls in doll house, truck in garage.

Communicative: Eye contact, turn taking, vocabulary building, use of noun phrase + verb phrase (NP + VP) utterances in spontaneous conversation.

Socioemotional: Interactions with clinician and at least one other child, turn taking with children, parallel play.

Motor (Fine and Gross): Gross body imitation, imitation of the articulatory movements, large muscle motor games.

Additional Goals: Rhythmic practice, i.e., hand games, rhythm band, and marching.

---

* The child's name and all personal details have been changed to protect the youngster's privacy.

Review and Reporting

These final reports in effect are a culmination of the nursery program. They reflect the periodic review for the term; recommendations are made from them. If any other referrals are deemed necessary then, they are made and the parents assisted in the follow-through. Once completed, the cycle begins again with the establishment of new goals for each child.

In the nursery, a parent group is maintained to augment the parent-teacher relationship (discussed fully in Chapter 9). Parents are encouraged to join in

Exhibit 5-4 Daily Group Plan

Session: A.M. (Sensorimotor)   Date: October 9, 1982

Group Members:* Ira McBain, Glenda Roe,   Clinicians:* Carol Clinician, Suzie Sharp
Shana Quigley, Wilden McFee, Raymond
Jones, Lulu March   Supervisor: E. Johnston

Opening Exercises: Children answer roll call by placing their picture on chart, look at and chart weather.

Group Language Activity: Experience therapy calls for making peanut butter sandwiches.

Free Play: Children have free choice of activities, clinicians to follow their lead.

Put Toys Away Before Refreshment Time: Clinicians use this as classification practice.

Refreshments: Children receive cookies and a fruit juice.

Story Time: Children look at picture books before being read to.

Music Time: Children participate in singing games and rhythm band, followed by marching.

McGinnis Circle: Clinician conducts single-word practice in McGinnis format.

Individual Therapy: Children are involved in individual therapy plans.

Put Toys Away: Children place them in cabinets and clean up the room before dismissal.

Dismissal: Children put pictures away. Clinicians tell parents what was done during the session.

---

* Names and all personal details have been changed to protect privacy.

---

discussions of language development and related matters and receive guidance and support so they can help make the most of their children's time in the language nursery.

In addition to their membership in this group, with the continuing activities it provides, parents are informed regarding all matters of program and their input is sought at each phase.

It must be remembered that while therapy is indicated for remediation of the severe problems found in the language nursery program, the children are very young and are able to attend for only short periods at a time. Consequently, care must be exercised to make individual sessions brief, interesting, and as meaningful as possible.

Exhibit 5-5 Individual Therapy Plan

Name: Ira McBain*   Birthdate: 4-12-79   Date: Oct. 9, 1982

Clinician: Suzie Sharp*   Room: 62-A

Semester Goals: eye contact, turn taking, vocabulary building, spontaneous use of NP + VP utterances.

Daily Objectives	Materials	Procedures
Imitation of gross motor actions		Game: child imitates clinician motions for token reward
Vocabulary building	Animal picture cards, toy, zoo, and farm	Child names pictures (after clinician model) and puts in zoo or farm
Eye contact, turn-taking, NP + VP	Puppets, Burt & Ernie	Puppet play eliciting NP + VP, using eye contact, and turn taking.

Evaluation of session:

* Names and all personal details have been changed to protect privacy.

The lessons must be appropriate to the children's cognitive level and interest and be within their ability to succeed reasonably well at the task. This must be accomplished with care and gentleness and in the spirit of play.

SUMMARY

The federal government has required all schools receiving financial assistance to implement a basic program for special children in attendance. Mainstreaming, least restrictive environment, and due process provisions of the law require compliance efforts among the states and their implementing educational agencies but results have been mixed. Little research data exist for evaluating progress.

Due process and Individualized Education Program provisions have forged a working partnership between the educational agencies and parents of handicapped children. As part of the legislative requirements, the schools must make periodic progress reports to the parents on how their children are progressing through the IEP.

Problems have arisen as educational agencies implement this legislation because of the cost of the program and the time spent in preparing the individual plans for every child and maintaining the many reports necessary. Other problems have arisen because parents and school officials disagree about interpretation and implementation.

Several provisions have been adapted and implemented in the language nursery school program: Individual Therapy Goals are established for each child and these then are incorporated into group lesson plans. Final reports of progress bring parents up to date on their children and prepare the way for establishment of new goals.

DISCUSSION QUESTIONS

1. What lacks or abuses was P.L. 94-142 intended to correct?
2. How are the terms "mainstreaming" and "least restrictive environment" different in the requirements they place on school officials?
3. What are the P.L. 94-142 requirements for making parents and schools partners in educating handicapped children?
4. How can preschools voluntarily adapt to the format of P.L. 94-142?

REFERENCES

Allen, J.E. *Mainstreaming in early childhood education*. Albany, N.Y.: Delmar Publishers, 1980.

Brenton, M. Mainstreaming the handicapped. *Today's Education*, 1974, *63*(2), 20–25.

Brinegar, L. The problems and pitfalls in implementing P.L. 94-142. In L.F. Buscaglia & E.H. Williams (Eds.), *Human advocacy and P.L. 94-142: The educator's roles*. Thorofare, N.J.: Charles B. Slack, Inc., 1979.

Buscaglia, L.F. & Williams, E.H. It's all in an attitude. In L.F. Buscaglia & E.H. Williams (Eds.), *Human advocacy and P.L. 94-142: The educator's roles*. Thorofare, N.J.: Charles B. Slack, Inc., 1979.

Cohen, S. *Special people*. Englewood Cliffs, N.J.: Prentice-Hall, Inc., 1977.

French, M. A personal perspective. In L.F. Buscaglia & E.H. Williams (Eds.), *Human advocacy and P.L. 94-142: The educator's roles*. Thorofare, N.J.: Charles B. Slack, Inc., 1979.

P.L. 94-142. *Education for All Handicapped Children Act of 1975*, 20 U.S.C. 1401, 1411. Washington, D.C.: Government Printing Office, 1975.

Streng, A.H.; Kretschmer, R.R.; & Kretschmer, L.W. *Language learning and deafness*. New York: Grune & Stratton, Inc., 1978.

Tremblay, J.D. & Vanaman, J.D. The constitutional and statutory right of handicapped children to a free, appropriate education. In L.F. Buscaglia & E.H. Williams (Eds.), *Human advocacy and P.L. 94-142: The educator's roles*. Thorofare, N.J.: Charles B. Slack, Inc. 1979.

Chapter 6

Management of Child Behavior

CHAPTER OBJECTIVES

After completing this chapter, readers should be able to:

1. Describe the ways current child management theory should be used to supplement ideas of discipline.
2. Compare and contrast five major models of child management as they apply to the nursery school.
3. Explain how to implement the Adlerian model in a nursery school setting.

KEY IDEAS

1. The current confusion regarding child management techniques must be settled in favor of a philosophy that helps youngsters assume and understand a reasonable, consistent role in the social system.
2. Modern models of child management agree that youngsters have purpose in their behavior patterns and that parents and teachers must understand that purpose to help them grow to the optimum level.
3. The children most likely to be in the language nursery will have communication problems so a language-based model of management is not likely to be as effective as a nonlanguage-based one.
4. Whatever model of child management is adopted in the language nursery, consistent implementation is necessary.
5. Teachers must be aware at all times that some problems children exhibit require specialized help and that this assistance must be obtained as necessary.

165

THE PROBLEMS OF PARENTS

Parents' expectations for their children are no different now from what they have been throughout the history of this country but over the last two decades, changes in the realization of these expectations are obvious. Parents attempt to raise their children in the same way as they and their parents were reared, but the results are not the same. In some instances, confused and resentful parents cannot endure the results. They do not know what to do to achieve desired behavior in their children. They are not secure in their parenting and do not appear to know how to make things any better.

Adults today would expect things to be better for the children but they are not. As misbehavior escalates, children become less confident or secure and probably could not explain what they want or why they are not satisfied. According to Dreikurs (1964), this fact is evidenced by the increasing number of severely disturbed children in schools, clinics, and hospitals—and they are younger than ever before.

While this book makes no pretense of being a philosophical treatise on maladjusted children, the magnitude and severity of present problems loom in the background. Professionals can hardly keep their own philosophies from showing through the discussions on disciplinary goals and procedures.

It is impossible to define the "secure" person, adult or child. A consensus would assign certain attributes as important components, more observable in children but probably no less true of adults. Children are most secure when they are loved and accepted, when they have productive things to do (play, hobbies, or work), when they understand where they fit into the order of things, and when they can see themselves as movers in the system.

This last fact relates also to the adequacy of human communication in that the very important semantic role of mover is one of the basic and earliest relationships learned in the emerging language. Confident adults or children appear to need to consider themselves movers in terms of actions done and of producing the language that expresses the steps taken.

The formal understanding of proper child-rearing practices probably originated in the tribal history of the culture. These practices were effective in a time when the culture evolved according to set rules and individuals learned their proper roles and played them out, first as children and later as parents.

With the development of democracy, many of the rules for child rearing became obscured. In a democracy there are fewer rules and rituals and there is much that is new. With the changing times, groups such as women's liberation, labor unions, senior citizens, and youths seem to be aggressively exploring the options of their new situations. When rules and roles are in a state of flux, children and adults are on their own. They must observe and react without firm guidelines, often without adequate feedback or guidance. They rely on their own observations for feedback but many people are poor observers and the conclusions so drawn are apt to be faulty.

It sometimes appears to the authors that as children they lived in an adult-centered world where children were to be seen and not heard. Now, as adults, they live in a child-oriented world where the young demand and occupy the central role.

While today's adults expect to be in a superior position to the children and to be treated so, the children expect to be equal with the parents and to be treated so. Herein would seem to lie a basic problem. According to the thesis of Dreikurs (1964) the result is not democracy but chaos, in which each faction strives to make its mark. The parents are inconsistent because they are not sure how to proceed and often swing from threats and punishment to reasoning and pleading. The parents' inconsistency and doubt produce confusion and insecurity in the children, who feel they must constantly try their limits in an effort to determine where they really are. According to Dreikurs, when democracy (or at least the American adaptation of it) becomes the established way, the result is the child tyrants with whom parents have such a difficult time.

At least in part, this situation is stimulated by faster and more comprehensive news media coverage of all aspects of life. When parents and children see the stylized and unrealistic young people presented in the media and the often-ill considered advice given on the talk shows, they become less confident of their abilities, rights, and responsibilities and less satisfied with their own real-life roles.

Purposeful Behavior

All human behavior is purposeful (Dreikurs, 1958, 1964; Harris, 1973). People do the things they do to achieve a purpose. In some cases, the more mature individuals are able to examine their motives and to know what prompts them to adopt a course of action. Most of the time, however, they do not identify their motives. Children generally are unable to state their deep motives, even though they sometimes know something of their surface motivation (Dreikurs, 1964).

It is important in dealing with and guiding the behavior of children for the adults to be able to identify the youngsters' deep needs or motivations. Children can be led to change deep motivation by a range of successful experiences, making them better able to interact with society. It would not be appropriate to confront them with their deep motivation; this would tend to take on the tone of an accusation and might indeed be harmful in the long run (Dreikurs, 1964).

All people, at least at an unconscious level, want to feel that they belong and gain attention, respect, and a sense of community. This often can be a factor in children's choice of behaviors as an attention-getting mechanism. They equate attention with belonging and seek it as proof that they are valued.

It often appears that parents equate a sense of belonging with the demands they allow their children to place on them. Being needed and having others express such need enhances their sense of value. However, this being needed produces ambivalent feelings in parents in that they want their children to be independent and self-reliant while at the same time they do not want to relinquish this aspect of their belonging.

These two factors confound the management regimen parents espouse, producing inconsistencies that then confuse the children. These inconsistencies are further complicated by the necessity of each child's having to reconcile a personal understanding of the social-communicative context with the parents' interpretation of it.

The Social-Communicative Context

Society defines (places restrictions on) what it accepts as adherence to behavioral and interpersonal rules and those involving linguistics and pragmatics. Information given and feedback received interact in intricate interpersonal patterns. Just as communication transmits a variety of information to a listener, so listener reaction provides a stream of information back to the speaker. This can either weaken or strengthen speaker performance as the individual attempts to adjust further communication to the feedback perceived.

The expectations placed on each individual are specific to the role played. Speaker perceptions of the group's demands are both stylized and personal. Adults and children must generate acceptable social, linguistic, and pragmatic interactions and establish a personal style with which to operate (Clark & Clark, 1977).

Children enhance their effectiveness by learning to operate within the behavioral restrictions, the linguistic code, and the pragmatic requirements of their social context. Through this interaction they master the context and the protocol of formal language. Their experiences at producing strings of connected sentences, that then are responded to, provide a medium for learning the discourse rules of the adult world (Kretschmer & Kretschmer, 1978) in essentially the same way that nonlinguistic behavior is refined.

The kinds and numbers of contextual rules mandated on behavior, language, and pragmatics vary from social class to social class, from family to family, and even among individuals within a single family. Much of this variation results from what are perceived as conflicting signals; these in turn may be caused by differences in individual interpretation, faulty perception, or even the presentation of unorthodox signals by the person doing the communicating.

Ervin-Tripp (1971) identifies three basic types of sociolinguistic rules: (1) alternation rules (which account for register differences children make for various listeners), (2) co-occurrence constraints (which may limit children's ability to use a dialect different from their own) and (3) sequential rules (which govern social routines). Each of these must be mastered and related to pragmatics, language, and interpersonal interactions if the children are to communicate. The effectiveness of the communication, as has been noted, is determined largely by individual perceptions and interpretations of these rules.

When interpersonal conflict exists between parents and children, regardless of the culture or dialect in which it occurs, the social context is likely to deteriorate and the youngsters' behavior becomes an issue. The effects of conflict on inter- pretation, and even perception, of aspects of the communicative context are far reaching and perhaps pernicious.

This often causes much soul-searching and anxiety on the part of both parents and children. This anxiety further disrupts the social planning children are able to do (Clark & Clark, 1977), which in turn has a direct effect on cognitive, linguistic, and pragmatic performance and on sociolinguistic successes. When these prob- lems arise early, they may prevent the children from making optimal interpersonal adjustments and developing the effective communication so necessary to all other progress.

The Family Constellation

All persons, by their placement in the family, experience a slightly different environment that has a profound impact on learning, development, motivation, and behavior. The child is a dynamic force, an agent, a doer of action who interacts in specific ways with the environment. An impoverished environment can have the effect of starving the development, while a hostile environment actually can damage development and destroy motivation. On the other hand, a positive environment enriches development and enhances the most productive elements of children's motivation.

In determining the motivation of children and relating this to their specific environment, it is clear that their position in the family constellation must be considered. Each child's unique position in the family has a profound effect on development (Dreikurs & Grey, 1970). Older children, who have been through the trauma of being dethroned by a younger sibling, develop similar traits. Second children seldom choose to compete with the older ones in areas where the older ones excel. Instead, they attempt to find "their" area from among those not already claimed. Middle children frequently have a difficult role to play out because, being neither the oldest nor the youngest, they may feel there is no special place for them. Younger children often have a difficult time selecting an area for personal excellence and may not always select wisely because they believe "all the good parts are taken."

If parents are asked what one facet of child rearing provides them the least satisfaction and the most anxiety, many respond with "discipline," the means used to train the children in what behaviors are acceptable in the social world. This choice of means is, of course, extremely important. It does appear, however, to be more accurately labeled child management in that it provides a way of planning and managing children's social learning and can be most productive when it is not limited to disciplinary measures.

The Preschool, the Child, and the Family

Whether children attend preschool or not, parents should make a reasonable and coordinated effort at training them to live in their environment. Their first educational ties outside the home are deferred until kindergarten. Parent training generally is aimed at the school skills needed for success in kindergarten, and parents and school cooperate from there. If normally developing children do attend some form of preschool, that becomes their first outside educational setting and the liaison between parent, school, and pupil begins at this point. A well-coordinated effort is important to ensure children the best possible transition.

If children are not developing as expected, for any number of reasons, coordinated and consistent intervention becomes crucial. For those who already are failing to demonstrate adequate organization and development, the world has not proved quite so hospitable. The psychological problems that often emerge from this frustration confound the children and they become more fragmented, more deviant, and more disorganized.

A comprehensive and well-integrated approach clearly is the only way to minimize such problems and to enlist the children's cooperation in personal development. This liaison produces a team composed of child, parents, pediatricians, teachers, and communication therapists (if indicated), and possibly other related specialists such as physical therapists, occupational therapists, etc.

The child's behavior is an important and ever-present factor in the success of the intervention program; consequently, the model used to base discipline upon is important at every phase. It must bridge the gap between the child and the environment in a way that is fair, consistent, and comprehensible to the youngster. The authors believe it is very important to use a management model that does not become part of the problem. For language-impaired children, this means that language, since it is the problem, should not be the central part of the management format.

IMPORTANCE OF MANAGEMENT TO LEARNING

Management of children's behavior is a factor in learning. Parents should try to use mechanisms, such as encouragement and example, to teach children to live in their home environment that also teaches them in the cognitive and socioemotional realm. Parents model the social behavior children learn. If they are considerate, generous, and fair, this is the behavior children acquire. If parents are able to disagree in a fair and equitable manner even when they are angry, their young observers learn the acceptable way to disagree.

The authors do not agree with the general viewpoint that parents should not disagree in front of children; this seems to be unrealistic and does not model behavior that children ultimately need to emulate. It appears that a more useful purpose would be served if children realized that in essence even the "top brass" do not always agree and also that when they do disagree, they are able to do so in socioemotionally acceptable ways, hurting no one.

By management of behavior, the authors refer to the planned and organized system of interactions used by parents and teachers as they build a dyad through which to train the child.

The Importance of Rule Systems

An appropriate way of managing behavior must be developed by parents as they build a dyad with the child. As noted, this implies a system that is fair, comprehensive, and comprehensible, a system children will understand and learn to operate.

In essence, the youngsters must do the same thing in learning the rule system of behavior as they do in learning the rule systems of semantics, syntax, pragmatics, and phonology. If the rules of behavior provide a calm, untroubled, and uncluttered environment, children will learn everything more efficiently. It also follows that if they have learned one set of systematic rules, that experience helps them learn others.

General Philosophies of Child Management

A number of effective child management models exist and all probably are effective at times. Regardless of adults' philosophical preferences or temperament, a model can be chosen for managing the children and educating them to live in the existing world. It is important for parents to choose management models that are compatible with their overall approach to learning and to their children.

Behavioral Model

Any number of variations can exist on this paradigm that basically operates on the philosophy of classical and operant conditioning (Mower, 1960; Osgood, 1963; Pavlov, 1927; Skinner, 1957 and others). According to this model, all behaviors, including language development (Houston, 1972), are learned by a process of stimulus, response, and reinforcement. The motivation for learning is arranged by the teacher (parent) who chooses a behavior, a specific bit of information to teach, elicits it, and provides reinforcement. The reinforced behavior develops into a pattern and the reinforcement schedule gradually is modified and reduced (faded) until it eventually plays no part in the behavior.

A behavioral model ordinarily employs operant conditioning. Small elements of the desired behavior are identified, as are specific reinforcers the children will regard as rewarding. The behaviors to be established are elicited and a reward is given. The association of the behavior and the reward increases the likelihood that the conduct will recur. Initially, a reinforcement ratio of 1:1 generally is emphasized and, as the conditioned response becomes stronger, is modified in various ways until it becomes unnecessary.

If undesirable behaviors are to be eliminated, the clinician rewards the children each time the behavior is withheld. This often involves the substitution of more acceptable behaviors in the same position, at least for the time being. When a better action has been substituted for one that is being extinguished, it eventually can be allowed to disappear, if it will.

Language production is elicited in this model primarily by four means:

1. the tact, specifying something present in the context;
2. the mand, specifying the response and the reinforcement it elicits;
3. echo verbal, a repetition of the stimulus;
4. autoclitic, either self-descriptive or behavior-descriptive utterances (Houston, 1972.)

Once the desired production is achieved, the children immediately (within three seconds) are provided with carefully chosen reinforcers, a reward they want enough to work for. Gradually, the number of rewards is lessened, then given on an irregular schedule that strengthens the response by making it less dependent on being recompensed, to the point where rewards can be discontinued and the desired behavior is maintained.

This behavior model is in wide use among educators and it does have considerable power. While it is highly effective with all children, its uses at times may be contraindicated. It is true that the children are trained to behave in specific ways but the training, unfortunately, is essentially mechanical and does not interact with cognitive elements. The children do not have the opportunity to reason through a transaction and learn to choose a better way.

When motivation is planned and applied from the outside, without interfacing with the cognitive process, the children may not develop such attributes as conscience, responsibility for personal actions, and self-motivation. They may not learn to survey the situation and choose an appropriate response from among the possible options available and may not learn to live with the consequences of their own actions.

The authors prefer that children make choices on a personal, cognitive basis because such a process teaches valuable lessons and builds social adjustment patterns that stay with them for a lifetime. Certainly, there are elements of automatic behavior that can be learned quickly and effectively from an operant model and, when they are noted, are incorporated into the overall picture.

However, the authors have an ethical concern that precludes adopting a behavior approach as the main or basic theory of child management. The authors question whether children should be ''conditioned'' to being conditioned whenever some outside force, person, or institution, however benevolent, wants to change an element, a pattern, or a complete system of behavior to better suit their needs.

Transactional Analysis Model

In transactions of any length between one person and another, a careful observer usually can identify responses from three different levels (persons) from within the other individual. If people turn that same observation on themselves, there is evidence that the same three ''persons'' operate from within them—a *child,* a *parent,* and an *adult.* A rather sophisticated format for improving interpersonal interactions has been developed around this notion. This transactional model is presented both as a way for adults to interact with their age peers and with juveniles (Harris, 1973) and as a management technique with young children (Freed, 1975).

The theory teaches that during the first few years of life, children are taking in a variety of information that is being recorded permanently in the brain in those three categories—*child, parent,* and *adult.* Harris (1973) concludes that the brain functions like a multisensory tape recorder capable of preserving exact feelings and impressions on a permanent basis. These can be replayed and recalled to mind by experiences throughout a lifetime. The information thus recorded is organized onto one of three tapes within the individual according to the type of information contained.

The *child tape* primarily records feelings and impressions—the helplessness, frustration, and dependency of the baby or small child. These include the child behavior that has led to parent disapproval and a feeling of failure. The *child tape* also records the joyous discoveries and creative urges of the very young learner, the happy play and laughter of childhood (Harris, 1973).

Even a happy childhood, however, produces tapes with more negative self-feelings than joy. These *child tapes* transmit a message of, ''You (parent or other adult) are big and strong and powerful and I am little and weak and dependent on your good will. You are OK but I'm not OK.'' If this is true of the taped reflections of a happy childhood, those of an unhappy childhood surely record a more hopeless and ''not OK'' tape to be played back periodically to the hapless individual.

The *child* in everyone is said to take over when people respond with emotional outbreaks of frustration, rage, or despair (Harris, 1973). This *child* needs love, comfort, reassurance, stroking. If individuals are to live harmoniously with the *child* within, they must learn how to recognize and understand that "person" and manage its outbursts.

The *parent tape,* being recorded during the same time frame, is focused on all the laws, rules, and admonitions heard by the young child, such as "Do this!" "Stop that!" "Never do that again!" "Always be careful to . . . !" This tape also carries the happy and sad impressions that are directed at the busy toddler. Because this tape records the data from the persons most important to the helpless child, it comes to represent "the truth and the way." It comes from those who represent parents' security. It is no wonder that small persons replaying this tape often form the conclusion that, "Even though I'm not OK, you are OK" and they continue to be hurt in transactions using this recording.

The *parent* in everyone is said to take over when the individual responds with ultimatums, arbitrary statements, or demands, as if all that needs to be considered has been (Harris, 1973). Interpersonal transactions are smoothed and made productive if both parties recognize the parent tapes and act accordingly.

The *adult tape* recording is said to begin at about 10 months of age (Harris, 1973) as babies learn that they can move about and make things happen. It is more advanced than the felt reactions of the *child* or the taught reaction concepts of the *parent.* It represents the thought-out beliefs or reactions of the *adult.* It probably marks the beginning of goal-directed behavior. The *adult* updates the information on the *child* and *parent tapes,* determining what is true, filters incoming information, and seeks to remain in control of outgoing responses.

The *adult* can be said to take over and be in control when responses are thoughtful outcomes of appropriately used information (Harris, 1973). This *adult* is able to draw the proper balance that says, "I'm OK and you're OK" and act accordingly.

The transactional analysis process is simply an evaluation of what tape is being played by the "other" and the skillful use of the individual's *adult tape* as respondent. People then are able to give tolerance, encouragement, and strokes where they are necessary and to help the other person learn to use the most *adult tape* available. The more the *adult* is allowed to speak, the more adept it becomes at recognizing the incoming tape and the stronger it grows for future use (see Exhibit 6-1 for suggestions as to how individuals can strengthen their own *adult*).

The use of this model for children, TA for Tots, works in a similar manner. Written in simple terms, it presents appropriate stories designed to help children come to know they are OK, that "They are *princes* and *princesses*" (Freed, 1975, p. i).

Parent Effectiveness Training Model

The Parent Effectiveness Training (PET) and Teacher Effectiveness Training (TET) programs (Gordon, 1975a, 1975b) provide parents and teachers with

Exhibit 6-1 Ways to Build a Strong Adult

---

1. Learn to recognize your Child, its vulnerabilities, its fears, its principal methods of expressing these feelings.
2. Learn to recognize your Parent, its admonitions, injunctions, fixed positions, and principle ways of expressing these admonitions, injunctions, and positions.
3. Be sensitive to the Child in others, talk to that Child, stroke that Child, protect that Child, and appreciate its need for creative expression as well as the NOT OK burden it carries about.
4. Count to ten, if necessary, in order to give the Adult time to process the data coming into the computer, to sort out Parent and Child from reality.
5. When in doubt, leave it out. You can't be attacked for what you didn't say.
6. Work out a system of values. You can't make decisions without an ethical framework.

Source: Quotations are drawn from *I'm OK, You're OK* by Thomas A. Harris, published by Avon Books, New York, 1973, p. 121.

---

training and support in the increasingly difficult arena of child management. The books and related classes are highly effective in helping these two populations find a better way to deal with children's behavior.

Central to the PET concept is the fact that parents seem to be getting the blame for everything that is wrong with youth, yet most are ill-trained for the task of raising the young, if they are trained at all (Gordon, 1975a). The people who have this job often are young, inexperienced, and confronting numerous other stresses in their lives. They do not know how to proceed in providing for the physical, psychological, social, and intellectual growth of the new little person who also must grow up to be a good citizen and a productive and happy individual.

The PET program claims to enable parents to raise cooperative and considerate children without punishment, in an environment free of strife and turmoil. This is done essentially by improving the quality of the relationship between parents and child. This total system is not limited to stress situations but instead presents a comprehensive new relationship fully as rewarding in times of joy as it is useful in times of stress. The parents are encouraged to produce an atmosphere that says to the child neither "You win" or "You lose." It is an environment in which no one loses, and this absence of stress may signify that everybody wins.

Parents are only people and reflect all the weaknesses and inconsistencies of other people in their child-rearing practices. Naturally, some parents have more tolerance for child behavior than others as a function of their own personalities. However, this model dispels two myths that appear to confound their best efforts:

1. There is the notion that parents must be consistent. While consistency certainly is desirable, parents, being quite human, will fail on occasion. This does not negate the rest of their efforts.

2. There is the notion that parents always must agree and support each other. This is not a natural outcome of parenting but merely a cultural attitude built into people's background. Disagreements, if handled with dignity, can have the twofold effect of letting children see they are not always the odd persons, disagreeing with the entire world, and of giving a model for how to go about disagreeing if that happens to be the case.

According to Gordon (1975a), parents must cultivate a way of listening that is accepting of children and give clear evidence of that attitude. The art of accepting and listening is a powerful tool. Through it, the quality of the relationship can be improved. When parents can communicate to a child that they are truly listening and accepting, open lines of communication can be maintained; family hostilities can be diminished; and meaningful help, guidance, and support can be given to each member.

It becomes important for parents to be able to distinguish between problems that belong to children (with which they can help the youngsters) and problems that belong to parents themselves and that they must resolve. Finally, problems that exist between parents and child must be solved, it is hoped in a manner in which no one loses. Gordon (1975a) pinpoints six steps in this method:

1. identifying and defining the conflict
2. generating possible alternative solutions
3. evaluating the alternative solutions
4. deciding on the best acceptable solution
5. working out ways of implementing the solution
6. following up to evaluate how it worked. (p. 237)

This model has proved effective in numerous instances and parents who espouse it are lavish in their praise. It holds many notions in combination with the theories of the late Dr. Alfred Adler, the Austrian psychiatrist, as presented by Dreikurs (1958, 1964); Dreikurs and Grey (1970), and Dreikurs, Grunwald, and Pepper (1982).

These theories employ the democratic process as a means of dealing with children's actions in an attempt to help them find a place in their world. The main difference appears to be the fact that the PET and TET models are highly verbal, using language at every level of interaction, while the Dreikurs model is based mainly on action and can be operated with a minimum of language.

Since language is one of the main problems in the Piagetian Preschool Language Nursery program, it is not felt that a highly verbal program can carry the messages of correcting children's behavior. Consequently, while some of the ideas are used in the authors' language program, the majority of work done there is at the less verbal level of Dreikurs's model.

Piagetian Model

According to Piaget (1977) and Piaget and Inhelder (1969b), children's socioemotional development is based on action and is constructed from within, just as is cognitive development (see Chapter 1).

> Piaget traces the parallel between emotional and intellectual life throughout childhood and adolescence. He consistently refers to the motivational aspects of behavior (interest, curiosity, will, determination) and the value systems (moral standards, ideals, goals, aspirations) as part of emotional life. (Pulaski, 1980, p. 135)

Children must be allowed to experience a variety of events in order to construct appropriate social and emotional responses to them. It is imperative that the experience and guidance they receive be at the proper cognitive level if any true benefit is to be gained (Sund, 1976).

During the time children are building cognitive abilities, they also are creating an internal sense of morality and learning how to adapt themselves to others in society, to see things from someone else's viewpoint. They are learning to be autonomous and secure in the more mature relationships of the adult world.

However, even the best intentioned activities possible do go astray and children may find themselves in extreme disagreement with the authority figures of the world. When this is the case, accepted Piagetian practices are designed to help the young persons examine the situation and come to accept a further course of action. They may be asked to make restitution or in some way to accept the consequences of the action (Kamii & DeVries, 1977).

In this matter, the Piagetian concept is at least partially compatible with the Adlerian principles chosen for the nursery program. Like Dreikurs's, Piaget's approach does not appear to be primarily verbal but is based more on action (see overview in Chapter 1). Also, like Dreikurs's, Piaget's approach calls for giving support and encouragement to the transgressors lest they become so discouraged that they quit trying, at which point things can only get worse.

Happily, the Piagetian socioemotional principles governing this nursery program can be blended with the practical philosophy and child management techniques presented by Dreikurs. This combination is both effective with the children and meaningful to the parents.

Adlerian (Dreikurs) Model

This well-constructed and complete model is promulgated by the Adlerian Institute with offices in Chicago and across the country, following guidelines set by Dreikurs (Dreikurs, Corsini, Lowe, Sonstegard, 1959). It is compatible with the

Piagetian directive of the nursery program and has been chosen as the primary child management approach to be used with it (see Chapter 1).

It is highly effective with children who have severe problems with language, probably because it is largely a motor-based method and does not rely heavily on language. The rest of this chapter describes this chosen method of child management.

GUIDELINES FOR MANAGING THE NURSERY GROUP

According to Dreikurs (1964), all behavior is purposeful. Nothing children do is random or purposeless. At an early age, infants begin to build a personal relationship with the world, their personality, and a strategy for obtaining what they want. Three factors are important in this development.

1. *Family atmosphere,* from which the children absorb the values, prejudices, attitudes, and priorities of the family. Fortunate children who are born into a tolerant, loving, accepting family are likely to be able to assimilate these qualities into both personality and action strategies.
2. *Family constellation,* which represents the position each person occupies in the family. As discussed earlier in this chapter, each child born into a family enters into a specific position and is likely to develop strategies and personality traits inherent in that position.
3. *Children's responses,* which shape the strategies and personality developed. "A child is an active and dynamic entity. He shares equally in establishing the relationships between himself and each other person in his environment." (Dreikurs, 1964, p. 32)

Expectations

All people act and react according to what they have come to expect from their environment. Actions relate to the context, to understanding of the persons present and past experiences with them. Self-fulfilling expectations become stronger each time they are repeated, confirming children's belief that they know what to expect. Those who have histories of opportunity, acceptance, and fair treatment expect this to be the outcome of their interactions. This expectation can do much to shape their behavior, and in so doing predispose events to come out the way they expected. High expectations encourage positive behavior, which brings good results. On the other hand, children who have experienced only frustration, failure, and hostility come to expect the worst, which alters their behavior and, in the long run, their results. When this expectation is confirmed repeatedly, there is no reason (in the children's minds) to try to be good or to encourage better results.

Low expectations work against the more desirable behavior, actually increasing the problems.

Children who come from a capricious and inconsistent environment, where they never really know what to expect, are frustrated and confused. The widely varying treatment they receive produces both high and low expectations. This confusion, combined with the mixed results they reap, produces anxiety and discouragement and a feeling that no matter how hard they try, they are likely to be rebuffed.

Children often enter the language nursery program with very low expectations. This obviously affects their ability to relate to the school or their peers. It becomes the task of the teacher/clinician to provide them with enough positive response so that they can raise their expectations. Ordinarily, higher expectations can be seen as changes in motivation, effort, and optimism. This raising of expectations helps the children get ready to go on to school and to interact more appropriately when that time comes.

Encouragement—A Vital Force

According to Dreikurs (1964), "A misbehaving child is a discouraged child." (p. 36) Every child needs encouragement to grow on as a plant needs sunlight and water. Confused and punishing approaches to discipline often are totally discouraging to children who already have begun to doubt their worth. As pointed out in the discussion of transactional analysis, children's observations in their world lead to the conclusion that everyone else is "OK" but that they (the small, helpless youngsters) are "Not OK."

Children's natural determination to succeed usually keeps them trying and they often are ingenious in their efforts. However, if clinicians or teachers continually point out by everything they do that the children have failed, discouragement can grow into a problem of clinical dimensions.

For example, 3-year-old Denis proudly went up to his mother and said, "I made my bed myself." If mother simply says, "Thank you. You are a big help to me," Denis will feel encouraged and will continue to try. If on the other hand she says, "Oh honey, it's all messy. Let me fix it," and does so, Denis will feel that he is not competent. Mother will have transmitted the message that his efforts were not acceptable (a message of "Not OK."). His continued discouragement with other things he tries to do could eventually cause him to quit trying, yet it is precisely when children are failing that encouragement is most needed—encouragement to keep trying, to do what is most difficult.

Emphasis always should be placed on the children's efforts, not on how good the result is. At this time an encouraging parent says, "Keep trying. You can make it." Encouraging words to children who have succeeded, especially those that focus on the quality of the result, tend to have the adverse effect of creating increasing anxiety in that the youngsters may doubt that they can produce another such good result or finally be able to live up to the parents' expectations (Dreikurs, 1964; Ginott, 1975).

On the occasions when the children's efforts fail, it is important to react to them and their intentions and, in effect, to say, "I understand what you intended to do and I appreciate your effort." Depending on the circumstances, parents also may be able to follow with, "Do you understand what happened to make it turn out this way?" This in fact can serve both to teach and to interact with the children's failure without emphasizing the discouraging aspects.

When children misbehave, the parents must be careful to phrase the reactions in such a way that they do not create additional discouragement. It is important to be able to separate the doer and the deed. Parents must be able to say to the child, "I love you but I do not like what you did." This is a comment a child can accept and learn from and it does not increase the discouragement. It avoids the ultimate increase in misbehaviors of the more discouraged child.

Overprotection often masquerades as love and affection when in reality it is a more discouraging and negative statement, saying to the children, "You are an incompetent. I cannot trust you. I must overprotect you." Certainly parents must be conscientious in protecting their children but there is a fine line between protection and overprotection. Parents somehow must find this line to provide a sufficient protection level and yet allow the children as much freedom as possible to develop and grow.

The clinicians/teachers in the language nursery program must become adept at interacting with each child in such a way as to acknowledge the doer, the intention, and the results with insight and to provide support and encouragement.

Independence and Self-Esteem

Parents hope their children will grow to be independent, to stand on their own two feet, to take care of themselves. Yet this ability does not come as if by magic when children are old enough to leave home. It grows, often painfully, over time, from practice at doing things for themselves, and it must begin when the children are small and cute and appear helpless. Parents must fight the temptation to do everything for the small persons, whether it is because they are so "cute," so "slow," so "messy," or some other reason, and give them time and opportunity to do things for themselves. A good rule of thumb is:

DO NOT DO THINGS FOR CHILDREN THAT THEY CAN DO FOR THEMSELVES.

Independence must be nurtured, self-esteem built. At each stage of development there are things children can do. Once learned, these should be expected of the children. For example, once 2-year-old Gregory is old enough to sit up at the table and eat independently, he should be expected to do so without any fuss or fanfare. He begins to learn that he is responsible for this one of his needs. Jason, who is 3, also is able to dress himself and can be expected to do this regularly as well as take care of himself at dinner. Amy, at 4, also is old enough to have some household chore to do that she and her parents have agreed upon. She carries her share of the household duties proudly.

When children can do things for themselves and when this ability is valued by those they love, they begin to build self-esteem. They feel like contributing members of society and take increasing pride in doing more and more independently. As successful interactions multiply and independence grows, they gain in self-confidence. Once started on this self-rewarding path, the course of development should be positive if the children are allowed to grow in an accepting and tranquil world that appreciates their efforts and provides the needed encouragement.

Preschool clinicians and teachers are in a position to do an enormous amount of good simply by providing the right environment for desired qualities to grow in, like a nursery operator provides young plants with a nurturing environment in which to grow.

In the language nursery a main goal is to encourage each child to become autonomous, to be able to do things independently, without undue reliance on others. This requires that an atmosphere be maintained that is calm and predictable and in which satisfactory results can be achieved best by each child's functioning independently (but with reasonable cooperation). This atmosphere must be a pleasant and supportive one in which the child is relaxed.

There must be consistent, good-humored interactions with adults. Whenever adults fail to control themselves, giving way to frustration and temper, they confuse and upset the children, causing temporary setbacks in the development of appropriate interpersonal behavior. Conversely, a calm and predictable environment gives children a safe learning ground where they can practice their independence, learn to respect themselves and each other, and grow in confidence and self-esteem. There they also can develop other desirable qualities such as empathy for others, gentleness of spirit, determination, and a good sense of humor, from the examples given by the adults they know and love.

Parents' or teachers' examples communicate more than words ever could. Sudden outbursts in any authority figure model uncontrolled temper in their charges. Verbal abuse destroys children's sense of worth, and sarcasm humiliates and confuses. Neither have any meaningful place in child management. Adults who explode into scoldings and spankings only teach their children how to fly at each other in hostile outbursts of violence.

The preschool setting provides space and time for each child to do certain things independently. As these are completed, the children gain in confidence. As they succeed, they help others and earn praise; their self-esteem grows and continues to develop both in their own minds and in the teachers'. By the time they reach adolescence, these experiences have enriched them and broadened their outlook. They are independent.

Teacher interactions with sensorimotor level children are likely to be mainly motoric. While modeling language extensively, care must be exercised to keep that language pleasant to avoid its becoming too heavily associated with discipline. As children become older they become increasingly symbolically oriented, most often developing verbal symbols. They become more able to use verbal symbols and logic in the process of settling their disputes.

They become pragmatically more able to make their growing language serve them, to do what they want it to do. They easily can see Dreikurs's management techniques (discussed next) as simply a part of the natural order. Language can be allowed to function in a more positive realm, providing information and pleasure.

MANAGEMENT OF INDIVIDUAL CHILDREN

When dealing with groups of youngsters it becomes clear that: (1) no child is a problem all the time and (2) each child is a problem at some time. The type and magnitude of problems varies from child to child, requiring the teachers to be able to make a variety of adaptations.

Dreikurs's Management Procedures

This management model, successful with children across the nation, is based on family or teacher counseling sessions in which all the principals meet with the counselor to discuss particular problems. Parents bring their problems but children also are listened to and the counselor then assists by making suggestions. Philosophically the model is based on the fact that behavior is goal directed and is done to accomplish a purpose. Parents are helped to understand their children's motives and to build ways of interacting with them that help the youngsters to fit into their world. While it could be very harmful for parents to confront their children with their antisocial or unproductive motivation (Dreikurs, 1964), the young people are gradually encouraged and led to changes in their motivation and to goals more acceptable to the family life style. Gradually the interaction model becomes a way of life.

Parents learn how to use three powerful techniques: (1) encouragement (discussed earlier in this chapter), (2) natural or logical consequences, and (3) disinvolvement in struggles for power.

Allowing children to experience the logical or natural consequences of their actions is an effective technique. It is most useful with the attention-getting mechanisms (Dreikurs, 1964). It is essential that this technique not take on the characteristics of punishment, so great care is required in its administration.

Children come to recognize the fact that they must reckon the consequences when choosing a course of action. This knowledge often does much to motivate them to choose the action more carefully so the consequences will be more pleasant.

The ability of adults to disinvolve themselves from the power struggle with children is the most useful technique for dealing with or eliminating the problem. The children who plan the contest intend to engage their parents in it. If, instead, the parents choose to remain calmly uninvolved, there can be no power struggle and the children must seek some other way to express themselves.

All family members benefit from mutual respect, which helps build an atmosphere of tranquillity and cooperation. When children bring unfortunate consequences upon themselves, they come to realize that they precipitated the events themselves and they blame no one else. Parents, on the other hand, can afford to let the children pay the consequences of the action and be sincerely sorry they are unhappy. All family members come to have respect for the social order and to understand how they can best fit in.

If these lessons are learned while children are young and the desired atmosphere is established, parents and teenagers can have smoother sailing in the difficult years ahead.

Specific Problems

According to Dreikurs (1964), children's motivation can be expected to fall into one of four major categories (see Table 6-1), from the least discouraged and productive to the most: attention-getting mechanisms (AGM), power seeking, revenge seeking, and finally the extreme discouragement of assumed disabilities. Once parents have isolated and identified children's motivation, they need to plan appropriate interactions with them. This remediates the problems and helps them improve specific motivation and methods of achieving it.

Attention-Getting Mechanisms (AGMs)

Everyone likes to receive attention but at the same time must be able to function autonomously without an undue amount of it. Children who make constant demands for attention do so because that is their way of proving their importance to themselves. Those who adopt active, constructive ways of gaining constant attention appear to have a need to convince themselves that they have value. While the active and passive constructive means that they choose are not likely to be problems, the attention-getting mechanism (AGM) itself requires modifying.

For example, Annette, 3½ years old, seeks to keep her clinician busy and gain more attention by her constant offers to "entertain." Her constant, "Me play piano," regardless of what else is going on, disrupts the activities of all the other children. If the therapist simply responds, "It isn't time to play the piano. When

Table 6-1 The Four Mistaken Goals of Misbehavior

Useful Behavior		Useless Behavior		Direction of Maladjustment
Active-Constructive	Passive-Constructive	Active-Destructive	Passive-Destructive	Goals
Success	*Charm*	*Nuisance*	*Lazy*	
The model child	The clinging vine	Show-off	Bashful, shy	
The teacher's pet	Vain	Obtrusiveness	Dependent	
Is very industrious	Cute	Mischief maker	Anxious	(AGM)
Exaggerated conscientious-ness	Flatters	Acts tough	Reading & speech difficulties	Attention-Getting (1)
Is very reliable	Sensitive	Tattles	Cries	Mechanism
Often tattles		Teases	Pokey	
Performs for praise and recognition		The "walking question mark"	Untidy	
		Instability	Frivolous	
		"Enfant terrible"	Fearful	
		Fresh	Lacks concentration	
			May have eating problems	

		Rebel	*Stubborn*	
The most frequent deteriorating sequence is from active-construc-		Argues, bickers	Forgetful	
tive AGM to active-destructive		Contradicts	Daydreams	Power (2)
power to active-destructive revenge		Temper tantrums	Dawdles	Seeking
(line a). Another frequent sequence		Lies	Indolence	
goes from passive-constructive		Spiteful	Loafing & idling	
AGM to passive-destructive AGM to		Provocative		
display of inability (line b). In most		Loiters		
cases this development goes		Bull-headed		
through a passive demonstration of				
power. Sometimes passive-con-		*Vicious*	*Violent*	
structive behavior can turn directly to		Contemptuous	Passivity	Revenge (3)
the open display of inadequacy (goal		Steals	Sullen	Seeking
4) (line c). Improvement does not		Insolent	Unmerciful	
follow the same lines. Even a		Violent	Enjoys watch-ing violence	
revengeful child, who generally		Brutal	Malicious	
presents the most disturbed behav-				
ior patterns, can become adequately			*Hopeless*	
adjusted if he can be convinced that			Pseudo-retarded	Display of (4)
he is liked and can be useful.			Listless	Inadequacy
			Sluggish	
			Lackadaisical	

Source: Reprinted from *Maintaining Sanity in the Classroom: Classroom Management Techniques* (2nd ed.) by Rudolph Dreikurs, Bernice Bronia Grunwald, and Floy Childers Pepper, published by Harper & Row, Publishers, Inc., New York. Copyright © 1982, by permission of Harper & Row, Publishers, Inc.

the timer rings, I will help you play the piano,'' Annette can learn to control her quest for attention and to wait until the appointed time.

Somewhat less productive attention-getting mechanisms employ active or passive destructive means. The goal again is to gain undue attention but the children may despair of getting it by constructive means and choose destructive ones. It may not be pleasant attention to have but it is attention. These destructive means may be met by logical or natural consequences, allowing children to endure the results of the misbehavior; however, at the same time, the conduct must not gain the desired attention.

For example, Nicholas, age 3½, keeps all available clinicians busy as he roams around during free play, knocking over blocks, grabbing dolls, generally getting attention by interrupting everyone's activity. In this case, the clinician must try to ensure that such activity gains no attention for the child but might show him a more acceptable way to gain a modicum of attention.

To be fair to children who have AGMs, clinicians or parents first must be sure they are given sufficient attention without having to demand it, then pleasantly but firmly refuse to yield to excessive demands. This actually must be seen as encouraging in the long run.

Mother says to the child, ''I love you very much. I expect you to become self-sufficient and independent. You do not have to depend on me for constant attention but you will always get the attention you do need.''

The clinician can incorporate both directives by saying to Annette, who has been nagging to have music time, ''We will have to wait until it is time for music. Then I will help you choose a record to play, so everyone can march.'' This does not give undue attention when it is demanded but it does assure the child a chance of obtaining attention that is appropriate.

Power Struggle

Many children achieve their status in their own eyes by attempting to keep their parents or teachers involved in a struggle for power, which the adults are sure to lose (Dreikurs, 1964). This is a difficult position for adults and one that requires a calm, detached approach. When children make a play for power, unwary teachers usually are drawn into the conflict. When teachers allow this to occur, they already have lost the battle (Dreikurs, 1964). Children feel free to use every conceivable weapon while teachers and parents must be constrained by their roles in life.

Two possible responses to the power struggle are available: (1) abstention from punishment and (2) refusal to participate.

Too often, when a power struggle rages, the logical or natural consequences assume the negative attributes of punishment and thus fail to help the situation. If a natural consequence can be allowed without the teacher's producing a punitive effect, it can be useful in resolving the struggle; if not, some other alternative must be sought.

For example, the nursery group is going outside to play but John has decided his clinician must put on his coat for him. Since John is able to put it on, the clinician must not be drawn into this service. If the clinician says pleasantly to John, "All right. I guess if you don't want to go outside, we don't have to. You can wait in the room with me. I have work to do anyway." John fails to involve her in a struggle. The coat should be put away and no further urging or scolding should be heard. The clinician should go on with the work and refrain from entertaining or providing for John. The child, who really did want to go outside, finds himself waiting in the room with nothing to do until the other children return but he perceives this result as something he brought on himself. He probably learns from this situation.

The response more likely to be effective for the clinician or teacher is to simply refuse to be drawn into the struggle. The adult simply leaves the child alone in the arena. Unable to struggle alone, the child then must turn to a more productive behavior. If this response is consistent, the child's attempts to embroil the teacher in a struggle for power will diminish.

For example, Elmer, 4 years old and new to the nursery program, is outraged by being expected to sit in the reading circle. He shows his displeasure by lying down in the reading circle and screaming. The wise clinician, refusing to be drawn into a confrontation, moves the circle to another corner of the room and goes on with the story. Elmer continues to rage but is not able to involve anyone else in his struggle so he finally quiets down and listens to the story from afar.

Revenge Seeking

Sometimes children can become so intensely involved in power struggles with parents or teachers that they ultimately spend much of their time seeking revenge against them. Such children are likely to be those who see only a very negative position in the family or classroom for themselves. In their minds, they are actively bad children. Because of their misery, they may strike out again and again to avenge themselves against parents or teachers.

Parents and teachers must be very careful in such instances to support and encourage the children even while dealing with the undesirable behavior. Punishment can only confirm the children's worst fears about their lack of value and urge them on to more retaliation. What they need instead is help to see a more positive place for themselves in the world and encouragement to try to fill it. These efforts must be appreciated as they strive to achieve an improved goal.

For example, Arthur, age 3, comes to school angry with his mother and continues the day angry with his teacher and therapist. Although able to go to the bathroom, he crawls under the sandbox and soils his pants to "get even with them all." Instead of reacting to his revenge, the teacher gives him a hug and says, "I'm sure you would like to be cleaned up," and sends an aide out with him. When he returns he has missed most of a favorite activity but nothing is said about the incident. He rejoins the group with no apparent feeling of having gotten even. After an interval of cooperative interaction, the teacher suggests an activity she is sure Arthur will enjoy. After a number of similar interactions, it is noted that Arthur is less revengeful than he had been and becomes more cooperative.

Assumed Inadequacy (Disability)

Children's most devastating negative motivation is the one that results in assumed disability. It represents children who are totally demoralized and so discouraged that they believe they cannot succeed at anything. They may hide behind an assumed disability that says to the world, "Leave me alone. I am no good. I can't do anything and I don't want to try again." It may be that they would rather have it said that they would not try to do anything than that they tried and failed again.

Just as success breeds success, this kind of failure only breeds more discouragement and failure. For example, Mitch, age 3, is so sure he will fail that he will not try to frost his cupcake, preferring to lie on the floor and watch the other children. Realizing that this occurs most often when Mitch does not know what to expect, his teacher wisely begins to give all the children a preview of the work to be done before they begin. When Mitch can see someone else frost a cookie first, he is more willing to try and, with each successful try, feels less discouraged.

If children are to realize that they are not worthless, they must be given encouragement and trust to change their motivation to a more profitable one. It is hoped that the encouragement will provide the incentive for them to try again, while the trust placed in them can instill in them the beginnings of self-esteem so necessary for development.

MANAGEMENT PROBLEMS WITH GROUPS

For everyone who has worked with children, the group represents a powerful factor to be used to guide and direct its individual members. The group develops a personality from the composite of its members. All of its children contribute to the group's activities and can think of more things to do collectively than any of them could singly. This group is capable of greater heights of achievement and lower depths of behavior than would be usual for individual members. If one child can be naughty, a group of children can be much more so.

Children in a group do, however, react to management techniques in predictable ways. If teachers are aware of important facts about group management, they can form their groups into closely knit and supportive units that operate at a higher level. Desirable characteristics, i.e., cooperation and mutual support, can be built by group activity while undesirable characteristics, i.e., competitiveness, can be extinguished by creative handling.

Teachers who are interested in effective group dynamics should be careful to include the children in all aspects of planning. The youngsters also must be included in councils where they can be involved in setting rules and limits for themselves. The members can gain experience in various positions of authority within the group while at the same time acquiring respect for system and order in the preschool.

In the Piagetian sense, members construct their socioemotional knowledge in group interactions. They learn how to minimize their disagreements and practice working cooperatively. All this social practice and group activity provides an ideal arena for the learning of pragmatic abilities that probably will be quite mature by the end of the preschool years.

Practical adaptations of this action-based model can become a way of life for both children and teachers. The model was chosen essentially because it is compatible with the Piagetian developmental theory on which the authors' program is based. Important to this compatibility is the fact that this model focuses on an action base. As noted earlier, it is not a method that puts heavy emphasis on verbalization, thus allowing the clinician to deal with the behavior directly and still stimulate the language without any direct interference from the children's misconduct problems.

THE POWER OF GROUP DYNAMICS

Working with children in groups is demanding but very profitable. The group has more impact on each of its members than would be accorded to a single member. It also generates momentum and can carry a developmental or learning force.

Teachers must take into account the awesome power of group activity. As noted, they must consider each member in all planning. If a particular child is having problems, teachers must evaluate their interactions with that individual (Exhibit 6-2). If a child is falling behind for cognitive reasons, they must plan ways of helping. When children make big gains, teachers should evaluate how and why so they can replicate the conditions.

In the language nursery, groups of children and teams of teachers/clinicians must interact with the least possible friction. Certainly some rules are dictated by the physical facility or the sponsoring agency; other operating rules can come about through a process of nursery council, a panel composed of the staff and the children. Younger children may not have much to add to this process but it is good for them to see it in operation; if they have ideas, they should be listened to. In this

Exhibit 6-2 Child's Troubles in Small-Group Activities

1. Does the child understand the daily routine? Can he anticipate times of the day? Does he know where his group meets each day? Does he need help getting started?
2. What materials and activities might he be particularly interested in? What is he successful at and how can that be included in small-group time?
3. Are small-group activities being structured too narrowly so the child can't work on his own level and be successful? Do things seem too hard or easy for him?
4. Is there another child he works particularly well with?
5. Can he be enlisted to help other children at small-group time? To share ideas and solutions?
6. Does he fall apart because he can't make ideas work? or because once he has tried one thing he can't find alternatives?
7. Does he need more support throughout the day? Does he work better at small-group time after he has had a successful work time?
8. What can be done to make the expectations of small-group time more clear?

Source: Reprinted from *Young Children in Action: A Manual for Preschool Educators* by Mary Hohmann, Bernard Banet, and David P. Weikart with permission of High/Scope Press, © 1979.

way they learn about the formulation of realistic expectations. (See Exhibit 6-3 for sample expectations to be resolved for both clinicians and children.)

A Word of Caution

The authors believe the Adlerian model so ably presented by Dreikurs, combined with certain Piagetian notions, constitutes an appropriate approach to children in general. It must be remembered, however, that children whose problems are specific and severe require more specialized management. If the children are not working properly, continuation of the general principles previously suggested could be counterproductive in two ways:

1. The actions taken might prove harmful or inadequate if not properly presented and followed through.
2. More specialized guidance (and its subsequent benefits) might never be sought when it was truly needed.

Therefore, it is incumbent on teachers and clinicians to become skilled enough in the theories and approaches they use that they can administer them properly. This probably requires that they seek specific instruction in the methods of their choice. If severe problems are encountered, a specialist in the crisis area should be consulted. For those following the suggestions of this program, some of the skilled counselors at the Adlerian Institute in Chicago could be contacted for guidance.

Exhibit 6-3 Behaviors for Adult Team Members and Group Children

---

The team should have common expectations for its members' conduct.

1. What about leaving the room to answer the phone, smoke, etc.?
2. What about talking across the room to each other or children?
3. How will team members maintain contact with each other throughout the day?
4. What if a team member really gets angry with a child or another team member?
5. What about talking about children while they are present?
6. How will the team respond to catastrophes, i.e., spilled paint, measles, accidents, etc.?
7. Will each team member's group perform the same activity at small-group time?
8. Should each team member stay in an area throughout work time?
9. What about the times team members come to school but don't feel like being patient with children or coworkers?
10. What about a child who prefers one team member over others?

Common expectations and limits should be decided on for children.

1. Can a child go straight to an area without indicating a plan?
2. Do children need to clean up before changing their plans?
3. Can children run or tussle in the center of the room?
4. Can children go outside during work time?
5. What materials in particular work areas can be used in other parts of the room?
6. Can children go to the bathroom by themselves?
7. Do all children have to wait for everyone to be ready for the next activity before it begins or can things begin when a small group of children are ready?
8. Does everyone have to clean up just the things they used or work until the whole room is cleaned?
9. What if a child won't clean up?
10. Does a child have to go to small-group time?
11. What if a child doesn't want to participate in the circle activity? What if he is disrupting it?
12. How in general will the team deal with typical 3- and 4-year-olds hitting, grabbing, and biting?

Source: Reprinted from *Young Children in Action: A Manual for Preschool Educators* by Mary Hohmann, Bernard Banet, and David P. Weikart with permission of High/Scope Press, © 1979.

Challenges

Democracy, to most Americans the most rewarding form of government known, makes demands at many levels on those who would live in its light. Among these is a demand for maturity and tolerance in interpersonal relationships. It surely requires more maturity for adults to live democratically than to live as dictators over their children.

Parents must grow into their roles. If they are to live democratically with their children, they must become mature enough to guide them without insisting on absolute control over them. They must encourage, stimulate, and support them, yet allow them the freedom to be their own persons and ultimately to live a life of emerging independence and self-motivation.

SUMMARY

Much confusion exists regarding the best approach to child management or discipline. Parents and teachers are at a loss in trying to do what is best for the development of the children in their charge. Society has changed enough that, to paraphrase Lincoln, the rules of the quiet past are inadequate for the booming present. At the same time, some of the advice available does not seem to work as it should.

The authors have found that without appropriate management techniques, the children in their care cannot accomplish the necessary learning tasks. Five modern management models were described: the behavioral, the transactional analysis, the parent effectiveness training, the Piagetian, and the Adlerian model. It was shown how the behavioral model can be used to accomplish changes in behavior at the conditioned level but this was coupled with a warning against too much dependence upon this model. Other models more consistent with the intent of the language nursery school were discussed and some ways in which teachers can build a personal model based upon the strong points of the more interactive models were shown.

Guidelines for managing the nursery school group that are consistent with the Dreikurs interpretation of Adlerian psychology and designed to foster autonomy and social responsibility in children were described. Problems exhibited by many children that reduce their ability to work in nursery school groups or in society at large were examined. Suggestions were made for designing a management program based upon logical and natural consequences so the children could develop the autonomy necessary. Similarly, several types of problems exhibited by some children in the nursery school were described, and suggestions were made for management of such situations. Finally, the concept of group dynamics was examined and related to the management model chosen as the most powerful for the authors' needs.

DISCUSSION QUESTIONS

1. How does the concept of purposeful behavior in all children agree with your concept of child discipline?

2. What do you think about the relative ethics of the behavioral model of child management and the other models presented?
3. How much attention should a teacher pay to the self-esteem of nursery school children? Are you prepared to defend your position?
4. Are children with assumed inadequacy in need of more help or in more trouble than any of the others nursery school teachers might encounter?

REFERENCES

Adler, A. *Understanding human nature*. New York: Premier Books, 1957.

Adler, A. *The problem child*. New York: Capricorn Books, 1963.

Clark, H.H., & Clark, E.V. *Psychology of language: An introduction to psycholinguistics*. New York: Harcourt Brace Jovanovich, Inc., 1977.

Dreikurs, R. *The challenge of parenthood*. New York: Duell, Sloan & Pearce, 1958.

Dreikurs, R. *Children: The challenge*. New York: Hawthorn Books, Inc., 1964.

Dreikurs, R.; Corsini; Lowe, R.; & Sonstegard. *Adlerian family counseling: A manual for counseling centers*. Eugene, Oregon: University of Oregon Press, 1959.

Dreikurs, R., & Grey, L. *A parent's guide to child discipline*. New York: Hawthorn Books, Inc., 1970.

Dreikurs, R.; Grunwald, B.B.; & Pepper, F.C. *Maintaining sanity in the classroom: Classroom Management Techniques* (2nd ed.). New York: Harper & Row, Publishers, Inc., 1982.

Ervin-Tripp, S. Social backgrounds and verbal skills. In R. Huxley & E. Ingram (Eds.), *Language acquisition: Models & methods*. New York: Academic Press, Inc., 1971.

Freed, A.M. *T.A. for tots, and other prinzes*. Sacramento, Calif.: Jalmar Press, Inc., 1975.

Ginott, H.C. *Teacher and child: A book for parents and teachers*. New York: Macmillan Publishing Co., Inc., 1975.

Gordon, T. *Parent effectiveness training* (PET). New York: Peter H. Wyden, Inc., 1975. (a)

Gordon, T. *Teacher effectiveness training,* (TET). New York: Peter H. Wyden, Inc., 1975. (b)

Harris, T.A. *I'm OK, You're OK*. New York: Avon Books, 1973.

Hohmann, M.; Banet, B.; & Weikart, D.P. *Young children in action: A manual for preschool educators*. Ypsilanti, Mich.: The High/Scope Press, 1979.

Houston, S.H. *A survey of psycholinguistics*. The Hague: Mouton Publishers, 1972.

Kamii, C., & DeVries, R. Piaget for Early Education. In M.C. Day & R.K. Parker (Eds.), *The preschool in action: Exploring early childhood programs* (2nd ed.). Boston: Allyn & Bacon, Inc., 1977.

Kretschmer, R.R., & Kretschmer, L.W. *Language development and intervention with the hearing impaired*. Baltimore: University Park Press, 1978.

Mowrer, O.H. *Learning theory and the symbolic process*. New York: John Wiley & Sons, Inc., 1960.

Osgood, E.C. Language universals and psycholinguistics. In J.H. Greenberg (Ed.), *Universals of language*. Cambridge, Mass.: The MIT Press, 1963.

Pavlov, I. *Conditioned reflexes* (1st ed.). New York: Dover, 1927.

Piaget, J. [*The language and thought of the child*] (M. Gavain, trans.). Cleveland and New York: World Publishing Co., 1969(a).

Piaget, J., & Inhelder, B. [*The psychology of the child*] (H. Weaver, trans.). New York: Basic Books, Inc., 1969(b).

Piaget, J. In H.E. Gruber & J. Vonèche (Eds. and trans.), *The essential Piaget*. New York: Basic Books, Inc., 1977.

Pulaski, M.A.S. *Understanding Piaget: An introduction to children's cognitive development*. New York: Harper & Row, Publishers, Inc., 1980.

Skinner, B.F. *Verbal behavior*. New York: Appleton-Century-Crofts, Inc., 1957.

Sund, R.B. *Piaget for educators: A multimedia program*. Columbus, Ohio: The Charles E. Merrill Publishing Co., Inc., 1976.

Chapter 7

Children's Play

CHAPTER OBJECTIVES

After completing this chapter, readers should be able to:

1. Describe the importance of play in children's lives.
2. Explain the relationships between play, cognitive development, and language.
3. Describe the types of play and the specific value of each.
4. Describe the sequential development of play and the potential for diagnosis inherent in this understanding.

KEY IDEAS

1. Play is the business of children.
2. Physical, intellectual, language, and social growth all depend to some extent upon the play activities children engage in.
3. Play exhibits distinct stages of development, as do other aspects of child growth.
4. Deficiencies or deviations in the sequential development of play activities may have far-reaching implications for children's growth.
5. Teachers or parents can use understanding of the play schedules of children for diagnostic purposes.

THE ROOTS OF PLAY

I shall contend that play as a process lies at the very core of human behavior and development. (Chance, 1979, p. xv)

Play, the vocation of the young, the avocation of the old—a medium for learning in society—is so close to everyone that they hardly see it function at all. It has long suffered from lack of being studied or appreciated. Many researchers and educators still pass it off as a waste of time, contributing little or nothing to the general good.

Nothing could be further from the truth. Play is one of the most important universal elements in people's lives. Play teaches patterns, motions, and attitudes that change over time, providing a relatively safe medium for learning and adjusting. Individuals play important but simple things as children, exploring the parameters of an ever-expanding environment. As adults, they play more formalized and complex games. In fact, they mark society's civility, the level of its achievements.

Not only have human children played games since the beginning of time, so, too, have animal babies. Everyone has enjoyed watching kittens, puppies, or other young animals play. Those who also have witnessed the more complex play of closer relatives, the chimpanzees, and of the sociable and playful dolphins, have seen that the more closely they resemble humans intellectually, the more their play contains complex elements that more nearly approximate our own.

Play is more than an interesting phenomenon to be noted and forgotten. It is a tool to be used in the teaching of children.

THE NATURE OF PLAY

The essential attribute of play is a rule which has become an affect . . . an idea which has become an affect, a concept which has turned into a passion. (Vygotsky, 1933/1976, p. 549)

Play is defined here as spontaneous activity in which the individual engages for fun. It is challenging in its own right and an end in itself (Chance, 1979). Regardless of its spontaneous and diverting nature, play is an important phenomenon that serves to transmit necessary social knowledge and functions to newer members of society.

Vygotsky (1933/1976) maintains that play is not random activity for children but is highly purposeful. It can be seen to develop over a lifetime from very simple beginnings to the more formalized and abstract play of adults, and it takes many forms. It is both systematic and rule governed (Garvey, 1977).

Initial play may stem directly from children's earliest social interactions in the mother-infant dyad. Its development appears to be parallel, and in various ways related to, the emergence of smiling, imitation, cognition, and language but the relationships implied are not yet fully defined.

According to Garvey (1977), the parallel between play and smiling is maintained throughout the preschool years until the children have a range of responses (smiling, laughing, giggling) to parallel the play behaviors they have developed. The element Garvey calls group glee—a spontaneous eruption of giggling, screaming, and clapping of hands—appears to be a combination of play and smile development. These episodes persist into the kindergarten year and she (Garvey) believes they actually contribute to the learning process because they channel the responses in desired directions.

As adults (professionals) watch young children learn to play, to work through the early stages Piaget identifies (Piaget, 1962, 1969a, 1969b, 1974, 1977; Pulaski, 1980), the relationship between imitation and play becomes clearer:

Level 1:   By 2 years of age, children have learned to imitate themselves doing something they actually are capable of doing. For example, Level 1 children might be able to pretend they were eating, crying, etc.

Level 2:   At age 2, these children imitate someone else doing something they themselves can do; they can pretend a doll is eating or crying.

Level 3:   By age 2½, the children can imitate (or play out) entire scenes and complex episodes. For example, they could play an entire scenario of preparing lunch for guests.

Chance (1979) discusses the importance of a reciprocal relationship between play and learning. Play must in fact have a role in focusing symbolic activity so essential to learning and it is "certainly implicated in early language acquisition" (Bruner, Jolly, & Sylva, 1976, p. 19). Indeed, careful consideration of the development of play highlights its contribution to all areas of development: physical, cognitive, emotional, social, and linguistic. According to Bruner et al. (1976), a formal parallel exists between rule-governed, structured play and rule-bound, structured language. They hypothesize that the evolution of play probably can be classified as a prerequisite to language and symbol acquisition.

Play containing the preceding developmental elements essentially is of four kinds (Chance, 1979):

1. *Physical Play:* This involves emphasis on action, developing muscles and reflexes, exploring physical relationships, gravity, resistances, etc. Jason, 18 months old, runs back and forth across the lawn, shoulders up and head forward, obviously feeling that he possesses great speed. Joyously, he adds the single word that expresses this physical play as he chants, "running, running, running."

2. *Manipulative Play:* This involves attempts to master the environment, grasping, reaching, hand-eye coordination, etc. Amy, who is 4, carefully arranges the sprinkler she is running through in the backyard so she can play at running in and out of the edge of it in the course of her planned game,

wondering whether she can so place it that it will just catch her as she climbs the apple tree.

3. *Symbolic Play:* This involves the use of symbols for "pretend-at-reality" role playing, puppeteering, block building, etc. Later, Jason, now 3 years old, carefully packs selected toys into the nose cone (laundry basket) of his rocket ship (family room sofa) before inviting his grandmother to go on a vacation to the moon with him. This flight of fancy is complete with sandwiches (blocks), juice (paper cups), and tickets (torn from the newspaper) for the movies on the moon.

4. *Game Play:* This focus is on rules or conventions of cooperative play, elaborate multilevel operations constructed by a group of children or taught to a group by one member, etc. Denis, age 9; Paula, 7½; Mark, 5½, and a group of their cousins occupied the long summer evenings playing a continuing game of flashlight tag with basic rules and various levels of structure that depended upon exactly which children were playing and which batteries wore out on their grandfather's flashlights. This game continued for years (whenever the cousins met at their grandparents' farm) and gradually became more sophisticated as the children matured.

Later play styles come from these beginnings and furnish an arena for practice as the children learn the business of living.

THE DEVELOPMENT OF PLAY

Play, so necessary to growth, develops over a lifetime and has its effects on almost all parts of people's lives. Its process is more important than the specific games it employs (Sylva, Bruner, & Genova, 1976). It is intrinsically bound up with all other development in the first few months: with pragmatic development as it comes from the interpersonal actions of the mother-infant dyad and phonological development as the children learn to babble, developing the prerequisite motor skills for vocalization.

"The importance of babbling as a basis for human speech can not be overestimated" (Hayes, 1952/1976, p. 619). This important stage ushers in a period of "sound play" that in itself is a developmental step. Pulaski (1980) emphasizes that Piaget (1963; 1977) distinguishes the beginning of play as functional pleasure. According to Pulaski, "In play he (the child) is assimilating objects and activities to his own satisfaction" just for fun (Pulaski, 1980, p. 82).

During the second half of the first year, children, usually interacting with the mother (see Exhibit 7-1), have learned to grasp an object, bang it on the table, and use it playfully and manipulatively (Garvey, 1977). For example, they can take a spoon and bang it on a highchair tray for fun and in various ways initiate games and rituals with mother (Bloom & Lahey, 1978).

Exhibit 7-1 Chronology of How Normal Object Play Begins

Age	Activity
9 months	The child grasps a nearer, brigher object and moves it to the mouth. Might well wave it or bang it on table. Uses few action patterns.
12 months	The child is likely to investigate each object before doing anything with it. Objects treated at random (mouthed, banged, waved).
15 months	The child inspects and investigates. More, and more consistent, appropriate uses of objects.
21 months	The child searches for object to go with another thing. Imaginary milk stirred with imaginary spoon. Doll put in truck and door closed.
24 months	The child feeds doll realistically, etc. Playing with toys increases.
30 to 36 months	The child manipulates the toys in symbolic way. Doll made to brush its hair and get dressed for church.

Source: Constructed from *Play: The Developing Child* by Catherine Garvey. Harvard University Press, © 1977, pp. 43–44.

At about 1 year, they advance from random manipulation and initiation of game behavior with the mother to increased approximation of correct use of such things as spoons and cups (Garvey, 1977). For example, they may be able to take a spoon and bang it on the highchair but also intersperse this with pretend stirring or eating with the same spoon. As early as the beginning of the second year, some children can relate to what Piaget terms ludic symbols, make-believe games (Pulaski, 1980). For example, they can rock a baby made of rolled-up newspaper. According to Garvey, children at 15 months can manipulate objects in more conventional ways and may begin to pantomime. By 21 months, they will search for an object to go with another one they are playing with. For example, they might find a (toy) saucepan and search for a spoon (or something to use as a spoon) to stir with.

The end of the sensorimotor period marks the beginning of a new era in the development of play. The children now can play quite realistically with familiar items (Garvey, 1977), having reached what Piaget identifies as Stage 1—pretending to perform a familiar action (Pulaski, 1980).

By the end of the sensorimotor period, children are likely to have passed Piaget's Stage 2 (Pulaski, 1980) and can pretend at a more abstract level—that a doll is combing its hair, etc. At this age (2 years old) they are capable of simple role playing, very simple language play, and symbolic play (Sund, 1976).

This period also sees the beginning of verbal language that, with pretend play, is based on symbolic formation (McCune-Nicolich & Carroll, 1981; Meers, 1976). By this age, children will have passed through a complete sequence of development enhancing cognition, language, and play (see Exhibit 7-2) that are interdependent at every level.

Exhibit 7-2 Developments in Child's Play from 1 to 3 Years

---

1. The child increasingly differentiates between various action patterns compatible with each object and fits together action and object appropriately (for example, he moves from mouthing every graspable object to putting only the spoon in his mouth).
2. He comes to combine objects that go together into functional relationships (he assembles the cup, saucer, and spoon).
3. He puts action patterns in sequence to form larger, coherent wholes (he links cooking, eating, and washing up).
4. He applies action patterns to himself (brushes his own hair), to others or replicas of others (brushes his mother's or a doll's hair). Finally, he attributes to replicas the ability to act (as when he causes the doll to brush its own hair or moves a toy dog while making barking noises).
5. He invents absent but appropriate objects or substances to complete action patterns (he stirs imaginary coffee with a spoon).
6. He transforms objects for use in actions and action sequences (he stirs imaginary coffee with a toy rake, used as a spoon).

Source: Reprinted from *Play: The Developing Child* by Catherine Garvey with permission of the Harvard University Press, © 1977.

Meers (1976), incorporating Cass' theories (1971), comments that as children grow and develop in all the other ways mentioned, their ability to play evolves through five stages: solitary play, spectator play, parallel play, associative play, and cooperative play. They create the ability to play in the larger groups of kindergarten. Each stage has its essential relationship with language.

During the first half of the preoperational period (2 through 4 years), children construct both language and symbolic play, centering on role playing, as they begin to explore and widen the parameters of their world. As language, cognition, and play develop they become integrated into the foundation for operativity needed by about age 7, the transition between the preoperational and concrete operational periods.

Children like to play make-believe and to represent things with other things—for example the blocks are houses and the coffee can is the car. Blocks are particularly fascinating at this age because they can represent so much symbolic thought and are so versatile. They seem to allow children to incorporate their abilities and motor skills at manipulating the blocks creatively in designing make-believe games. Children achieve equilibrium as they accommodate to reality and assimilate information from it, using the tactic of imitation. By the beginning of the preoperational period, both assimilation and accommodation have become well enough developed to observe. Between ages 2 and 4, symbolic play is at its peak (Pulaski, 1980).

Children at that age are egocentric and not yet capable of playing in a truly cooperative manner "with" other children. They merely are playing their own games while in the company of another child. Below the age of 4, children do not realize that rules are for everyone and that they operate by mutual consent. They do not really follow any rules (Sund, 1976).

These two factors—children's egocentricity and inability to operate with rule systems—probably mitigate against their playing in truly cooperative ways. When they have passed these milestones, they are ready to take another big step in the advancement of their play: to truly cooperative, rule-governed play.

As children turn 4, they are able to operate within a rule system and more creative games become possible. The well-developed play of this age sometimes is seen as compensatory in that it provides a temporary respite from earlier consequences and frustration (Sylva, Bruner, & Genova, 1976). Children play out events or actions that in reality are forbidden or frightening. Play enables them to act out painful emotions that then become stylized or ritualized, orderly, and sociable, and from them proper roles in society are learned. As children become old enough and mature enough to begin kindergarten, they are ready for the collective symbolism of group games (Pulaski, 1980).

Throughout the period of preschool development, play has been an important and serious activity, channeling children to further growth. When they enter school, play is somewhat more limited as the larger, more complex society imposes ever greater demands and restrictions that permeate their interactions with the world. By adolescence, play again has become very serious business as it fills more adult needs (Vygotsky, 1933/1976) by providing outlets for aggression, frustrations, and fears.

THE IMPORTANCE OF PLAY

Two basic precepts that attest how important play is to development are that:

1. The organism is constructing and adapting an internal model of self and/or context, and
2. These models must exist so the organism can act on them to produce new learning. (Fagen, 1976)

This approach is compatible with Piaget's basic constructionist view of the learning process.

The authors' observations of children who have had no opportunity to play because they are handicapped or environmentally restricted, when compared with children from a rich play environment, indicate a notable difference between the two groups. Children with extensive play backgrounds become adept at all kinds of play, learning to construct rules and adapt them to various contexts. They develop personal strength and individuality in the play arena. Those who have limited experience do not have these advantages and their development may lag far behind.

Children's games help them perfect a sense of social interactions. During the activity, the children learn how to approach various social situations and react appropriately. A sense of fair play and honesty develops from these interactions and the insights they bring. Piaget states that, "All morality consists (of) a system of rules, and the essence of all morality is to be sought for in the respect which the individual acquires for the rules." (Piaget, 1965/1976, p. 413)

Before children go out to play with peers, they must learn many social rules and roles from early interactions with parents (Piaget, 1965/1976). This is the way roles and attitudes are passed from older generations to the younger. Children go out using many of the same adaptations as their parents would have. This is satisfactory when the parent models are adequate but can become a problem when they have been inadequate. The importance of play can be seen by what happens (for the lack of such activity) to the youngsters in the play or school group.

POTENTIAL EFFECTS OF PLAY

It can be seen that developmental play is crucial because it does such a variety of things for children. Of course, toys provide the materials for play and creative children adapt and make them fit their needs, but the most important element is the development of language (Levenstein, 1976). Bradley and Caldwell (1976), studying the relationships between home environment and cognitive development, report the most significant factor in stimulating children's intellect is appropriate play materials. As cognition expands through interaction with such materials, so does language. Children learn and develop many abilities through play, making it possible to expand their play through language.

Manipulative Play

Through manipulative play, children learn physical problem-solving skills. This play with objects and the actions performed with them enables children to solve mechanical problems related to the operation of toys and other articles in the physical world.

Water Play

This type of play is instrumental in helping children experience and construct their understanding of capacity and volume. The activities of filling and pouring from containers also fosters an understanding of three-dimensional space and size and shape relationships among containers (Leacock, 1976). Once these concepts begin to be learned through water play, they continue to expand in the sandbox and other situations as well.

Role Play

This type of activity allows children to learn social roles while interacting with their peers. In role playing, they gradually learn not only to understand various roles but also to relate to how others see various things. It would seem very likely that this type of play becomes necessary and possible only when the children are ready to begin the transition from egocentrism to social play. At this same time they are learning the appropriate pragmatics of a number of social contexts by the ordinary means of trial and error.

Physical Play

Like other physical activities, physical play is important because it smoothes and expands motoric abilities. Since those correlate highly with language development, this type of play probably is prerequisite to further language development for many children. Physical play enables them to develop motor skills that serve as foundations for further development. In addition, it functions to release tension, unused energy (Chance, 1979), and frustration.

Symbolic Play

This very creative form can be used by children to minimize the consequences of their actions (Bruner, 1976). By playing out questionable real-life situations, they arrange to do their learning in play, a less risky situation than real life and one with less permanent consequences.

Amy, at 4, was anxious to start kindergarten. She practiced her role and prepared for the rather scary event of starting school by playing it out repeatedly before class actually started. She would get a large book and a lunch box and, with her grandmother, play that she went on the school bus (bottom of the end table). After a time she would return home (couch) and report on her day, sometimes pretending she had a good day at school and sometimes that she did not.

Deep Play

Activities in which children play "dangerous games," such as Russian roulette or "dare," where the stakes are unreasonably high are used most often by adolescents to minimize some of the larger risks they must take in growing up. Play in which the stakes are so high that one can lose more than can be gained is viewed as a sign of deep, unresolved problems (Bruner, 1976). When this occurs, children play the game because they cannot tolerate taking such large risks in real-life situations that promise to cost so dearly. Obviously, this type of play is not to be expected of all children, nor is it desirable for all. It signals the presence of serious unresolved problems that young people have in relating to today's culture. They can use it creatively as an escape mechanism when such a need arises. While this type of play is more common in adolescents, it is not unknown in pre-schoolers.

Social Play

Here children incorporate all of the individual basic skills into social interactions of a wide variety. This type of play intensifies and preserves the culture for transmission to succeeding generations (Chance, 1979) and to those who come new to the culture. Through the rhymes, stories, songs, and games the players learn to understand and appreciate their social and cultural heritage (Leacock, 1976), which they preserve with pride and transmit to their children.

Game Play

Playing games emphasizes the learning of sets of rules. The players must agree on and obey the rules if the game is to function (Coleman, 1976). This activity has long constituted one of the major ways people learn. Players see the consequences of their and other players' actions and understand how those relate to predictable and consequently controllable outcomes.

Academic Play

This play, in the form of mental stimulation games, contributes to children's belief that they can control their own destiny. Academic games come in a wide range of difficulty, are used creatively by capable students to illustrate various learning principles, and can be used by teachers to hold the interest of the entire range of pupils.

In a study reported by Coleman (1976), the U.S. Office of Education concluded that "one attribute strongly related to performance on standardized achievement tests is a child's belief that his future depends on his own efforts, rather than on a capricious environment" (p. 462). He adds that many disadvantaged children lack this belief. It becomes clear that play at some earlier level might have made a critical difference to them.

Competitive Play

These games can take any of a number of forms. The important feature is allowing the players to pit themselves against one or more adversaries (e.g., nature, evil, life situation, etc.) and play out a controlled aggression. It also permits quantification of the win-lose feature and generally can be counted on to provide players with experience at both winning and losing.

Electronic Play

This new form, still an unstudied phenomenon, provides a totally different experience. It appears to be both highly sensory and reflexive and yet demands both cognitive reactions and strategy. The authors are intrigued by the diverse possibilities for learning through electronic games but somewhat apprehensive about their possible social and cultural implications.

Therapeutic Play

This type of play, designed to remedy specific psychological problems, is a powerful tool. Play therapy is used in carefully controlled clinical situations by trained professionals to help children play through serious problems. It should not be used, in the psychological sense, by anyone untrained in its application.

Play can have less formal therapeutic results when it is simply used appropriately with children who learn from the chosen play settings. The ordinary benefits each child stands to receive from appropriate play are the emphasis of this chapter and a strength of the Piagetian Language Nursery Program.

It is important to note that many types of learning are inherent in each play situation. It is not possible to so construct a play situation that only one type of learning can result, nor would it be desirable to do so if it were. The social rules of taking turns and respect for others' rights and desires, for example, probably permeate all play situations above the level of parallel play.

THE INFANT-MOTHER DYAD

As noted earlier in this chapter, children acquire their first learning through play in close interaction with parents and siblings. The sequence of mother-infant play, and with other adults and children in the family, leads eventually to activities with peers in relatively uncontrolled situations. Yet it appears clear that the mother-child play of infancy is prerequisite to all other play. Murphy (1972) comments: "Moreover, the playful capacity underlying creativity is supported by good feelings as well—partly, I believe, because it evokes the joy, the delight, the fun of the earliest mother-baby duets" (p. 126).

Studies of play patterns between mother and infant primates yield data that appear to correlate rather highly with observations of mother-infant dyads in humans. In studies of monkey mother-infant dyads, Suomi and Harlow (1976) find that infant monkeys raised without mothers to teach them to play, who then are literally forced onto the playing field, are delayed in learning how to play and have infantile play patterns when, after a number of months, they are introduced to their peers.

They are very aggressive and their play is underdeveloped. They compare them to human children who are "mama's boys," raised by mothers only and who, they say, rarely are popular or effective playmates, combining both aggressiveness and social withdrawal. "All work and no play makes for a dull child. No play makes for a very socially disturbed monkey" (Suomi & Harlow, 1976, p. 492).

Current theory indicates that infants are born with more abilities than was thought previously (Eimas, Siqueland, Jusczyk, & Vigorito, 1971). They are ready very early in life to begin interacting with the "other" in their world. William, 8 weeks old, is "beginning to enjoy" reciprocal vocal play with adults and is becoming "skillful" at maintaining eye contact with others (Snow, 1972)—cornerstones of both the development of play and the development of language.

Early interactions between mother and infant are crucial for many reasons. Through them the baby learns many things. Motherese, the characteristic language used innately by the parent, is well suited to this task. These early verbal interactions help teach the language by providing a highly organized yet simplified model for the child to listen to (Snow, 1972). Early physical play aids in the development of both physical and perceptual motor skills (Chance, 1979).

Experience through play makes possible the systematic progression of cognitive abilities. According to Chance (1979), one of the chief benefits of physical play is that the child gets practice in making transformations and exploring the possibilities of the world.

Some authorities believe play provides a catharsis. There is plenty of evidence that play contributes to emotional health. Children who have learned to play have built the ability to escape unpleasantness when that is necessary. They learn to use play as a protection or as a cathartic. They also learn to create a protective fantasy but at the same time know it is not real. It is this ability that makes them better able to distinguish what is real from what is fantasy (Chance, 1979). This is good mental health. Chance discusses Sutton-Smith's assertion that children who daydream or live lives of high fantasy are most likely to become highly successful and creative adults.

Social development also is implemented by the mother-infant dyad, stressing as it does eye contact and primary social accommodations, for these are the ways and times when infants learn most easily and upon which they can make further adaptations.

ENVIRONMENTAL IMPOVERISHMENT

It has been seen that play serves as an organizer for sensorimotor, emotional, perceptual, cognitive, and linguistic elements and that it helps children form many of the patterns that will grow for a lifetime. However, the deprived children, brought up by tired, depressed mothers in disorganized and crowded ghettos, fail to learn to play (Murphy, 1972) because their mothers have little or no personal resources with which to nurture them. Consequently, these children manifest problems in school and in social situations. According to Murphy (1972) such children appear to generate little or no curiosity and have an inadequate vocabulary. Instead of free and open play, they often sit in ill-furnished flats with nothing to play with, where the light is poor, the television or radio is blaring, and the people yelling over the noise, increasing the confusion. The young people cannot construct the patterns and rule systems that normally develop into language and the skills for school.

If the mother is overworked and exhausted by poverty, she has little of herself to give to the relationship. She does not play with, fondle, or communicate with her child, leaving the infant to struggle alone in a bleak and joyless world. Early intervention with poverty mothers to help them build satisfactory relationships with their infants is focused on building the play relationship. Only in this way can the mothers teach the children to play and only in this way can those youngsters learn many of the things necessary to childhood.

DIAGNOSTIC PLAY

In diagnostic play, as in other areas of diagnosis, clinicians always are looking for patterns of development or of disability. Observation of play behavior in various contexts can provide significant insights into all aspects of children's development.

The way they manipulate objects in play is an index of what they understand about relationships between themselves and the articles (Bloom & Lahey, 1978). For example, children who cannot play at placing markers in specific positions on a game board may well be demonstrating a lack of understanding of basic spatial relationships. To children, to play a thing is to learn it and to know a thing is to be able to play it. There then must be room in the development of both play and cognition for the initiation of this sequence.

Diagnostically, clinicians can answer some of their own questions regarding the children by introducing an appropriate play format and making observations. The children project much of themselves into this play, enabling the diagnosticians to make cognitive, emotional, and social inferences (Chance, 1970).

Hutt and Bahavnani (1972/1976) found that they could categorize children 3 to 5 according to how they played with a new toy into either "specific" or "diverse explorer'' categories; their study describes the behavioral features of each. These features provide an understanding of the way the children operate and can be used to build diagnostic insight.

Hutt and Bahavnani (1976, p. 219) also describe "inventive boys (as) highly divergent thinkers, more so than girls; they were also socially less well adjusted than the inventive girls.'' It appears consistent with other facts known about play to assert that this inventive-divergent thinking quality is the precursor of the creative artist or scientific genius. The authors hypothesize that, diagnostically, children's play can be divided into four major categories:

1. play and language commensurate with age level
2. adequate play and impaired language
3. adequate language and impaired play
4. inadequate language and inadequate play.

Children who have both language and play skills at or above their age level should encounter no major problems with learning or development. The language serves as an index as to the adequacy of cognitive development and the play as to both cognitive and social development. These children ordinarily are not found in the language nursery. (The exception would be children with some severe speech problem that did not involve their language.)

Children with adequate or more sophisticated play behavior and depressed language abilities are more likely to display learning disabilities than are those who have equal play and language development, according to Johnston (1981). Their play behavior reflects the strength of social and emotional development while the lack of language ability is the index of the learning disability. These children, depending on the severity of their problem or syndrome, are likely candidates for the preschool language nursery. Their problems may be diagnosed as learning disability, developmental aphasia, developmental apraxia, or idiopathic language disorder.

Children who display adequate language and depressed ability to play present unique problems in diagnosis. They may have language commensurate with age but emotional stress or frustrations may reduce their ability to play constructively (Barker, Dembo, & Lewin, 1941/1976). They also are likely candidates for some form of help and in some circumstances may be enrolled in the language nursery for pragmatic assistance even though their primary problem is not language. In extreme cases, some of them may be diagnosed as emotionally disturbed, schizophrenic, or, in some instances, autistic.

Children who have sensory problems may demonstrate disorders of play and/or language but these are more closely related to the sensory deficit than to the other parts of the diagnosis. They require therapy to eliminate the deficit that came about as a result of the sensory problem and so may be enrolled in the language nursery group. The sensory deficit should be minimized as much as possible by medical, surgical, or mechanical means, i.e., glasses, hearing aid, pressure equalization tubes, etc.

Children who have both inadequate play and language skills show that they have neither social nor cognitive development commensurate with their ages. They comprise the wide range of mentally retarded individuals, along with some few with very complex problems that make them appear to be retarded. They may be among those enrolled in the language nursery.

Horne and Philleo (1942/1976) compare the spontaneous creative play of normal and retarded children and find the normals better. The lower level of the retarded population can be used to provide diagnostic insight. It emphasizes the need for providing these children with specific play training.

While much of the evaluation of children's play is through informal observation, some formal scales do exist. The Westby *Symbolic Play Scale* (1980, p. 163) developed in 1976–1977 for severely mentally retarded children but since expanded to include normally developing children, provides a format for rating play for children ages 9 months to 5 years. This scale categorizes play and language behaviors into ten stages (Table 7-1) and identifies implications for therapy. According to Westby, play assessment assists clinicians in making a priority list for prospective language clients and in indicating specific language therapy. This scale can be incorporated easily into the language diagnostic area and furnishes additional insight into a number of others. Its format and rationale are compatible with the Piagetian philosophy so basic to this language nursery program.

In the overall diagnostic process, developmental analysis of play can provide meaningful insights and direction for the recommendations that must be made.

REMEDIATION THROUGH PLAY

Children's play consists mainly of the patterns they comprehend and use to relate their physical and social environment to themselves. Whether they play for these reasons or the play is initiated by adults as a training procedure, the operation is the same. Children use their physical world as the training ground, the play is their action upon it, personal integration is what they realize from it. Leacock (1976) comments: "Theorists of progressive education have continually stressed that free and 'playful' manipulation of their environment is important for children's learning" (p. 467).

According to Bloom and Lahey (1978), children's play is hierarchical in nature. The nonspecific play of the second year of life is a milestone in the developmental order. At that time children act on many objects in the same way, drinking from cups, playing with hats or toy trucks in the same way. In the next stage, object-

Table 7-1 Categories of Language and Symbolic Play

Stage/Age	Play Behavior	Linguistic Behavior
I 9–12 months	Develops object permanence and means-end behavior.	Performative gestures and vocalizations.
II 13–17 months	Explores toys and identifies action parts.	Chained single words.
III 17–19 months	Starts autosymbolic play, begins representation	Symbolic single-word utterances.
IV 19–22 months	Extends symbolism to other agents and patients.	Two-word combinations, varied semantic relationships.
V by 24 months	Begins role play, pretends at activities and represents experiences.	Short sentences; present progressive tense.
VI by 2½ years	Represents; uses frequent events in role play.	Language used selectively to analyze perception. Questions asked and answered.
VII 3 years	Relates several schemata to each other in sequence.	Expressive in language; past and future tenses used.
VIII 3–3½ years	Plays with less ritualistic toys.	Marked growth in descriptive vocabulary, linguistic concepts.
IX 3½-4 years	Hypothesizes about future events, problem solves.	Most language used; modals and conjunctions begin.
X 5 years	Plans or pretends situations in advance, coordinates sequences.	Quite full use of language; relational terms, then, when, etc.

Source: Adapted from "Assessment of Cognitive and Language Abilities Through Play" by Carol E. Westby, in Language, Speech & Hearing Services in Schools, 1980, 11(3), pp. 154–168. Copyright ©, 1980, by permission of the author and the American Speech-Language-Hearing Association.

specific play, children act on specific objects in prescribed ways. For example, they will play at drinking from canteens, rowing toy boats, or driving toy cars. The third stage, object relation, is the period in which they play with two objects in relation to each other, i.e., playing with dolls in relation to doll dishes or toy planes.

This developmental sequence of play behavior is necessary for certain language goals. Children who use nonspecific play probably are at the level of single words and/or successive utterances; object-specific play probably is at the level of early two-word utterances, and the object relation stage probably accompanies two-word utterances with some early elaborations. All three levels must be attained before the interrelationships of the language areas can be generated.

Toys

While play does not depend on toys to maintain it, they often enrich it. Children can play any number of games without toys, can make their own toys from materials at hand, can adapt toys they already have to other play, or can play with commercial toys in the way they were designed to be used.

Play can be improved and children's imaginations and social adaptations greatly enhanced by the appropriate choice of toys (Bradley & Caldwell, 1976). The choice of toys should take several factors into account:

1. Toys should be sturdy and constructed so they will not injure the children.
2. Toys should fit into the play expected at the children's age level.
3. Toys should be sufficient in number so all children will be able to play at the same time (not necessarily the same kind of play).
4. Toys should be provided in a variety of types to stimulate all sorts of activities.
5. Toys should be versatile enough to stretch children's imaginations, to encourage creativity, to invite fantasy.
6. Toys should provide stimulation for symbolic and role-playing activities.
7. Toys should challenge the children to problem solving.
8. Toys should appeal to sensory, motor, and intellectual needs.
9. Toys should catch and hold children's attention and provide stimulation for exploration and repetition of action.
10. Toys should be in a variety of sizes, textures, and shapes.
11. Toys should use clear, bright, primary colors and nontoxic paint.
12. Some toys should make sounds; fidelity is important when sounds are produced.

Once the toys have been chosen, improved play can be fostered if they are provided to the children along with sufficient opportunity to use them. An environment must be created that places high value on creative, spontaneous play (Chance, 1979). All children should be encouraged to participate in the play activities. This implies that they must be free either to lead or to follow, to play alone or with someone else. They must be allowed to play what has meaning for them at the time.

Rough-and-Tumble Play

This sophisticated play form is both highly structured and social. Younger children at first watch, then when they acquire enough physical skill, gradually begin to take part. Rough-and-tumble play has distinctive physical and vocal characteristics, e.g., running, jumping, yelling, shrieking, laughing. It is engaged in most often by boys, but girls do enter in on occasion. This combination of action patterns, performed at high speed, is playful in nature, allows the release of energy, and fosters development of physical skills. While it can take place anywhere, it requires open space and is tolerated more easily by parents and teachers when it occurs outdoors.

Rough-and-tumble play contains seven patterns: running, chasing, wrestling, jumping, beating at each other with an open hand (not actually hitting), beating at each other with an object (not actually hitting), and laughing (Jones, 1976). These activities serve the function of allowing physical practice and of providing an acceptable channel for normal aggressiveness. They are not associated with hostility in preschool children (Jones, 1976) but rather are an essential motor aspect of play.

Pictures and Books

While active play uses toys, more reflective but nevertheless important recreational activities use books and pictures. Pictures provide children with a way of making symbol-object-picture relationships. They also are an excellent medium for learning to label, to categorize, and to respond to and represent stories. The skills the children begin to learn as they look at pictures are the precursors to later developing skills for schoolwork (Levenstein, 1976).

Children's picture and story books are important early to sow the seeds of later reading development. The books must be appropriate to their age, interest, and background. With these to build on, subsequent books should extend and broaden the children's literary fields. This can be implemented by discussing the story and examining the illustrations (Levenstein, 1976). In addition, the children can tell companion stories and draw additional illustrations. (Chapter 10, on the language arts, explores these relationships further.)

Music

Musical play can replicate all other types of play and adds the dimensions of melody and rhythm. Musical games are a particular source of satisfaction as the children experience the pleasure of the game and the joy of the musical experience.

The making of music, either by singing or playing at musical toys or with instruments, can be a spontaneous and creative activity that allows the children to stretch and expand their horizons. Refinement of hearing, auditory discrimination, perception of patterns, social cooperation, and physical dexterity all can increase as the children listen, respond, and perform to music.

Singing and singing games teach a major part of the cultural and social background of the peoples of the world. Children thrill to the songs and rhymes of their homelands, they treasure the verses passed down from their parents, and ultimately will tell them to their own children. In fact, countless children have learned the alphabet through the "Alphabet Song" and their earliest numeration from the "Counting Song" or "Ten Little Indians."

Language Play

Children progress through a developmental sequence in their vocal/verbal play. Garvey (1977) identifies the following developmental sequence:

1. Play with noises and sounds. The most primitive level of this is phonation or articulation of sounds.
2. Play with the language system. This includes word play and early play with environmental sounds.
3. Social play. Spontaneous rhyming and word play with the patterns of rhyme, rhythm, and inflection.
4. Play with fantasy and nonsense.
5. Play with conversation. (pp. 61–76)

As children play with language and toys together, they expand their vocabularies to include the names and actions of the toys, thus learning the language of symbol-object relationships.

With the acquisition of symbolic formation and the relations that exist among toys, children enter into the prime period for symbolic play. They expand their cognitive field by role playing or by playing out elaborate symbolic scenarios, working their toys into the overall scheme of the activity.

Verbal/vocal play, in addition to being fun for the children, helps them learn to classify words into verbal categorizations, i.e., colors and shapes, making the language a more useful tool (Exhibit 7-3). As they progress to school age, they play in different ways but language play goes on. Through language play, they come to the pleasures of reading and writing, the excitement of the literate world.

BENEFITS OF INTERVENTION THROUGH PLAY

Research relating to intervention in the mother-child relationship through intensive verbal play and stimulation has proved positive. Levenstein (1976) concludes that there is a close relationship between children's verbal and intellectual growth. She adds that this growth can be influenced by the quality and amount of verbal interaction with mother. This growth is related specifically to the attempt to stimulate heightened verbal interactions. This fact furnishes a powerful justification for early intervention with young language-impaired children in situations outside the home.

Exhibit 7-3 Verbal Categorization

Verbal categorization calls for the clinicians or teachers to:

1. Give information (label, form, color, size, etc.)
2. Describe their own toy manipulation
3. Elicit responses
4. Verbalize social interactions (invited, direction)
5. Encourage reflections (alternatives, consequences)
6. Encourage divergence (independence, curiosity)
7. Engage interest in books (fostering representational competence)
8. Give positive reinforcement (verbal support, help)

Source: Adapted from "Cognitive Development through Verbalized Play: The Mother-Child Home Programme" by Phyllis Levenstein in *Play: Its Role in Development and Evolution* by J.S. Bruner, A. Jolly, and K. Sylva published by Basic Books, Inc., New York, pp. 287–288, copyright © 1976.

SUMMARY

Throughout this chapter, play has been seen to be fundamental to the development of each child. The various roles of play in cognitive and language learning have been discussed, as well as how children use play to relate themselves to things and people in their world, to learn their life roles, and to practice relating to each other.

Children who learn to play with many objects and situations before they attempt problem solving in school or in society will have better success with it because the skills they learn during play, such as self-initiation and direction of effort, also will help them solve problems. By learning to use toys and to figure out how to make them do specific things, they also learn how to use tools (a problem-solving activity) and make them do what they want them to do (Sylva, Bruner, & Genova, 1976).

In view of the central nature of play in learning processes, this medium clearly is the primary building block in the Piagetian Language Nursery. It is incumbent on teachers to learn how to assess play skills, plan for expansion and enrichment, and remediate them when deficient.

DISCUSSION QUESTIONS

1. What will you say now to the next teacher or parent who complains that all the children do in nursery school or kindergarten is play?
2. What will you do when it is evident that Sammy, almost 5, plays beside but not with the other children? What will you say to his mother?

REFERENCES

Baker, R.G.; Dembo, T.; & Lewin, K. (Originally published, 1943.) Frustration and regression. In J.S. Bruner; A. Jolly; & K. Sylva (Eds.), *Play: Its role in development and evolution*. New York: Basic Books, Inc., 1976, 521–527.

Bates, E. *Language in context: The acquisition of pragmatics*. New York: Academic Press, Inc., 1976.

Bloom, L., & Lahey, M. *Language development and language disorders*. New York: John Wiley & Sons, Inc., 1978.

Bradley, R.H., & Caldwell, B.M. The relation of infant home environment to mental test performance at 54 months: A follow–up study. *Child Development*, December 1976, *47*, 1172–1174.

Bruner, J.S. (Originally published, 1972.) Nature and uses of immaturity. In J.S. Bruner; A. Jolly; & K. Sylva (Eds.), *Play: Its role in development and evolution*. New York: Basic Books, Inc., 1976, 28–64.

Bruner, J.S.; Jolly, A.; & Sylva, K. Introduction. In J.S. Bruner; A. Jolly; & K. Sylva (Eds.), *Play: Its role in development and evolution*. New York: Basic Books, Inc., 1976, 13–24.

Cass, J. *The significance of children's play*. London: Batsford, 1971.

Chance, P. *Learning through play*, Pediatric Roundtable: 3. New York: Gardner Press, Inc., 1979.

Coleman, J.S. (Originally published, 1967.) Learning through games. In J.S. Bruner; A. Jolly; & K. Sylva (Eds.), *Play: Its role in development and evolution*. New York: Basic Books, Inc., 1976, 460–463.

Eimas, P.E.; Siqueland, E.R.; Jusczyk, P.; & Vigorito, J. Speech perception in infants. *Science*, 1971, *171*, 303–306.

Fagen, R. Modeling how and why play works. In J.S. Bruner; A. Jolly; & K. Sylva (Eds.), *Play: Its role in development and evolution*. New York: Basic Books, Inc., 1976, 96–115.

Garvey, C. *Play: The developing child*. Cambridge, Mass.: Harvard University Press, 1977.

Hayes, C. (Originally published, 1952.) Chimpanzees, alas, do not babble. In J.S. Bruner; A. Jolly; & K. Sylva (Eds.), *Play: Its role in development and evolution*. New York: Basic Books, Inc., 1976, 619–620.

Horne, B.M., & Philleo, C.C. (Originally published, 1942.) A comparative study of the spontaneous play activities of normal and mentally defective children. In J.S. Bruner; A. Jolly; & K. Sylva (Eds.), *Play: Its role in development and evolution*. New York: Basic Books, Inc., 1976, 512–520.

Hutt, C., & Bhavnani, R. (Originally published, 1972.) Predictions from play. In J.S. Bruner; A. Jolly; & K. Sylva (Eds.), *Play: Its role in development and evolution*. New York: Basic Books, Inc., 1976, 216–219.

Johnston, J. Foreword. *Topics in Language Disorders*, 1981, *1*(2), xxi.

Jones, N.B. (Originally published, 1967.) Rough and tumble play among nursery school children. In J.S. Bruner; A. Jolly; & K. Sylva (Eds.), *Play: Its role in development and evolution*. New York: Basic Books, Inc., 1976, 352–363.

Leacock, E. (Originally published, 1971.) At play in African villages. In J.S. Bruner; A. Jolly; & K. Sylva (Eds.), *Play: Its role in development and evolution*. New York: Basic Books, Inc., 1976, 466–473.

Levenstein, P. Cognitive development through verbalized play: The mother–child home programme. In J.S. Bruner; A. Jolly; & K. Sylva (Eds.), *Play: Its role in development and evolution*. New York: Basic Books, Inc., 1976, 286–297.

McCune-Nicholich, L., & Carroll, S. Development of symbolic play: Implications for the language specialist, 1981, *1*(2), 1–15.

Meers, J.J. *Helping our children talk*. London and New York: Longman Ltd., 1976.

Murphy, L.B. Infant's play and cognitive development. In. M.W. Piers (Ed.), *Play and development*. New York: W.W. Norton & Company, Inc., 1972, 119–126.

Piaget, J. *Play, dreams and imitation in childhood*. New York: W.W. Norton & Co., Inc., 1962.

Piaget, J. *[The origins of intelligence in children]* (M. Cook, trans.). New York: W.W. Norton & Co., Inc., 1963.

Piaget, J. (Originally published, 1965.) The rules of the game of marbles. In J.S. Bruner; A. Jolly; & K. Sylva (Eds.), *Play: Its role in development and evolution*. New York: Basic Books, Inc., 1976, 413–441.

Piaget, J. *[The language and thought of the child]* (M. Gavain, trans.). Cleveland and New York: World Publishing Co., 1969(a).

Piaget, J., & Inhelder, B. *[The psychology of the child]* (H. Weaver, trans.). New York: Basic Books, Inc., 1969(b).

Piaget, J. *[The construction of reality in the child]* (M. Cook, trans.). New York: Ballantine Books, 1974.

Piaget, J. In H.E. Gruber & J. Vonèche (Eds. and trans.), *The essential Piaget*. New York: Basic Books, Inc., 1977.

Pulaski, M.A.S. *Understanding Piaget: An introduction to children's cognitive development*. New York: Harper & Row, Publishers, Inc., 1980.

Snow, C.E. Mother's speech to children learning language. *Child Development*, 1972, *43*, 549–565.

Sund, R.B. *Piaget for educators: A multimedia program*. Columbus, Ohio: The Charles E. Merrill Publishing Co., Inc., 1976.

Suomi, J.J., & Harlow, H.F. (Originally published, 1971.) Monkeys without play. In J.S. Bruner; A. Jolly; & K. Sylva (Eds.), *Play: Its role in development and evolution*. New York: Basic Books, Inc., 1976, 490–495.

Sylva, K.; Bruner, J.S.; & Genova, P. The role of play in the problem solving of children 3–5 years old. In J.S. Bruner; A. Jolly; & K. Sylva (Eds.), *Play: Its role in development and evolution*. New York: Basic Books, Inc., 1976, 244–257.

Vygotsky, L.S. (Originally published, 1933.) Play and its role in the mental development of the child. In J.S. Bruner; A. Jolly; & K. Sylva (Eds.), *Play: Its role in development and evolution*. New York: Basic Books, Inc., 1976, 537–554.

Westby, C.E. Assessment of cognitive and language abilities through play. *Language, Speech & Hearing Services in Schools*, 1980, *11*(3), 154–168.

Chapter 8

The Parent Group

CHAPTER OBJECTIVES

After completing this chapter, readers should be able to:

1. Describe the importance of the parent's group to the Piagetian Language Nursery.
2. Explain the rationale for insisting on parent participation in the child's program.
3. Explain the nature and importance of the goals for forming the parent group.

KEY IDEAS

1. Parents of language-impaired children often need emotional support.
2. Obtaining parent support and cooperation in the nursery school is important to the development of both the children and the parents.
3. The parent group provides a format for its members' education regarding the program curriculum.
4. Parents, as they become familiar with the aims, rationale, and procedures of the program, are able to help their children by extending some of the therapy procedures to the home.

IMPORTANCE OF THE PARENT GROUP

Observation demonstrates that while normal people are destined to develop language if they have adequate auditory stimulation, they do not learn it in a vacuum. When professionals' attention is focused on young, language-impaired children, this fact becomes very important. The quality of home interaction clearly has an impact on the children's language development, even though in most instances it probably is not causative.

To provide the most intensive preschool language group situation, it is essential that it be augmented by a parent group. This entity is organized and arranged as part of the language nursery program. Through this program, parents are given information about children and guided in ways to help them make the most of the language intervention they are receiving and to implement it further at home. Parents have proved to be well motivated and highly effective in this capacity.

The Parents' Contribution

The group of parents usually is diverse and may range from college graduates with careers, to student families with their many struggles, to blue-collar workers, or to the anxious and depressed poverty populations.

Ordinarily, most parents are not highly sophisticated in matters of speech, hearing, or language development. They bring many elements to the group that are problems to them and that become the subject matter of group discussion:

- anxiety about whether their child ever will talk and how later development will progress
- ambivalent feelings about their child, often containing elements of guilt and/ or rejection
- a certain level of understanding and personal resources with which to help their child
- personalities tired from their day-to-day interactions with their problems
- love and a sincere interest in the welfare of the child, for most.

They possess the "big picture" of the child within the continuity of the family. They are many things to the child, but above all they are very important to the youngster, who also is important to them. Parents do bring at least one other very positive element that is essential to the intervention plan: They have known this child and whatever problems there have been in the youngster's lifetime, and they know them well. Since they have their child's interest at heart and can be expected to listen carefully and try to implement suggestions from the nursery, parents together can accomplish a great deal for and with their sons or daughters in this supportive situation.

The Teacher's/Clinician's Contribution

While levels of training and experience differ from one professional to the next, those are the two most important ingredients teachers and clinicians bring to the language nursery. By training, these clinicians have become factually acquainted with the range of children's problems to be worked with. This enables them to identify specific elements and to relate them to each other. When in the presence of one problem they are able to determine what other factors need diagnosing and to draw lines of therapy and management that extend from diagnosis to treatment and incorporate parent guidance. They possess the research skills that enable them to seek additional information and a professional interest that keeps their information current.

During their experience they have amassed materials and ideas and a keen sense of which can be appropriately tried with whom. Wise and experienced professionals can draw from the children the most they have to give and can use this ability to build their self-images and motivation. Through past experiences, the staff professionals will have known a variety of children and parents and from this knowledge will have gained wisdom, insight, and empathy that they use in guiding and relating to parents.

Clinicians and teachers have formed sets of appropriate techniques that enable them to deal successfully with children, parents, and other professionals.

The preschool staff members understand the relationship between communication with the parents and some level of counseling (McWilliams, 1976). They can help parents build effective communication as each party learns to reciprocate in coding and decoding messages (Gordon, 1977).

Regardless of the myriad of factors—fears, hopes, and concerns—evident among the group members, it is essential to the healthy operation of all phases of the preschool that lines of communication be kept open. "Perhaps the greatest practical problem . . . is the scheduling of time for the essential communication between them, . . . without interfering with programming for the children themselves." (Furman & Katan, 1969, p. 25)

The parent group that is constructed to accompany this nursery functions both like a wistful child, needing to be guided by the teacher and eager for whatever relief can be afforded, and a productive coworker, able to help both children and therapists in the language intervention process.

THE FORMAT OF THE GROUP

Once the group is formed, the practical problems of establishing its routine and conducting its operations are important (Gordon, 1977). Functioning on an appropriate schedule, the group provides guidance for the preschool operation and in turn is guided by it. In this context parents guide through the information they provide for teachers and clinicians, both factual and experiential with particular children.

Membership of the Group

Ordinarily, parents have taken their children to the Piagetian Preschool Language Nursery because the youngsters were not developing communication effectively for their ages. These parents tend to be uninformed about the course of normal language development and are both confused and concerned about what their children are doing. Their growing sense of frustration may have been related to latent hostility directed at the children, which in some ways often is a manifestation of guilt they feel.

Whatever the dynamics operating on individual parents, they all are experiencing needs, doubts, confusion, and discouragement that culminated in their taking children to the clinic. Both mothers and fathers are encouraged to join the group but mothers are the most frequent enrollees. Parents can benefit from membership in the group as they are guided by the leader and as they form meaningful exchanges with each other (Todd & Gottlieb, 1976). The authors recommend that parent membership be mandatory in most cases.

In learning how to react to their children's language problems, parents come in contact with new management approaches (Dreikurs, 1964; Furth & Wachs, 1975; Ginott, 1975; Gordon, 1975). They learn to work effectively with children with whom they cannot use the ordinary medium of language and become informed as to both the verbal and nonverbal methods of coping with them (Middleman, 1968).

Some parents may require specialized counseling that is beyond the capabilities of the language nursery staff. When this occurs, it is essential that prompt referrals to qualified counselors be arranged and that parents be urged to follow up. If the need for outside guidance and professional counseling is not competitive with the emphasis of the language nursery, parents can benefit from both.

Special consideration must be given a parent who is directly involved in an abuse syndrome. Each state has specific laws for reporting abuse cases. These regulations must be obeyed carefully, and teachers and clinicians, who may be in a unique observational position, must be conscientious in meeting this ethical, moral, and legal obligation. Whether a child abuser or a victim of spouse abuse, the parent must be involved in specialized guidance of some nature. If the teacher and the psychological specialist determine that the individual can be incorporated effectively into the parent group, that membership can serve as a support service for the counseling. If there is interference between the two counseling emphases, the parent should be guided into specialized psychological counseling geared to alleviate the primary problem and of course, through it, the child's. The parent can be included in a language group later if the need persists.

The one exception to compulsory group membership may be a parent who has more serious psychological problems and actually requires the help of a specialist. A severely disturbed parent may react in ways that can either (1) defeat the psychological counseling that is so necessary or (2) be destructive of the group. In either case, this individual's participation in the parent group is contraindicated. Instead, this parent should be encouraged to follow the psychological recommendations.

In addition to parents, the group includes all the teachers and/or clinicians who work with the preschool nursery program.

Scheduling of Meetings

Various teachers' attendance at meetings depends on their availability since the children must always have some professionals present. Group meetings should be scheduled to allow each staff member to attend a percentage of time. This is important to preserve the complete exchange of information required by all.

The meeting schedule is more than a mechanically regulated format. The frequency and length of the sessions varies throughout the year to relate directly to various needs and activities. Initially, parent meetings should be scheduled at frequent intervals:

1. to get the term off to a good start
2. to establish working relationships among parents
3. to take advantage of the parents' initial interest in the preschool program
4. to provide as much of the needed information as possible early in the program.

In many instances these will be weekly meetings. After parents' initial needs have been met, the schedule may be relaxed. The authors prefer to limit meetings to the number necessary for presenting the material fully. The frequency in the second year may be different from the first year and should be chosen expressly to coordinate with the subject matter and the parents' stated needs.

The Group Leader

The role of group leader appears to fall logically to one of the professional staff. While this implies a "set" leader and meeting format, it is in no way permanent. The leadership also can be a rather temporary role, moved from one member to another depending on the activity of the moment.

The professional who has ultimate responsibility for the group should attend meetings regularly enough to maintain a good rapport with the parents and to assure understanding of the children's progress and problems. This person also should try to maintain some contact between sessions or over vacations to maintain continuity.

Parents' Attendance at Meetings

No parent group—or any other group, for that matter—can succeed without good attendance. This is particularly important when the initial group is small. Consequently, parent attendance at group meetings is required because: (1) without good attendance, the group will falter and become ineffective, to the loss of all concerned, and (2) without attending regularly, parents will be unable to uphold their obligations in the therapy partnership. They cannot keep informed and follow through with their children.

Certainly some allowances must be made for absences but the authors recommend establishment of a rather strict attendance rule. It soon becomes clear that if the meetings are organized and meaningful, parents will not have to be forced to attend.

THE PARENTS' FEELINGS

Much progress can be made once the members of the group have become acquainted and have gotten past the rather aloof mutual attitude that says, "I don't know about your case and I'm not exposing anything about me or my child." Many types of family dynamics are represented. Each parent and child combination approaching therapy is in an individualized relationship involving family dynamics. Clinicians must be able to help each parent-child dyad advance to a more satisfying and productive level of relationship. The various parents actually share a great deal of powerful emotion. As they sit in meetings or in the waiting room while the children are in therapy, they begin to talk and a bond develops among them, supporting and encouraging each parent.

Initially the emotion most often discussed is fear that the children will not be able to progress. As parents expose their own fears, the others provide support. Therein lies the ultimate strength of the group as this bond of support encourages parents to continue to help each other. This often evolves into generally constructive mutual discussions of each parent's problems that help at least some of them resolve their difficulties.

From this point, parents often informally discuss guilt and hostility, enabling them to express themselves and work out personal problems that may have existed for a long time. This discussion should totally avoid any element of moralizing or blame. Although this dialogue is not a parents' group activity, it is a healthy side effect of their group membership. When parents feel better and have each other for support, all children are indirect beneficiaries.

Moses (1975) presents an important theory that explains many parent reactions to handicapped children. He describes what parents go through upon learning they have a handicapped child as essentially a mourning process, not unlike what occurs with the death of a loved one. He regards this as a normal, automatic, and natural process. Moses theorizes that the parents initially mourn for their "normal" child, who essentially has "died," before starting through a grieving process to final acceptance.

The stages run a range of emotions:

- Denial: "I don't believe this!"
- Guilt: "My own actions must have brought this tragedy."
- Depression, anger, and self-pity: "It isn't fair."
- Bargaining: "God, please alleviate this and I promise to . . ."
- Acceptance of the problem
- Emergence of the ability to work meaningfully with the child.

Some parents require assistance at each of the phases while others appear to need it only in some instances.

Clinicians working with any parents who are going through a process of this magnitude must play the required role of listening with empathy and being ready to offer constructive help. The clinicians must be direct and accepting in this relationship, accompanying the parents as they evolve from the most discouraged level to the most productive one. It also must be realized that at times the parents' frustration, anger, and hurt may be focused on the clinicians as a symbol of something they cannot or do not want to accept. As the family progresses, the clinicians will be in a position to help establish constructive goals and activities.

In a model similar to Moses', Simmons-Martin (1976) describes four stages of parents' reaction as they gradually achieve acceptance of their handicapped child:

Stage 1—Shock: The parents may have been inwardly aware of the diagnosis for some time but they may truly suffer a shock reaction when the professional confirms their worst fears.

Stage 2—Panic: Many parents run from professional to professional in this time of doubt and confusion, seeking an answer they can accept but usually only increasing their confusion.

Stage 3—Retreat: Parents in this escapist period may be unable to shoulder the heavy responsibility and may appear to refuse to accept their unwanted role.

Stage 4—Realistic Expectations: Parents by this time sadly accept the problem and begin to deal with it.

Throughout these stages, parents need a skilled counselor who will provide the amount and type of support they need but will not do so much for them that they fail to begin to do things for themselves.

GOALS FOR PARENTS

In this often complex interaction, specific goals are established with and for parents—goals designed to help parents and, indirectly, their children.

Normal Behavior

Since most parents are not actually trained for the parenting job they must perform (Gordon, 1975), it is unlikely that many will have a clear idea of what normal development is. Some seem to expect too much from their children while others do not expect enough. Without systematic training in this area, parents have no clear idea of normal development, which leaves them floundering among their expectations. In this context it is not possible for them to fully understand delayed language or abnormal development. As a step toward understanding the strengths and weaknesses of their own children, parents must be given a basic understanding of normal language development.

At this same time they must be cautioned about the fallacy of comparing one child with another, i.e., their "language-delayed child" with their "advanced niece or nephew." They must come to believe that each child is an individual person, with individual strengths and weaknesses, not to be compared with anyone else.

Children with Problems

When parents understand about the norm but also about each child's right to be an individual, clinicians should be able to help them begin to understand how their children feel. The parents can begin to empathize with feelings of frustration, rage, fear, or discouragement in the youngsters. They can begin to see the interrelationship between their own feelings and reactions and those of their children. It is to be expected that in the course of this rather introspective activity, parents naturally will examine the ways in which their own parents first introduced them to the treatment they now administer to their children.

Understanding these relationships often provides a platform from which parents begin to construct new ways of interacting with their children. The authors have noted that parents introduced to transactional analysis terms frequently find them very useful in resolving conflicts of this nature. They learn that it is possible to verbalize the necessity of having their "adult" rather than their "parent" interacting with the young people in their homes.

Parent-Child Interactions

One result of this specific counseling emphasis usually is improved parent-child interactions. When parents understand that their verbal interactions with children can produce conflict, and when they comprehend what the resulting behaviors can be, they are motivated to develop better interactions that will not produce these negative feelings and actions (examples are listed in Exhibit 8-1). Parents who have begun to understand both themselves and their children better can turn to considering the importance of encouragement and logical consequences and of removing discipline from the tenuous relationship it has with language because their child's language is not adequate for this job (Dreikurs, 1965; Dreikurs & Grey, 1970).

For example, efforts to keep encouraging the child may require modifying certain practices around the home. If parents understand the pervasiveness of children's feelings of "Not OK," they may be able to arrange for them not to be sent to bed unhappy if there is any logical way of circumventing it. The authors believe that children who cry themselves to sleep probably do not rest well and may awake with the same foreboding feelings of sadness as when they went to bed, while those whose problems were resolved before bedtime (even though they may have committed the same offense) probably rest better and awake to get a fresh start on a new and better day.

Later, when the children are of school age, the principle becomes even more important. Those who go to school happy, encouraged, and without any forebodings of evil certainly work harder, learn more, and in every other way gain more from the school day than those who already have had major confrontations at home before they even start the day with the teacher.

This is not to say that the logical consequences fail to apply but rather that by school age the children may well have learned a comfortable routine on which to

---

Exhibit 8-1 Inappropriate Parent Behavior Elicits Unproductive Reactions from Children

Uninformed and unprepared parents too often do and say things to children that are countereffective and have a high probability of:

1. Causing the child to resist the parent's influence efforts by refusing to change the behavior that is unacceptable to the parent
2. Making the child feel the parent does not think the youngster is very bright
3. Making the child feel the parent has no consideration for his or her needs
4. Making the child feel guilty
5. Tearing down the child's self-esteem
6. Causing the child to defend himself or herself vigorously
7. Provoking the child to attack the parent or get back at the parent in some way.

Source: Adapted from *Parent Effectiveness Training* (PET) by Thomas Gordon, published by Peter H. Wyden, Inc., New York, p. 109. Copyright © 1975.

operate. Even on the rare occasions when logical consequences still must apply, parents need not yell and threaten. They can be truly sorry the consequences are so unpleasant for the children, who then will not perceive the parents as the enemy.

Parents' discussions may lead them to the no-lose solutions of parent effectiveness (Gordon, 1975), a more language-based articulation of a similar model.

In their attempt to find more productive ways of interacting, parents may become solution oriented (Ginott, 1975; Gordon, 1975). This approach leads to higher levels of problem solving for both preschoolers and adolescents between parents and children. Ginott (1965) says parents are led to three steps for survival:

1. We accept the fact that children will make us angry.
2. We are entitled to our anger without guilt or shame.
3. Except for one safeguard, we are entitled to express what we feel. We can express our angry feelings provided we do not attack the child's personality or character. (p. 50)

The self-defeating patterns of threatening, bribing, promising, sarcasm, moralizing, and rudeness are counterproductive. If parents expect to maintain stable rapport when their children are teenagers, with all that this implies they must establish that relationship of stability, warmth, and trust while they are young (Ginott, 1969).

In connection with this Piagetian preschool program, parents also are introduced to Piaget's theories (Piaget, 1962, 1969a, 1969b, 1974, 1977) of the development of all knowledge and become adept at stimulating children's thinking by using the Piagetian style of questioning implemented by Furth and Wachs (1975).

Parent-Parent Interactions

Throughout the course of the language intervention, group parents seem to become closer to each other regardless of any social, political, or economic differences. Each parent feels the warmth and companionship of the others who have many of the same problems and fears. They provide each other the empathy, tolerance, and support each appears to need. From each other they get suggestions for solving their problems. They do appear to benefit mutually from the fellowship they construct.

It has been the authors' experience that these parents begin to go out for coffee or shopping or other places around town. Their attachment to each other is shown by the fact that they get together during vacations. One parents' group whose children "graduated" some years ago still has an occasional reunion.

GOALS FOR TEACHERS AND CLINICIANS

Just as there are specific goals for parents to achieve, so also are there goals for clinicians. These usually relate to assisting parents and to planning and administering the program.

Referrals and School Placement

The continued monitoring of children's progress and the tracking of their further needs usually produces considerable additional information about them. Sometimes this material indicates the need for either additional testing or for services from another agency. In such cases, clinicians help parents in a number of ways. Clinicians can:

1. provide the initial screening that points to further testing
2. assist parents to understand the implications of testing
3. assist parents in finding the most appropriate referral for what must be done
4. assist in getting an appointment and send reports to the referral agency
5. interpret the agency's findings and help parents implement them
6. assist with school placement when this is needed.

It falls to the clinicians to advise parents whenever they have information that would help find the most appropriate placement, level, or possibly specific teacher. After the placement has been made, the clinicians may be called on to consult with the principal serving the youngster. Their effort serves to coordinate programs for the children, eliminate redundancy, and ensure a comprehensive treatment effort.

Program Guidance

Any program that has such broad goals, covers such an extended amount of time, and involves as many people as this preschool operation does can be expected to require much coordinating. A coordinator-administrator role obviously exists, although it probably is not a full-time position. Other roles also must be filled in accordance with the setting that houses the program. There must be:

1. someone to coordinate-administer the program, to keep things running smoothly
2. sufficient teachers/clinicians to work with the children
3. aides, if they are available and can be used effectively

4. housekeeping personnel
5. possibly a board of directors.

These are the essential staff roles that serve to keep everything current, operating, and organized.

The combination of teachers and clinicians established must be appropriate for the agency that sponsors the program. (In the authors' university setting, speech-language-hearing student clinicians are used exclusively, under careful supervision.) It is important that each person filling one of these roles meet established criteria for the position. The program needs a suitable number of teacher/clinicians to work with the small groups of children and provide the recommended amount of individual therapy.

The program the authors developed operates as a language intervention setting. If a program as described here were to include other, more traditional nursery curriculum items, it clearly would be more necessary to seek teachers with a broader background in early childhood education and separate the teacher and clinician roles.

The role of the parent group in program guidance is similar to that of an executive board or council. In this context, suggestions and advice on dealing with children can be expected to come from the parents. As they provide suggestions they are thinking through numerous problems that also may relate to the home. When problems with policy or general arrangements for the nursery arise, parents can help find answers.

Child Advocates

An advocate is one who understands the rights and responsibilities of the clients and conscientiously acts to protect them. Advocates also must know the parents' rights and responsibilities and their counseling must reflect this. This may give the parents information or it may provide them with the support and guidance necessary for them to act in the children's best interests.

In the climate of P.L. 94-142 (Buscaglia & Williams, 1979, discussed in Chapter 5) and increased awareness of the rights of the individual, the teachers/clinicians must be aware of its many provisions. It is highly unlikely that children enrolled in a language nursery would need an active advocate. Nevertheless, it is the responsibility of the clinician or teacher to understand this role and, should it become necessary, be prepared to act on it.

Parenting Skills

While teachers and clinicians in the preschool setting are not necessarily trained in all types of counseling, they must be proficient at doing so for families of the communication handicapped. This counseling is specific in some ways but it can be expected to have ramifications in a number of related areas. It remains, however, very important for professionals to remain conscious of the scope of the counseling, keeping it within their range of expertise.

Under no circumstances do the authors recommend that any teachers or clinicians who are doing communication counseling allow themselves to be drawn into the unprofessional position of providing counseling for which they are not qualified. Continued self-monitoring of the content of the parent counseling is essential, and when the therapists reach their own professional limits, a referral must be made to a qualified counselor for continuation if necessary.

There still is an extensive role for specialists who are involved in the parent-child communication dyad. Their intervention should be planned to:

1. provide parents with essential knowledge about communication that would enable them to be more productive in interactions with their children
2. analyze the strengths and weaknesses of the existing dyad and determine ways in which the weaknesses could be minimized and the strengths maximized
3. instruct and demonstrate these suggestions for improved interaction
4. provide sufficient feedback and encouragement to establish the more positive interactions in the continuing home relationship between parents and children.

These goals often can be met both in counseling sessions with parents and by observation as they watch clinicians work with their children in the nursery. As the children improve and become more encouraged themselves, this encourages the parents to keep trying. Success brings success, so the clinicians' task is to provide the initial success upon which to build.

Therapy Planning

As has been stated several times earlier, continuing therapy planning must be maintained to keep pace with children's progress. The therapists/teachers evaluate progress and further needs and from them set various appropriate goals for therapy (Furth & Wachs, 1975). As noted, these are cognitive, linguistic, social, and, occasionally, motor. As children's needs are reassessed and new goals set, the therapy usually must be modified.

While this type of planning is primarily the clinicians' responsibility and theirs is the final decision, the process often can be enhanced if it takes advantage of information from the group. Parents occasionally suggest a positive, or warn of a negative, element to be encountered. The group leader can occasionally suggest something that might be motivating for the children that could prove useful in the classroom or would allow the youngsters to do something they cannot do now.

TOPICS FOR PARENT GROUP DISCUSSION

The choice and arrangement of the topics discussed in the parent group varies from year to year and always is chosen by and for each specific group. Some topics are relatively standard and each succeeding group always chooses them; some are picked only occasionally. (Most of the topics are discussed fully in the various chapters here.)

Program Schedule

This rather standard topic ordinarily is the program for the first meeting. Parents have just brought their very young children to the clinic and placed them in a group, hoping they will go peacefully into the room, sit down, and cooperate. Unfortunately, this does not occur very often. Instead, children tend to go off crying, and parents are filled with doubts and misgivings. It helps them greatly if they are allowed to watch the nursery for a few minutes (to see that nothing is really wrong) and then are invited into an indoctrination meeting.

During this time parents are given the basic rationale of the program. They are introduced to the preschool staff and receive an outline of the activities and schedule for their group. They also are told about the day-to-day activities in the nursery room and about the special events and activities that will be held. For the most part, when parents leave this opening meeting they are optimistic and enthusiastic.

Normal Development

The importance of understanding normal development has been stated earlier. Most parents new to the nursery program need information of just that kind. A clear understanding of normal language development is essential before there is any frame of reference against which to understand or measure abnormal or delayed development. The parents learn about the normal range and that it actually encompasses a broad range of behavior. They begin to identify elements of delay in terms of this norm.

At the same time, they are informed of the fallacy—and, indeed, the problems—generated by using the same norm to label or classify their children. The undesirability and inflexibility of labeling children is described.

This discussion of normalcy is extended to its companion topic: deviancy. The authors are convinced that pushing children or holding them responsible for achieving some minimal level of achievement is inherently damaging. Those who are pushed become anxious and tend to develop negative self-concepts. Pushiness as a language stimulation technique is not productive in any way. The authors believe that the harder some children are pushed, the more firmly they are determined to dig in and stay put or move in another direction. The end thus may be worse than the beginning.

The final element parents are warned about in this initial meeting is the negative results so often revealed when children are asked to show off. Although they actually can perform the task requested, they become embarrassed and tend to fail to do anything they can be proud of. If this happens too often, the rather negative effects can begin to generalize to other situations.

The Nature and Development of Language

This topic deals directly with the main concerns that brought parents and children to the language nursery. Parents are encouraged to construct a notion of the nature and importance of language. Growing appreciation of how much their children need practice with this essential but highly complex network of rules usually increases parents' empathy for the youngsters and their tolerance of the time involved in the learning process.

The areas of cognition, pragmatics, semantics, syntax, and phonology (discussed in Chapters 1 and 2) are explained to parents along with examples and demonstration through role playing.

Once parents understand how much is to be learned, the usual question is, "How do we do that?" They are exposed to the fact that numerous theories of language development exist but the major emphasis is on the model that is most compatible with the Piagetian language nursery: (1) motherese and (2) rule inductions and hypothesis testing. Parents are encouraged to practice some of the key techniques of parallel talk, self-talk, modeling, and expansion. The essential role of experience is stressed and they are shown how to incorporate it into their daily lives.

The main emphasis is to help parents become comfortable with their role in language development. The hope is that they will come to view the experiences, the modeling, and the feedback they give not as something of a nuisance but simply as a way of life for language stimulation.

The Role of Discipline

When their main questions about initial language development have been answered, they usually ask next about discipline and child management. The authors always make it clear that they do not specialize in child management. It is a fact, however, that nonverbal children present management problems that are different from the ordinary, and speech-language pathologists are professionally as well prepared to deal with this combination problem as anyone else.

The authors' choice of a method that does not rely heavily on children's language ability is discussed with the parents. They may be introduced to a number

of management theories (see Chapter 6); through discussion, and often suggestions from other parents, they may be assisted to find personal solutions.

While the authors are enthusiastic in their support of the Adlerian (Dreikurs)
model, they are careful not to suggest that simple applications of a few Adlerian
principles will take care of all problems. That method, like most others, must be
studied extensively and applied very carefully if it is to work. This may well
require careful study beyond what can be provided. When this is the case, the
parents are referred to a specialist in the areas. The authors refer any parents whose
problems appear to be out of their own professional limits to the appropriate
agency for assistance.

Independence of the Children

One of the emphases in the parent group is on children's growing independence.
When independence is discussed in the group it appears that no parents want their
children to grow up dependent in any way. Yet few have examined the relationship
between early independence—the "I can do it all by myself"—and the kind of
self-reliance that enhances the quality of life. Nevertheless, when parents look at
this relationship and realize that the children must have practice at developing
independence and must start early, they are more willing to endure the wasted time
and occasional messes that occur.

It is a cardinal rule of this nursery program not to do things for children that they
can do for themselves. This, of course, also requires that they be given time and
guidance in doing things. It is more effective to praise children for their attempt
than for the result. This provides the "Thank you, that was a good try," to children
who need encouragement while at the same time not placing too much importance
on the success of the project.

Encouragement of Children

It should be remembered that encouragement is important to all aspects of
learning and motivation. This is equally true for parents, teachers, and children.
The lack of this clinical entity called encouragement can be responsible for failure
in a number of ways.

Children who lack encouragement begin to have doubts about their self-worth
and capability. It is important in all interpersonal interactions to observe where an
idea is coming from. Once that is determined, a specific plan must be attempted to
encourage the child and increase self-esteem and cooperativeness. This should be
attempted by parents/teachers/clinicians cooperatively. The choice of action may
be in a Dreikurs model or in some other one chosen by the group. It probably will
be noted that as soon as the children improve, everything else improves—again,
success brings success.

The opposite attribute, discouragement, represents the antithesis of everything that is productive in the learning environment. Truly discouraged children do not believe they have value or potential. Their actions are likely to say, "Please don't bother with me. I'm nothing and I never will be." When children feel like this, they and those who work with them need a specific plan and guidance in administering it. Nursery leaders who do not feel capable of providing this guidance should refer the parents and children to a more qualified professional for guidance.

The Value of Play

Unfortunately, many people working with the schools and with early childhood programs fail to appreciate the value of play (see Chapter 7). At times parents present an ardent desire for their children to sit in their seats and work. They tend to dismiss play as simply activity used to pass the time away. These parents require specific counseling about the essential nature of play before they will be able to appreciate the nursery program or their children's progress; they must come to respect play as the medium of instruction.

In the language nursery, play occupies a primary position. Through various kinds of play children construct sensorimotor knowledge from the toys they manipulate, logicomathematical knowledge as they learn about the logical operations that can be made by manipulating the physical world, and socioemotional knowledge as they play at interacting with the people in their world. Children develop language through play and, conversely, develop play through language. At every level of diagnosis or intervention, a given child will encounter some elements of play.

Toys and Their Place

In general, play must be a fluid and flexible medium, changing as the children or the context changes. Toys must be chosen to fit this model. The most creative toys available appear to be those that are sturdy, nondangerous, flexible enough to be used in a variety of ways, and simple enough to encourage the children to use their creative abilities in dealing with them.

The nursery program must be stocked with a variety of such toys. These should be arranged in specific areas where they lead to different play adaptations. The more the children are free to use their imaginations in play, the more the imaginations can grow and the youngsters can learn to think and experience more.

The general emphasis of the parent group when discussing toys is related to specific children and the home environment. The discussion answers the question, "What can we give the child for Christmas?" so often heard in preschools and parent groups. The authors consistently attempt to guide parents to the purchase of toys such as those just described. In their opinion there is little place in the play life of the preschooler for the automatic toys that appear to have a life of their own. It is not productive of language, cognition, or any other interpersonal ability for children to wind up (or plug in) a new toy and just sit down to watch it do its thing.

Individual Therapy

When children are old enough to be enrolled in individual therapy, it is done as part of the nursery program format. They are taken from the group by a clinician who works in the setting. Individual therapy has its own goals, motivation, and techniques. It concerns itself with a selection of targets chosen as (1) most necessary for the child, and (2) most likely to be correctable.

The report written for the individual therapy is incorporated into the overall preschool program report. The types of individual therapy are as different as the needs, personalities, and specific problems of the children. Some have only minimal needs; in fact, some may never need individual therapy. However, others have extreme needs for long-term individual therapy. Indeed, some may remain in individual therapy long after their need for the preschool language nursery group is resolved.

Videotaping Parents and Children

By the time the school year is half finished, parents may have become quite sophisticated in their discussion of language development, play, and encouragement. At that point, they are videotaped playing with their own child. Initially the idea of videotaping may cause some concern but as parents get further into the activity, they forget to be anxious and many finally enjoy the activity. If they choose to, they may bring toys from home. The only instruction given is that they all stay within camera range.

Afterward, the individual parents and the group leader view each tape. The leader must not be especially critical and may use the occasion for encouragement. Since the parents have become quite well informed in areas relating to the preschool program, it is likely that they will critique their own tapes as they view them. They can be helped to identify their weaknesses and their strengths in, for example, the mother-child interaction. The leader then can provide specific suggestions to help the parents improve their skills in this important interaction. This training enables the parents to make language development a way of life in the home.

Guided Observation

Parents have been encouraged to observe the program regularly. Following the videotaping, parents observe the language nursery again, this time guided by the group leader or clinician. During this observation, the leader points out the techniques, prompts, and/or feedback being used. The parents gain experience in observing the children's intentions and the reactions that follow success or failure. Parents observe how the clinicians use language to articulate the youngsters' intentions, to model the appropriate utterances, and to resolve discrepancies that occur.

Parents As Nursery Aides

Following the guided observations (in a planned sequence) parents are encouraged to take a turn assisting in the nursery. Parents interact with the clinicians and teachers on specific projects and begin to get the feel of a successful operation. This gives them an opportunity to interact in the group setting with children other than their own. When the children are not their own, parents seem to be free from the anxieties and tensions that probably color their interactions with their own. This practice also prepares the families to make language stimulation a part of their lives. The authors believe children benefit directly from this.

SUMMARY

Parents seen in the Piagetian Language Nursery Program have one characteristic in common: they have children who are not making normal progress in language development. Otherwise, they exhibit characteristics as diverse as any other group of parents of preschool children. Many do share another characteristic—tenseness—regarding their children's problems. Therefore, it is essential that they participate in certain facets of their youngsters' programs. This allows them to learn more about helping their children develop and to gain understanding of the situation and of the emotional support needed.

The parent group provides guidance and assistance to the professionals working with the children while at the same time learning more about cognitive and language development and the management approaches used in the nursery program. As parents observe the professionals, gaining understanding of the program's content, the clinicians also are counseling parents, helping them work toward acceptance of their children's communication situations. Acceptance of the situation is prerequisite to helping children profit to their optimum level.

Nursery clinicians, having become intimately acquainted with the children through the whole intervention program, are in position to aid parents in making decisions about further diagnosis, therapy, or simply later placement in public schools or other, more specialized facilities. Preschool professionals must be careful not to overstep the bounds of clinicians' ethical accountability but also must accept the responsibility to counsel with the parents on all aspects of the nursery program and the children's communication needs.

DISCUSSION QUESTIONS

1. Do you agree or disagree with the reasons for insisting that the parents be part of a group working closely with the Preschool Language Nursery program staff? Why or why not?
2. What other ways might the nursery staff use to accomplish the goals established for the parents' group?
3. Do you agree or disagree that the topics listed for parent group discussion are legitimate concerns of the language nursery therapists or are they interfering in affairs that are none of their concern? Why or why not?

REFERENCES

Buscaglia, L.F., & Williams, E.H. *Human advocacy and P.L. 94-142: The educator's role.* Thorofare, N.J.: Charles B. Slack, Inc., 1979.

Dreikurs, R. *Children: The challenge.* New York: Hawthorn Books, Inc., 1964.

Dreikurs, R., & Grey, L. *A parent's guide to child discipline.* New York: Hawthorn Books, Inc., 1970.

Furman, R.A., & Katan, A.K. *The therapeutic nursery school.* New York: International Universities Press, Inc., 1969.

Furth, H.G., & Wachs, H. *Thinking goes to school.* New York: Oxford University Press, Inc., 1975.

Ginott, H.G. *Between parent and child.* New York: The Macmillan Company, 1965.

Ginott, H.G. *Between parent and teenager.* New York: The Macmillan Company, 1969.

Ginott, H.G. *Teacher and child: A book for parents and teachers.* New York: Macmillan Publishing Co., Inc., 1975.

Gordon, T. *Parent effectiveness training* (PET). New York: Peter H. Wyden, Inc., 1975.

Gordon, T. *Leader effectiveness training* (LET). New York: Peter H. Wyden, Inc., 1977.

Kamii, C., & DeVries, R. Piaget for Early Education. In M.C. Day & R.K. Parker (Eds.), *The preschool in action: Exploring early childhood programs* (2nd ed.). Boston: Allyn & Bacon, Inc., 1977.

McWilliams, B.J. Various aspects of parent counseling. In E.J. Webster (Ed.), *Professional approaches with parents of handicapped children.* Springfield, Ill.: Charles C Thomas, Publisher, 1976.

Middleman, R.R. *The nonverbal method in working with groups.* New York: Association Press, 1968.

Moses, K. *Counseling in communicative disorders.* Paper presented to the Southwestern Ohio Speech & Hearing Association, Cincinnati, October 1975.

Piaget, J. *Play, dreams and imitation in childhood.* New York: W.W. Norton & Co., Inc., 1962.

Piaget, J. *[The language and thought of the child]* (M. Gavain, trans.). Cleveland and New York: World Publishing Co., 1969(a).

Piaget, J., & Inhelder, B. *[The psychology of the child]* (H. Weaver, trans.). New York: Basic Books, Inc., 1969(b).

Piaget, J. *[The construction of reality in the child]* (M. Cook, trans.). New York: Ballantine Books, 1974.

Piaget, J. In H.E. Gruber & J. Vonèche (Eds. and trans.), *The essential Piaget.* New York: Basic Books, Inc., 1977.

Simmons-Martin, A. A demonstration home approach with hearing-impaired children. In E.J. Webster (Ed.), *Professional approaches with parents of handicapped children*. Springfield, Ill.: Charles C Thomas, Publisher, 1976.

Todd, M., & Gottlieb, M.I. Interdisciplinary counseling in a medical setting. In E.J. Webster (Ed.), *Professional approaches with parents of handicapped children*. Springfield, Ill.: Charles C Thomas, Publisher, 1976.

Webster, E.J. (Ed.). *Professional approaches with parents of handicapped children*. Springfield, Ill.: Charles C Thomas, Publisher, 1976.

Chapter 9

The Physical Surroundings

CHAPTER OBJECTIVES

After reading this chapter, readers will be able to:

1. Summarize some state and federal standards for licensing nursery schools or other preschool child care facilities.
2. Describe some of the requirements for the space and facilities that house the language nursery program.
3. Explain why it is some times better to "find" space and/or furniture and equipment than to purchase it, even when finances are available.

KEY IDEAS

1. State and federal governments have licensing requirements for preschool child care facilities but there is much variety from state to state in the requirements.
2. The buildings and other facilities of the language nursery program have an educational function almost as important as the clinician/teacher.
3. Each simple activity—eating, playing, toileting—and the facilities for them must be designed with the children in mind and must be seen as contributing to their growth in cognition and language.
4. It often is more educational for children to have material, facilities, and equipment that are adaptable rather than single-purposed.

THE PHYSICAL SETTING

Clearly, important learning can and does occur in the absence of adequate physical surroundings. The lack of a fine facility does not necessarily mean the lack of a good program. However, the physical setting in which children study is very important as it colors all the learning experiences they will have in it.

As with other endeavors affecting the welfare of children in this country, nursery school programs have been the subject of concern at both the federal and state levels. Various titles have been given to programs designed for children of preschool age—nursery schools and day care centers are the most common. This book is concerned with the nursery: program, facilities, and values. State and federal requirements (Decker & Decker, 1980) do not differ greatly between the day care center and the nursery school and the description of them here does not attempt to differentiate between the two unless the variances are pronounced.

This chapter discusses the physical requirements for nursery schools: space considerations, equipment, and supplies, and the general contributions these physical characteristics do and should make to the facility's program.

STATE AND FEDERAL STANDARDS

The federal and state guidelines for licensing infant care centers cover all aspects of the physical facilities as well as the program but one striking fact is the great diversity among the states' regulations, from practically nothing to stringent. The overall concern is minimum standards to protect the health and safety of the children but this is interpreted in numerous ways.

Decker and Decker (1980) report a move toward registration rather than licensing family day care homes. They state that at this time "85 to 90 percent of family day-care homes have remained unlicensed" (p. 64). They attribute this to the legal problems of licensing private homes, the difficulty of managing the licensing, and the focus of the licensing efforts, which is on child care centers. They remark, "Licensing seems to have little to do with the quality of care families look for in choosing alternative facilities" (p. 64).

Careful study of the rules and regulations in a particular state is necessary for anyone attempting to operate a nursery school. One of the areas of divergence is the agency in charge; in some states, the department of welfare is the licensing agency; in others, it may be the department of health or the department of education; in some states, there is shared responsibility. Some of the variances may result from economic and political considerations.

Interpretation of needs for preschoolers varies just as much from state to state as do the requirements for facilities. Highly specialized needs must be met in the care of a group of children 2 to 5 years old in any situation. Any problems with facilities are compounded by the special needs of the children who represent the focus of this book. (This population is discussed in Chapter 3.)

Generally the children being planned for here are language impaired and between the ages of 2 and 5. While some may have severe handicaps, e.g., deafness, cleft palate, cerebral palsy, developmental aphasia, etc., others may have no handicap except the idiopathic language disorder.

State standards occasionally prohibit the very young from being in group care arrangements, which probably means that there are many very young children in illegal, unlicensed homes and centers (Evans & Saia, 1972). Generally, however, the child of 3 or older may be legally included in nursery schools. The authors regard such prohibitions on younger children as shortsighted and possibly detrimental to their well-being.

It should be noted that children in the language nursery program really are involved in therapy. The program described here is neither a day care center nor a true nursery school. It is group language therapy in a speech and hearing clinic in which children are on an intensive schedule. Consequently, the nature of the program makes it subject to a different set of regulations. Each preschool facility must determine which state and federal regulations apply. The key factor for language impaired children is that a belated start in therapy could have far-reaching, negative consequences on the children's development so an optimum schedule must be set for beginning treatment for them.

Licensing

Several states exempt from licensing requirements certain types of programs such as those controlled by educational institutions or state-owned or state-controlled institutions. Social, medical, or recreational organizations are not required to meet the licensing standards in the same manner, and religious bodies may establish programs in some states without having to be licensed (Evans & Saia, 1972). Again, only examination of a particular state's requirements can provide guidance.

Space

States that regulate day care centers or nursery schools usually have special requirements on the amount of space allotted to each child. These, too, vary, ranging from 20 to 35 square feet per child indoors, with most of the states requiring 35. Some writers (Evans & Saia, 1972) regard this as the minimum allowable for active children who are busily engaged in using and developing large muscles. Space required for each child outside is greater, from a low of 40 square feet to a high of 200. There seems to be some consensus that approximately 100 square feet per child outdoors should be required (Evans & Saia, 1972).

Meal Time

An important part of the program, from several viewpoints, involves food and drink. In the language nursery, each child is given a midsession snack as part of the developmental activity.

Eating is important not only for maintaining life but also for the developing of emotions and behavior patterns. In fact, the infant's earliest feelings of comfort or discomfort, trust or distrust, are concentrated mainly on satisfying his hunger. As he grows older, the child's appetite and behavior at mealtimes are sensitive indicators revealing his inner feelings. Therefore, it is important to provide a pleasant environment for eating, not only to ensure adequate nutrition but also to encourage personality development. (Evans & Saia, 1972, p. 84)

To make the most of this very important time devoted to eating and drinking, the physical aspects of the area should have certain characteristics. The kitchen should be closed off from the playrooms but near enough to allow easy serving and cleanup. Child-sized tables and chairs are a must and surfaces must be hard, easily cleaned, and sturdy. Food storage, preparation, and serving requirements also vary greatly, with the health aspect naturally being the prime consideration. Basic requirements are the sterilization of dishes and utensils, a sanitary method of garbage disposal, adequate refrigeration facilities, and a ventilated storage area (Armstrong, 1974).

For cost-saving reasons many institutions are beginning to draw upon central food preparation facilities, with the meals transported in insulated, wheeled carts as needed (Shaver, 1968). There are other benefits: a greater variety of food, better preparation, less confusion and mess, and lower prices because of bulk buying by the supplier. This allows teachers/clinicians to concentrate on the learning elements of nutrition. They should be careful to make eating times a part of the daily program that is accepting, encouraging, free from tensions, and conducive to learning a variety of operations.

Nap Time

Children seldom spend enough time in this preschool language nursery program to require a nap but under many circumstances it may be desirable to have provisions for the younger ones to sleep or rest. Each child could have a personal cot and blanket, clearly labeled with the youngster's name and placed in the same location every day. For sanitary and health reasons, cots must be stackable in such a way that air may circulate around them. Because that requires storage space that at times and in some situations may be at a premium, the authors like using mats or blankets brought from home and taken home to be laundered, instead of cots (IAAS, 1974; Passantino, 1977).

Toilets

As with mealtimes, toileting must not be seen as simply meeting children's physiological needs. "Toileting is a significant experience in the life of a young child for many reasons. The circumstances surrounding his toilet training may be conducive to promoting feelings of self-confidence and self-esteem or failure and inadequacy" (Evans & Saia, 1972, p. 90).

Construction or arrangement of a toilet must be done in such a way that children will have positive feelings toward the whole process and environment. Furniture should be child-sized and easily accessible or steps should be provided. The toilet seats, when adult sized, should be modified so a small child will not fear the possibility of falling in (Evans & Saia, 1972). Standards prepared by the Department of Health, Education, and Welfare provide that, until the age of 5 or 6, boys and girls may use the same toilet but there should be two toilets and basins regardless of the size of the group increasing to a ratio of one toilet and basin for each 10–15 children (Armstrong, 1974). All children must have their own washcloths and towels, although some advocate paper towels for sanitary reasons. If paper towels are chosen, they must be located as far from the toilets as possible to keep children from putting them in and they should be cautioned not to do so.

Storage and Isolation

Standards have been written in most states for two other specialized areas: storage and isolation. The isolation room must be available when an emergency occurs or when a child just needs to be alone. The room must be situated near an adult station so the child will not feel lonely, and for contingencies that might arise. Bathroom facilities must be accessible and first aid supplies should be stored nearby (Armstrong, 1974). This area also could be used for children who need more sleep, should the need arise.

Storage facilities for toys and other equipment must provide adequate space, have doors wide enough to allow large, wheeled items to be placed inside, and have enough shelving and bins for a large amount and variety of assorted materials. Movable storage bins are recommended. It also has been suggested that the general storage space be a walk-in closet, with the possibility that children might use it for privacy, exploration of their space, and general sensory activities, such as experiencing darkness, etc. (AASA, 1967).

THE FACILITY

It has become apparent in recent years that there is more to the building housing a program than just shelter from the elements or a place to hang one's hat. The building itself now is regarded as a part of the educational program. When a building is designed specifically for a nursery program, much thought must go into creating space that helps in educating children.

People respond to space in individual ways, often shutting out various elements because they are ugly or do not meet their needs or desires of the moment. Children do not do this (Passantino, 1977). They have not learned adults' reactions; they respond to many kinds of space—large and open as well as small, cozy, and hidden private places.

"The right kind of space creates activity. A child sees the space and his imagination begins to soar. He does not think, 'now there is an interesting space, what can I do with it?' His mind jumps past that, begins to create scenarios of action, play, make-believe." (Holt, 1975, pp. 141–142)

As buildings are considered for use for the very young, the outdoors must be integrated into the overall plan. Some think the most desirable arrangement is a continuous indoor-outdoor area where the children can play in both areas simultaneously or flow easily from one to the other. Windows must be arranged so teachers can supervise both groups at the same time (AASA, 1967).

Indoor Instructional Space

Specific instructional space designs must consider such factors as flexibility in the physical and educational sense. It must provide for adequate supervision of individuals and groups. Multiple uses of each area are important. They help control the number and types of activities that can be provided, the simplicity and directness of traffic patterns, and "the degree of physical and emotional comfort of the occupants." (Gibson, 1968, p. 19)

Young children seem to be more acutely responsive to their environments than are older children or adults so it follows that sterile, unimaginative space has a negative learning value (Passantino, 1977). Every new sensation or stimulation of children's senses has potential for learning, for development of the insights that together comprise their intellect.

The physical environment of the nursery school must contribute its share to growth just as much as does furniture, materials, and the activities. Moore (1975, p. 98) says, "Children have their own 'biological curriculum' which, if given a suitable channel for expression, can form a visible basis for action." The developmental needs are many and varied and everything that can be controlled in the children's environment should contribute to fulfilling these needs.

The way to provide the range of individual needs for expression is to ensure that the environment isn't highly structured, but rather open ended, and changeable, so varied that each child can find a space to meet personal needs at the moment of sensing them (Moore, 1975).

Diversity is the key factor in indoor building and classroom space. There seems to be a rather distinct dichotomy in thinking regarding the needs of indoor space, however. On one side are those who see large expanses of uncluttered space as the answer to creative programming. Their emphasis is on free flow of traffic, a minimum of barriers and walls, and areas that can be supervised by an adult simultaneously (AASA, 1967). Flexibility is acquired by having movable storage bins and racks and by wall closets. All the movable structures often are pushed back against the wall to allow more unobstructed space to provide a "spacious and open" sense (Fitt, 1975, p. 93).

An opposing view emphasizes close and intimate space where children often can be alone in pursuit of the things that interest them or can work in small groups, three or four at a time, in quieter, more intimate relationships. It was noted earlier that even very young children seem to need privacy occasionally. The play of 2- or 3-year-olds may be parallel but there are occasions where they delight in crawling by ones, twos, or threes into a large box such as a piano carton or into a closet. The smaller, more intimate spaces require the ability to interact with one or two others in close proximity or simply allow a child to retreat into a "private" office for some time alone.

The type of space available has much to do with the kind of program possible for the children but it must not be the controlling factor. Gibson (1968) comments:

> Space design controls such important factors as the adequacy of supervision in individuals and groups, the number and types of activities and experiences that can be provided for children, the degree of orderliness and convenience with which these activities may be carried on, the accessibility of areas, the possibilities for multiuse of space, the simplicity and directness of traffic patterns, how well children and adults see and hear, and the degree of physical and emotional comfort of the occupants. (p. 19)

There is wide agreement that facilities in which children are placed are important factors in the formation of their growth and developmental patterns. Children limited to a sterile, plastic world, where much more attention has been paid to the ease of cleaning and maintaining the facilities than to the uses they can make of their environment, miss out on much necessary stimulation. In another context, Heyman (1978) notes: "Many schools provide a harsh environment. The colors may be pleasant, but paint cannot do much for these halls." (p. 25) If this be true for elementary schools where the children already are less involved with their environment, how much more disheartening for the 2- to 5-year-olds to face the cold plastic and tiled walls and floors. An environment that is static and bland is not stimulating. It is an opportunity lost for maximum growth for impressionable young children (Passantino, 1977).

Outdoor Instructional Space

The outdoors area must be designed with the same care as indoor work and play space. When educators accept the idea that children learn the most basic and important things from activity that stimulates their imagination, they can see the need for variety and continuity. The transition from indoors to outdoors must be fluid and simple, allowing free (and even unconscious) flow from one to the other. An outdoors area has potential well beyond the indoors because of the variety of surfaces possible. One can have hills, valleys, and streams for children to run up or through, thus challenging their sense of spatial relationships (Gibson, 1968).

Too often, textures of the indoors areas abound in easily cleaned and maintained steel, concrete, and plastic while the outdoors can have a great variety of textures, shapes, and colors. Sand, water, mud, and growing things, while possible and sometimes necessary indoors, are natural to the outdoors. Trees for climbing and shrubs for hiding in all contribute their own special stimulation (Baker, 1968) to the growing mind (AASA, 1967).

Buildings

The thinking in the early 1980s on buildings to house educational facilities for the very young has emphasized a variety of textures on all surfaces. Each surface is seen as having potential for the children's use, so from the floor up attention needs to be paid to textures. Half of the floor should be covered with vinyl and half with sturdy carpet that can be cleaned easily. The floor should invite sitting to work on various projects, to listen to a story from an adult, or just to lie on and rest briefly. Whether carpet, vinyl, or some other substance, the floor material should deaden sound so that a falling block tower, for example, will be less distracting to the group across the room listening to a story or otherwise engaged in quiet activity.

Wall textures should demonstrate utility as work surfaces for industrious children. This, too, requires a variety of textures, fabric, brick, wood, wallboard, linoleum, and even, for some areas, tile. Much of the children's play may involve painting and drawing or constructing articles that will be displayed. Display requires wall surfaces or other horizontal or vertical space that can take tacks, pins, or tape.

The building surfaces themselves can contribute to children's identification of structures, textures, colors, and relationships and can provide data and opportunity for classification, seriation, directionality, and reversibility. A building that lends itself to adventure and exploration in a multitude of shapes, textures, and colors, while at the same time possessing the facilities necessary for caring for the comfort and health of the children, can be of any age, shape, or previous use.

Built Space

In recent years, with the sharp rise in the need for nursery schools and day care centers, there has been much thinking about how to provide for the increased space needed. Architects can analyze the curriculum or program before beginning the design of such buildings. The point is made by the AASA Commission (1967) when it says:

> A statement of the objectives of a school program leads to a spelling out of its details . . . ; the nature of the teaching, learning and community activities and the characteristics of the space and facilities needed; the spatial relations of these facilities to others; the types of materials and equipment involved; and similar considerations of who is going to pay for the facilities become important questions. (p. 88)

'Found' Space

An alternative approach has been so popular for a decade or so that a term has been coined to identify the idea: "found" space. Passantino (1977), says the approach:

> illustrates how people with purpose and a resourceful imagination have transformed the discarded, overlooked and inexpensive spaces or objects of an abundant and sometimes wasteful society into useful places and things for learning. To the young child such materials and spaces take on intrinsic values; they have a character all their own, full of new impulses for learning. (p. 5)

With the children's responsiveness to the environment, a remodeled building often provides more challenge for the imagination than one of the "built" plants with all the careful attention to ease of maintenance. Experience has indicated that found space often can fulfill the environmental needs of children at a much lower cost than new construction (Passantino, 1977). In addition to the economic considerations, Passantino notes the remodeled space has other pluses. He notes:

> The advantages of found space are numerous. A child jumping into a pile of hay in a converted barn, a group listening to a story in front of an ornate Victorian fireplace, children swinging from ropes suspended from a high ceiling—all [provide] marvelous learning experiences, and all capitalize on existing features in found spaces . . . expensive features if they were to be built new, but great free assets when they happen to exist. (p. 5)

Some of the financial advantages occur because there is no search for land or purchase and mortgage considerations because the owner of a little used, unused, or abandoned space often will permit it to be taken over with little or no payment. It also is possible to arrange shared use without a conflict of functions, as in use of Sunday school space. Many cooperative parent group nursery schools or day care centers have been able to operate with found space and equipment where otherwise they could not have functioned at all. It also is true that these types of space often exist in places where the need is greatest, such as in densely populated but older areas.

Children's learning experiences are most meaningful, whether in terms of cognitive growth, language growth, or physical development, when the environment responds to their needs. The important point is not whether they are housed in a nursery school built for the purpose or in found space that has been remodeled; the environment must support, enhance, implement, and help guide the learning activities planned by the teachers/clinicians. The authors agree with Gardner (1968): "There will be a place for playing and space for contemplation; space for groups of differing sizes and space for privacy. The facility might include many shapes and spaces, tall, low, large and small, and with this spatial variety, a variety of finishes and materials." (p. 4)

CREATIVE USE OF FOUND SPACE: A MODEL

It is essential that individuals responsible for designing, obtaining, or organizing space for preschool programs be fully cognizant of the essential relationship between physical facilities and the cognitive activities and growth expected to go on within them. The design by architect Patrick M. Armstrong (1982) discussed in this section illustrates one possible use of found space (with the addition of some new space). It suggests a number of innovations, each of which might be incorporated into existing plans. It also illustrates the concept that the physical space can become a part of the learning model. The design is planned to encourage creativity with elements widely available in urban, suburban, and rural areas. It was with this in mind that a typical structure (a service station that had been closed in Oxford, Ohio) was selected to be the model this project transformed into such a school. The site was measured, the needs of a preschool were examined, and the plans were drawn.

Financial, spatial, program, and building code regulations and constraints usually require some combination of old (found) and new space. Whatever space is selected, certain criteria must guide the renovation and construction.

Any plan for using found space must start with a flexible design process and construction so that the work can be done in phases. The design must provide a feeling of spaciousness so the children are not overcome by the adult scale. It must be energy efficient to minimize operating costs and it must encourage children to manipulate their environment. If possible, it should have a variety of views. It should contain colors, textures, light variations, acoustic experiences, and materials. All aspects of the building can be designed to provide learning experiences and to be fully accessible to all, incorporating elevators, ramps, and other features for the physically handicapped.

The model here is realistic in that it starts with a readily available, if not highly desirable, structure in a less than ideal location for a nursery school program. It is bounded on the north by a heavily traveled state highway, on the south by an active railroad, and to the east and west by a service station and a residence, respectively. Most of the site is paved with asphalt and to the south the ground drops off to the railroad tracks. The existing structure is too small for the 20 children plus staff that it was designed for, and is unacceptable to the building code in several respects.

Although the site has some undesirable features, the design utilizes these fully. For instance, an eight-foot drop to the rear is used to add a grade level exit/entry to the lower level and to allow more daylight to reach certain areas. Some of the asphalt was saved for activities requiring hard pavement. Safeguards for the children from the highway and railroad were provided but no attempt was made to obscure either since it was felt that these sights could provide positive learning events. The fences were designed in keeping with the image of the school and as another means of exploring texture and pattern variations of light and color. They are shown as trellises for morning glories (upper drawing in Figure 9-1).

The outdoor play area is oriented to the west toward the residence, with parking to the east and the adjacent service station, creating an effective use of the space. The original structure (lower drawing, Figure 9-1) was extended to the south to obtain the needed new space shown on the plans as the kitchen, outdoor storage, director's office, foyer, restroom, and stairway. It also provides additional windows for passive solar heating and daylighting. A small addition on the north side created the foyer, with a window seat. The structure also was extended upward to accommodate the elevator, testing rooms, stairway, and observation room (Figures 9-2, 9-3, and 9-4).

Figure 9-1 Remodeled Preschool Facility and the Original Building

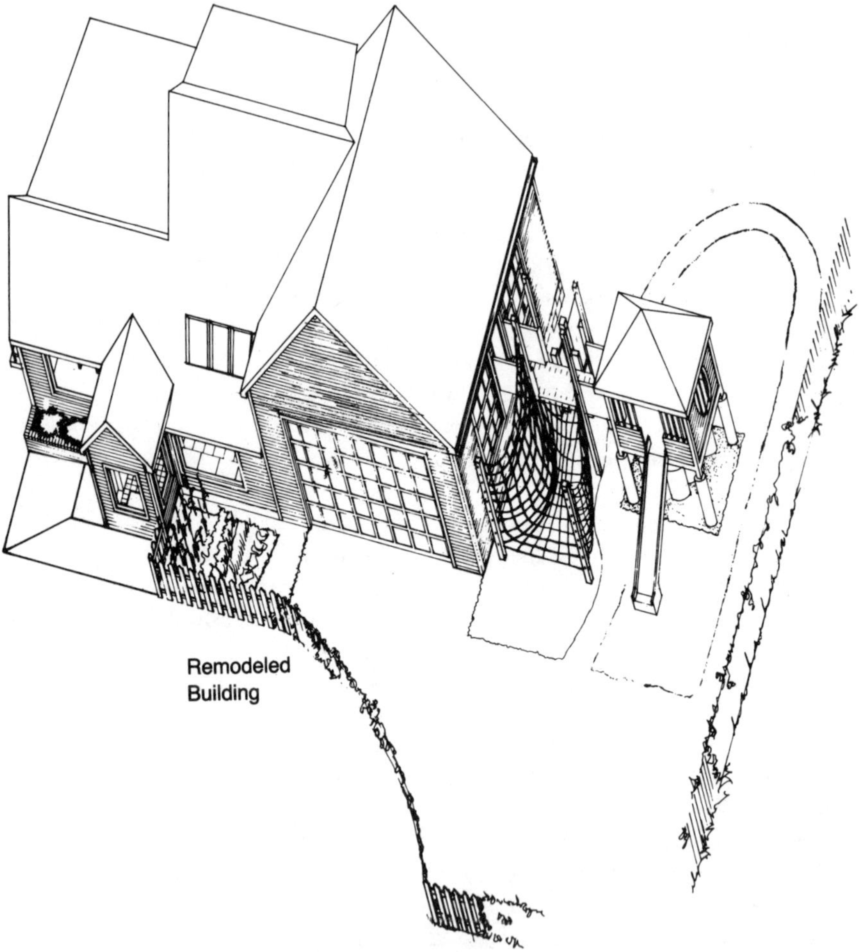

Remodeled
Building

Original
Structure

Source: Patrick M. Armstrong, Mason, Ohio, © 1982, with permission of the architect/artist.

Figure 9-2 Lower Level Plan

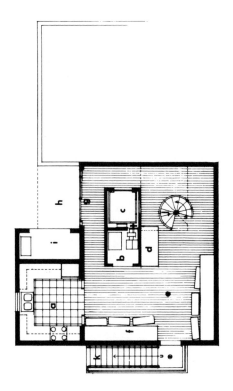

a. kitchen
b. mechanical
c. elevator
d. cot storage
e. nap/meeting room
f. fold-down tables

g. sliding doors to outside
h. outdoor covered play area
i. outdoor storage
j. circular stairway
k. exit, stairway to main level
l. parking

Source: Patrick M. Armstrong, Mason, Ohio, © 1982, with permission of the architect/artist.

Figure 9-3 Main Level Plan

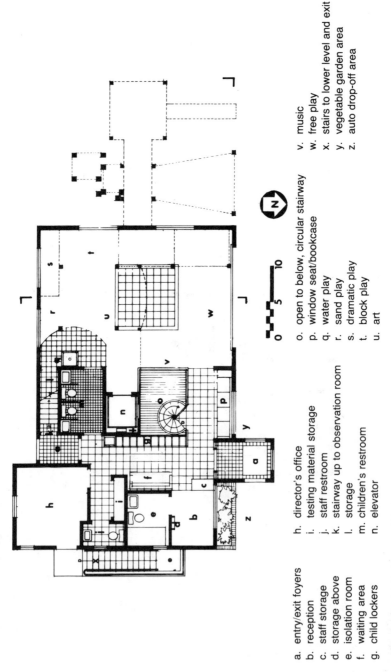

a. entry/exit foyers
b. reception
c. staff storage
d. storage above
e. isolation room
f. waiting area
g. child lockers

h. director's office
i. testing material storage
j. staff restroom
k. stairway up to observation room
l. storage
m. children's restroom
n. elevator

o. open to below, circular stairway
p. window seat/bookcase
q. water play
r. sand play
s. dramatic play
t. block play
u. art

v. music
w. free play
x. stairs to lower level and exit
y. vegetable garden area
z. auto drop-off area

Source: Patrick M. Armstrong, Mason, Ohio, © 1982, with permission of the architect/artist.

Figure 9-4 Upper Level Plan

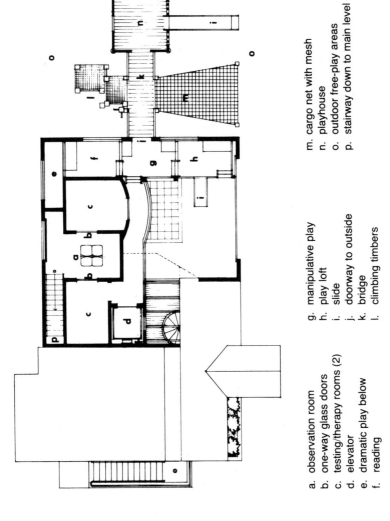

a. observation room
b. one-way glass doors
c. testing/therapy rooms (2)
d. elevator
e. dramatic play below
f. reading

g. manipulative play
h. play loft
i. slide
j. doorway to outside
k. bridge
l. climbing timbers

m. cargo net with mesh
n. playhouse
o. outdoor free-play areas
p. stairway down to main level

Source: Patrick M. Armstrong, Mason, Ohio, © 1982, with permission of the architect/artist.

The Lower Level

The lower level (Figure 9-2) is utilized for eating, sleeping, and large gatherings—multiple uses that necessitate movable seating and tables. It also includes mechanical equipment, elevator, kitchen, outdoor storage, and the stairway and exit to the slope of the southern (rear) part of this site.

Materials used include a natural hardwood floor for durability and color. The metal circular staircase has carpeted tread and railings supplemented with nylon mesh to prevent children from falling through. There is a plexiglass window into the elevator shaft to enable children to see the operation of the brightly painted mechanism.

The design provides a diagonal view up into main levels to give a more spacious feeling and flow of space as well as better supervision, and for natural lighting, which does not reach the nap area.

The Main Level

The main level entry (Figure 9-3), on the north side, opens into a foyer that prevents heat loss through the doors and provides a view into the free play window seat area, the outdoor play area, auto drop-off area, and vegetable garden. The foyer leads to the reception area, a small counter that also serves as lockable staff storage. From this reception area, the view is outside to the door and auto drop-off.

Adjacent to reception is the isolation room, equipped with a cot, toilet, and sink and a small window for light and natural ventilation. A Dutch door allows privacy with inconspicuous supervision. This area is carpeted with material that is easily cleaned and durable. Storage above the isolation room is possible since the design utilizes a cathedral ceiling, obtained by repositioning the original ceiling and exposing the existing trusses. This gives a more spacious feeling and provides shadows and patterns for the children to observe. Skylights help achieve these ends as well as letting more light into the circular staircase area.

A window-seat/bookcase is on the north side of the building to be cooler and with no intense sunlight. Children can sit in the window and "read" or look into the garden toward the auto pick-up/drop-off point.

The indoor free-play area includes sand, water, blocks, etc., and is carpeted in the central region with carpet tiles to create a checkerboard pattern encouraging large-scale games, with vinyl tiles around the sand and water areas. Lofts, fronted with nylon safety mesh, provide changes in elevation for the children and small areas where they can play by themselves. Under the lofts, areas of varying height are created to enable even the smallest children to find a space of their own (see Figure 9-5). Attached to the large windows in the free play area are movable interior shutters, constructed of a variety of materials. These can be operated by

Figure 9-5 Cross-Sections of Architectural Design

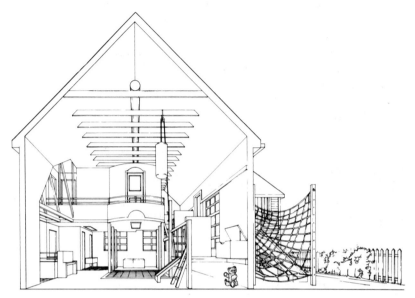

Top Two Levels, Facing East

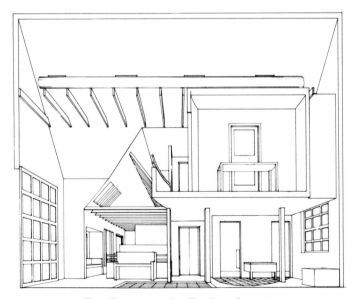

Top Two Levels, Facing South

Source: Patrick M. Armstrong, Mason, Ohio, © 1982, with permission of the architect/artist.

the children, who thus can explore variations of light patterns, intensity, and amount. They also serve as insulation over the windows at night to limit heat loss.

A carryover from the building's past history as a service station is the large garage door on the north side. This was left intact, except for the addition of insulation on its interior surface, to serve several purposes while exemplifying the concept of reusable space. It can be opened for natural ventilation and light and to create a unifying continuation of space from indoors to outdoors.

The Upper Level

The upper level plan (Figure 9-4) shows the two testing/therapy rooms with the observation room between them (also see Figure 9-5). One-way glass doors from the observation room into the testing rooms provide unobtrusive supervision as well as an alternative exit from the area by way of the rear staircase. The walls, floors, and ceilings of these rooms are of materials that absorb sounds from the other activity spaces.

Finally, the design incorporates outdoor play space (Figure 9-4) that includes a bridge to a playhouse, a climbing area, mesh lined cargo net to play in, a sheltered area under the playhouse, a covered play area, and as much free and open play space as is available.

In its totality, this design exemplifies a model learning setting designed to provide children with a wide range of sensory and motor experiences and opportunities to manipulate the environment, so necessary to sensorimotor and preoperational youngsters.

MATERIALS AND EQUIPMENT

As with the space itself, the furniture and equipment must contribute to the nursery school's continuing educational program. Versatility is the single most important characteristic involved; whenever possible, the equipment should be designed to encourage children to think of different ways to use it. Youngsters are not spacebound and shapebound as adults so often are. They might play for many minutes at a time with chairs turned upside down so they can crawl under the seat and have a "cave" to explore. A plastic frog intended as a toy box has become a place to hide, with the top pulled over and a raft going down a wild jungle river and shooting the rapids (a short set of stairs, not a particularly satisfying experience, but thrilling), and countless other concepts unknown to adult observers. Active children, involved in creative play, put all kinds of things to many unpredictable uses.

Purchased equipment often is too elaborate and polished or refined to provide the challenges needed for growing intellects. "A surfeit of plastic apparatus may look good, but misses the point entirely'' (IAAS, 1976, p. 23). Children become bored with the articles that present no challenge to their imaginations and often turn from the expensive, highly engineered toys to romp with large cardboard boxes until they have destroyed them.

Many teachers have become adept at figuring ways to use items no longer of commercial value, the found objects that often are available merely for the asking. Today's throwaway society is inclined to jettison many perfectly usable objects that, with little effort by teachers or clinicians, may become the favorite location for children to pursue the ''important'' tasks of the moment. They also offer values to teachers (and sometimes parents and other volunteers as well as the children) who become involved in creating more usable, or sturdier, or more aesthetic items for classroom use from found objects.

Two examples of found objects that became tremendously important to teachers and their groups of children illustrate the idea. One required only the time and effort involved in getting it into the classroom (kindergarten) while the other was reworked entirely by the teacher to become a real treasure, something children worked assiduously to earn.

The first item was a four-legged bathtub the teacher had removed from an old farmhouse she purchased. Her husband and sons took it to her school and set it up in a corner near the bookshelf, partially behind a screen of other bookshelves. With a couple of cushions in it, it was an instant success, so much so that the teacher had to work out a schedule for its use. Children vied for the time to be spent in whatever imaginative use they could make of the tub. The teacher commented that it had been everything from a bathtub to lie in and read to a boat exploring mighty rivers to a ship cast adrift among the stars.

The other item was a surplus parachute given to a teacher. For a while it was used in the gym for her children to run under after they had flipped it up into the air. Then she got the idea of making a special storytelling or reading place. The parachute was cut up and sewn into an envelope with a tube to a window fan. The highlight of the day, any day, was the time spent sitting inside the ''reading igloo'' in an intimate cluster, with the teacher reading or telling stories. Putting it up and taking it down takes a couple of minutes each, and it stores in a space about two feet square.

With some imagination and occasional guidance from the teacher, junk seems more valuable and exhilarating to children than finished equipment or toys that have been purchased. A playground construction made of old telephone poles, railroad ties, and other sturdy, surplus lumber is more challenging to children than a bright, shiny, antiseptic jungle gym. Cable spools, old tires (particularly truck and tractor tires that are big enough to climb into), and sturdy packing crates put together to form small ''buildings'' all challenge the imagination and facilitate running, jumping, sliding, crawling through, or just sitting and thinking.

This is not to deny the value of well-built, sturdy slides, swings, and other manufactured equipment. A well-stocked playground at a nursery or preschool is essential to provide for the release of energy, the development of large muscles, coordination of eye-hand and grasping motions, and all the other physical development necessary to the age level.

The outdoors must not be seen as just a place for children to release pent-up energy. As they learn through play, the outdoors must be integrated into the total educational environment. Ideally, there should be a balance between quiet, covered areas and open, sunlit ones (Haase, 1967), between large objects that can be climbed or swung on, and small flower beds or sturdier shrubs and trees where insects or birds can be watched. Small ecology centers, nature trails that take children past a small pool, perhaps a vegetable garden and fruit trees, all can contribute enormously to learning (Passantino, 1977).

One of the values of the found objects in the learning environment that is important to children's imaginations is the articles' abstractness or neutrality. When children interact with an abstract but real sturdy object, or set of objects such as an arrangement of telephone poles or railroad ties, a set of very large old tires, packing crates, etc., their imaginations supply the details necessary to transform these articles.

The children can place themselves in whatever situation occurs to them. As they interact with the many objects in the environment, various learnings are taking place. Haase (1968) remarks:

> A child's response to his environment is far more direct and energetic than an adult's. He is constantly making discoveries about highness and lowness, nearness and farness, hardness and softness, light and dark. The physical objects through which he explores these concepts can stimulate this imagination and reinforce his joy of learning. Space itself, color, texture, and light quality influence a child's attitude and can provide visual clues that guide his behavior. (p. 9)

The point seems to be that a nicely manufactured swing set, jungle gym, or slide with its finished surfaces and assigned conformity and relationships, its "completeness," is just that—complete. The children know what it is and what it is used for.

A jungle gym is an excellent piece of apparatus to climb on, to swing from, and to exercise with. It clearly is not a tree that also can be climbed, swung from, and exercised on. A tree also can be the home of a troop of monkeys, or a flock of birds, or a myriad of things children can think of. A clear-cut object does not challenge in the same way that an ambiguous one does. Representational art or design is deadly for preschoolers; objects should not be made to resemble real articles in their world too closely.

"A real boat can be fun for a while but it may soon be taken for granted and lose its appeal. It cannot easily become a fire engine." (IAAS, 1976, p. 37)

Classroom Furniture and Design

All surfaces in the classroom are potential work and display areas as well as settings for the furniture. Construction techniques and materials must take this into consideration so the room is designed for the use to which it will be put. Items of indoor furniture and equipment, like that for the outdoor learning environment, must meet the criterion of being learning tools in themselves. They cannot be too elaborate or single purpose, limited to a single activity. They must be simple, versatile, and capable of facilitating the quick and frequent shifts in mood and activity that occur in the nursery school.

All equipment and furniture probably should have wheels so it can be moved from one spot to another as need dictates. This type of equipment can double as room dividers or can be put against the wall out of the way for a game requiring much space. It can be placed all together in the center of the room or strung out as an obstacle course so tricycle riders face a challenge as they hold their own demolition derby.

Blocks of different sizes, shapes, weights, colors, and composition are a must in the preschool setting. Children gain experience from many things but these objects all require storage, thereby providing opportunity for cleanup practice and also for the use of trains or trucks to haul the toys away. Movable storage bins make delightful and often used parts of a train. All equipment or furniture should be multipurpose, mobile and stimulating.

Sitting arrangements need special consideration. As with all furniture, the heights of chairs and benches must be at the children's level but designers must be aware that most sitting probably will be on the floor and on cushions, beanbag chairs, easy chairs, soft cubes, and small boxes. There also must be some carpeted space where the group can sit.

Activity Areas

Regardless of whether the facility is a newly built structure or a found one, the wise use of the central space is a first concern. Since the preschool is a time of varied activity, the facility must be flexible enough for many uses and provided with materials to enable children to construct a variety of experiences. This can be handled effectively in a number of carefully equipped centers or areas that always are available, with others that can be set up at specific times.

Overcrowding can be prevented if a picture is mounted by each activity center that shows how many children can be there at one time, or if only a set number of picture holders is mounted by each center and the children mark their attendance by putting their own pictures in the slots. This way, when the slots are filled, the area is filled.

Sandbox

Generally, children's desire to pour, dig, etc., is met with a sandbox. There they interact in a multitude of ways with containers and sand or, in some cases, water. For variety, cornmeal or the plastic wrapping bits so often shipped with electronic equipment make interesting items.

Music Corner

Music in some form should be an important part of each child's day. This corner must make a variety of musical experiences available but teachers probably will need to control the use of the area to maintain its effectiveness. There should be a piano (for teacher use), rhythm band instruments, records and a record player, and other listening materials.

It is important to remember that the repertoire of instruments or records need not be high but fidelity of sound is important. It is worth the money to have good quality equipment because children will learn a great deal about sound from such articles and should have high-quality examples to learn from.

Listening to recorded music is good under many conditions but the authors do not believe just allowing the record player (or anything else) to play in the background is good for anyone. What that appears to teach children is how to "tune out" the background sounds and shout over them, neither a good listening or attentional skill. Consequently, while youngsters have times to listen or sing or march to music, or to play rhythm band, they should not have it as background noise while they are doing other things.

Reading Corner

Here a variety of picture books, story books, etc., must be available, along with a comfortable place to use them. It has been the authors' experience that if reading and writing materials both are available, the preschool child will both "read" and "write" creatively. In this corner children interact with stories in any ways that suggest themselves and in doing so begin to lay the foundations for later literacy (see Chapter 10).

Playhouse

This most popular center provides the ideal place for role play. It is equipped with dishes, food containers, and a wide variety of dress-up clothes. Children can put themselves into any interpersonal experience they choose by changing a hat or an apron and can practice their understanding of social roles, their symbolic formation, their language, and pragmatics.

Block Corner

One of the most versatile of play corners, this is a very popular place. Sturdy blocks of several kinds can be mixed and matched to produce "real" structures: "I am building a barn;" or very imaginative ones, "Look, I'm making a cave for this dragon;" or "See the space ship I built." Since these have the potential for becoming so many things, it is logical to keep the wheeled toys nearby so children can integrate them into block play.

Arts and Crafts

Parents and teachers hope to see children do new and novel things. They seek to bring out the youngsters' freshness of creativity. This can best be done by providing them a wide variety of art media, time to create, and appreciation for what they have attempted. It is to be hoped that most preschoolers have ample opportunity to face a large blank page with a choice of artistic materials to use on it and begin to produce something original. To foster this creative artistry activity, it is important to provide each child with paper, markers, glue, crayons, paints, glitter, macaroni, sand, or some other assortment of materials and the encouragement to try something new.

Cooperative Play

While not in position to be used at all times, a number of other group activities should be available for children to use at stated periods. For example, a grocery store, with shopping carts, play food, cash register, paper bags, and "money," occupies children for a long time and is very productive. A puppet theater with a variety of puppets provides an opportunity for group role playing. Large riding toys with sets of road and railroad signs promote interactive motor play. A very large cardboard carton with windows and doors cut in it provides endless hours of drive-in banking, hamburger stand, or, most often, school play.

Toys and Materials

The toys purchased for use by a large number of children must meet certain requirements (see Chapter 7) and must be chosen carefully. Children can play without many elaborate toys if allowed creative freedom to construct new play notions. Throughout, this chapter has discussed the importance of interesting but nondefined materials so children will construct their play.

However, there still must be more traditional toys available to fill their standard roles in symbolic play. There must be dolls, balls, trucks, tricycles, and jungle gyms interspersed with the more ''creative'' materials to allow children to make the blend of play most appropriate for them and for the activity at hand.

Therapy Materials

Since the children focused on here probably are in speech/language/hearing therapy, some highly specialized materials also must be available for use with the therapist. Videotape and audiotape equipment is highly effective in therapy and also useful with parent groups. Either a puretone audiometer or a speech audiometer, and an impedance audiometer must be available. Auditory trainers or language masters also may be desirable.

In addition, once the specific therapy has been chosen, the clinician and child begin to acquire the specific materials needed. It is suggested that a locked closet be provided for therapy equipment, which cannot be taken out without the therapist's permission. Each child who receives therapy also could be provided with a cubby for individual therapy materials.

Testing Materials

Since the preschool language nursery is heavily involved in various types of diagnostic and monitoring testing, a variety of appropriate tests must be available. The exact choice of which tests are chosen must be made on the basis of the specific goals of the setting and the general nature of the population to be served (see Chapter 3). These tests should be valid and reliable and must be chosen to cover all aspects of communication. The materials required for administering the tests also must be furnished.

Tests and materials should be kept in a cabinet, with access limited to those who will be using them. Under no circumstances should children be allowed to play with these materials because that can distort the reliability of the results. If youngsters have played with any materials, they may develop notions about their use that will be counterproductive or they may have been taught (either deliberately or accidentally) to use them, thus negating the test results; and/or the materials simply may not evoke the level of interest and involvement that the examiner requires.

SUMMARY

Today more than ever, professionals are aware of the role the environment plays in children's education. The space in which they are housed as they work, play, and learn, may be nearly as important as the teachers/clinicians themselves.

Because the subjects are the very young in a specialized situation, attention must be paid to the learning potential of the facilities themselves. Children cannot sit in straight-backed chairs and listen to teachers and learn. They must be manipulating their environment, playing with objects, spaces, substances, materials in continuing patterns, and talking or trying to talk about everything that is going on.

DISCUSSION QUESTIONS

1. Should the federal government establish licensing requirements for nursery schools and day care centers that would be binding on all states?
2. Do you agree or disagree that the facilities that house a nursery school are almost as important educationally as the teachers or clinicians? Why, or why not?
3. Would you rather work in built or found space, assuming all health and safety standards are up to code? Why, or why not?

REFERENCES

American Association of School Administrators (AASA). *Report of the AASA Commission on School Buildings*. Washington, D.C.: Author, 1967.

Armstrong, P.M. *Architectural design for preschool*. Unpublished architectural paper, Miami (Ohio) University, 1974.

Armstrong, P.M. *Found space in architectural design for Piagetian preschool language nursery*. Unpublished project, Miami (Ohio) University, 1982.

Baker, K.R. Extending the indoors outside. In S. Sunderlin (Ed.), *Housing for early childhood education*. Washington, D.C.: Association for Childhood Education International, 1968.

Decker, C.A. & Decker, J.R. *Planning and administrating early childhood programs* (2nd ed.). Columbus, Ohio: Charles E. Merrill Publishing Co., 1980.

Evans, E.B., & Saia, G.E. *Day care for infants: The case for infant day care and a practical guide*. Boston: Beacon Press, Inc., 1972.

Fitt, S. The individual and his environment. In G.D. Thomas & B.D. Wright (Eds.), *Learning Environments*. Chicago: The University of Chicago Press, 1975.

Gardner, D.E. An ideal environment for learning. In S. Sunderlin (Ed.), *Housing for early childhood education*. Washington, D.C.: Association for Childhood Education International, 1968.

Gibson, C.D. Preschool Educational Housing. In S. Sunderlin (Ed.), *Housing for early childhood education*. Washington, D.C.: Association for Childhood Education International, 1968.

Haase, R. Space which allows. In S. Sunderlin (Ed.), *Housing for early childhood education*. Washington, D.C.: Association for Childhood Education International, 1968.

Heyman, M. *Places and spaces: Environmental psychology in education*. Bloomington, Ind.: The Phi Delta Kappa Educational Foundation, 1978.

Holt, J. Children are sensitive to space. In T.G. David & B.D. Wright (Eds.), *Learning environments*. Chicago: The University of Chicago Press, 1975.

Institute of Advanced Architectural Studies. London: RIBA Publications, Ltd., 1976.

Jefferson, R.S. Indoor facilities. In S. Sunderlin (Ed.), *Housing for early childhood education*. Washington, D.C.: Association for Childhood Education International, 1968.

Moore, R.C. Anarchy zone, kids' needs and school yards. In T.G. David & B.D. Wright (Eds.), *Learning environments*. Chicago: The University of Chicago Press, 1975.

Passantino, R.J. *Found spaces and equipment for children's centers*. New York: Educational Facilities Laboratories, 1977.

Rosner, S. A place in space. In S. Sunderlin (Ed.), *Housing for early childhood education*. Washington, D.C.: Association for Childhood Education International, 1968.

Shaver, J.A. Nursery school facilities. In S. Sunderlin (Ed.), *Housing for early childhood education*. Washington, D.C.: Association for Childhood Education International, 1968.

U.S. Department of Health, Education, and Welfare. *Environmental criteria: MR preschool day care facilities* (Grant number RD-1-MR#07000). College Station, Texas: Research Center, College of Architecture and Environmental Design.

Chapter 10

The Language Arts from Listening to Reading

CHAPTER OBJECTIVES

After completing this chapter readers will be able to:

1. Describe the pragmatic abilities children should bring to a beginning reading situation.
2. Describe the ways in which listening contributes to overall language development.
3. Discuss the relationship between oral language development and later beginning reading instruction.
4. Describe the role of the nursery program in relation to perception.
5. Describe the importance of the various Piagetian tasks such as classification, directionality, reversibility, etc., to the children who soon will start reading instruction.

KEY IDEAS

1. Many of the activities that are a normal part of the nursery program are important to children's development of language.
2. Reading is a necessary and natural extension of the communication abilities of every child.
3. All language systems—pragmatics, syntax, semantics, phonology—are important foundations for later reading instruction.
4. Each of the developmental tasks studied by Piaget has its own role to play in expressive and receptive language and reading.
5. Nursery school teachers/clinicians or parents can greatly facilitate a successful start on reading by helping to build print awareness and a literary ''set.''

BASES FOR ENTRY INTO LANGUAGE NURSERY

Ordinarily the young who constitute the language-impaired or otherwise linguistically dysfunctional population (discussed in Chapter 3) would be scheduled into the language nursery basically for four reasons:

1. They are so severely language impaired that their entire developmental process is being distorted, both cognitively and emotionally.
2. They have need of a very comprehensive treatment program aimed at remediating the entire range of language, developmental, and social deficits.
3. They need the contact with other children.
4. They are at an appropriate age and/or level of cognitive development to fit into one of the existing groups.

Because of their condition, it is obvious the children's initial entry into the linguistic world was not effective. Some have purely idiopathic language disorders, no causative factor having been identified. Others have other identified problems known to either cause or contribute to the failure to develop communication. These youngsters will be blended carefully to preserve an acceptable ratio of mentally retarded and/or emotionally disturbed children to maintain the normal nature of the group.

Once scheduled into the nursery, diagnosis and intervention are established, then modified continually to meet the changing needs of the children in the sensorimotor, socioemotional, and logicomathematical learning areas as well as in language development: pragmatics, semantics, syntax, and phonology. During this period, parents are involved in some level of group participation.

GRADUATION FROM THE LANGUAGE NURSERY

Specific group management arrangements vary from setting to setting and actually may dictate dismissal and/or transfer policies. If the program operates on the basis of two sessions (one sensorimotor and one preoperational) there must be sufficient flexibility to allow children to move from group to group. For those who appear to be in too young or too old a placement, there should be some provision for moving to the appropriate group. Once appropriate placement is achieved, clinicians try to keep groups stable because their viability seems to depend on it. It is less disruptive to a group if children are moved at the end of a term or at term break.

Guidelines for Scheduling Children out of the Nursery

There comes a time when each child has gained the optimum amount possible from the group and should be "graduated" from the nursery program. There are many reasons for this, such as:

- The child can be served more appropriately in some other placement.
- The child no longer is delayed sufficiently to warrant the training program.
- The child is to begin public school and can obtain the necessary therapy there.
- The child no longer needs the nursery group but may require regular individual therapy.
- The child no longer is appropriate for either cognitive group.
- A wide variety of other reasons can mandate a change.

Appropriate Communication Norms

It depends, of course, on the reason for dismissal from the nursery program what normative data must be considered (see discussion of diagnosis in Chapter 3). To be effective, any norms established for enrollment or dismissal must be established by the staff at the facility after consideration of the characteristics of the population. However, general guidelines such as the following can be recommended:

- For "graduation" as dismissed or corrected, the children's receptive and expressive language must be appropriate to their age level and speech community.
- For transfer to public school, the children must meet criteria for acceptance there and be accepted in a suitable program.
- For referral to other facility, the children must have reached a point where some other facility probably can serve the existing needs better and the desired service is available.
- For dismissal from the nursery group yet remaining in individual therapy, the children should have nothing more to gain from the group programs available but still have need of individual therapy, which is available.

Appropriate Follow-Up Settings

Depending on the setting in which the language nursery group is housed, a wide variety of other services might be or become available. The staff persons responsible for making dismissals and referrals should be required to establish (and keep up to date) a list of available referral points. The list should contain current information to help guide parents to the most advantageous sources.

For example, the following data might serve as a base line: name of agency, address, types of service, age limits, any specific requirements, especially strong (and weak) areas, cost, calendar, sponsoring agency, waiting list, etc. Obviously, if this much background information is available about each agency, referral can become a more exact and personal service.

IMPORTANCE OF COMMUNICATIVE DEVELOPMENT

This area (discussed in both Chapters 1 and 2) is of primary importance at all stages of life. In fact, the importance of language development to later schooling cannot be overemphasized and is the focus of this chapter. The linguistic areas of syntax, semantics, and phonology are essential to success in school and to children's development in other ways as well.

Pragmatics defines an area that is a part of the communication system and at the same time extralinguistic, technically outside the limits of the language itself, as it guides and directs individuals' use of language.

Pragmatics is identifiable in infants before they use verbal language and is vitally important as it carries basic gestural communications. Infants learning appropriate pragmatics are developing a strong interpersonal framework, a foundation upon which to build language. Babies begin at a very early age to gather pragmatic abilities through eye contact, mother-infant synchrony, attention to joint activity, verbal turn taking (Snow, 1972, 1981), and referencing. Even at this early age, they make their earliest vocalizations perform some communicative task for them.

Pragmatics is crucial to language in that it provides the appropriateness values of usage. It is the way people use language to make it do what they want it to do. As language develops, so does pragmatic ability to incorporate rules for use of conversation, for topicalization, for use of register, and for signaling information through syntax. Children who have appropriate pragmatics (tool use of language) can make their language serve them as they choose (Bates, 1976; Bates & Johnston, 1979). They can use the proper discourse rules to conform to the appropriateness postulates (politeness, sufficiency of information, truth value, relevancy, and context and person specificity). In addition, they know what to expect from the language of others and how to make language do specific things (such as ask and answer questions, greet people, ask for help, give directions, make suggestions, etc.).

Obviously, children who possess these essential pragmatic abilities can operate effectively if they have adequate language, while those with an insufficiency will have many problems operating the language code.

Pragmatics continues to be important as the children go from spoken language to reading. Indeed, it becomes even more important and complex as the elements supporting and guiding the visual use of language for written communication develop. While the youngsters will maintain and expand the existing pragmatic abilities for a lifetime, certain additional understandings also are necessary if their use of reading is to reach its appropriate level. These abilities relate to building a "literacy set."

Pragmatics in reading involves the use of the formal code (written language) rather than the informal one (spoken language) plus the presuppositions of the reader, such as what the person expects from print. Expectations based on the visual display of the printed page, on more extensive use of surface structure, and on the more intense use of implicature (implied material), etc., are elements of pragmatic usage.

Pragmatics in school involves children's expectations of the teacher-child relationship; the use of more sophisticated question-and-answer forms; and the school requirements for following and giving directions, for decoding and encoding idioms, and for relating to the facility's "book and test" format or "read alone followed by a written test." Children must learn about the structure of the school day and become responsive to the general order and routine.

All these presuppositions provide a new set of ground rules for using appropriate communication in school. For children who have appropriate pragmatic abilities, the school transition usually presents no more than minor problems; however, for those who start school without adequate language/pragmatic skills, the transition may be impossible. They may be unable to generate the pragmatics so necessary for success in school, leading to disastrous results.

ON TO READING

Children being graduated or transferred from the language nursery vary greatly in language development. The authors are interested and involved in studying the importance of the great differences in language background, usage, knowledge, and ability to communicate that children bring to school. Variations in learning style, learning rate, and experiential background, which have been the focus of concern for many years, appear less important than language development in determining true readiness for school achievement (Smith, 1978).

It is known that children with functionally mature language for their age level, with adequate instruction, can learn to read, whatever their learning style, learning rate, or experiential background. It also is known that children who are severely delayed or deviant in language, whatever the cause (physical, mental, or experiential), are likely to experience difficulties in learning to read. Typical children entering school possess a considerable and rapidly expanding language facility. It has been described by Heilman, Blair, and Rupley (1981) as "the greatest force for socialization that exists and . . . is the most potent single factor known in the development of individuality'' (p. 46).

As important as language is in learning to read, little attention has been paid to language factors in general, and particularly to the preschool child's achievement of various language aspects in considerations of reading readiness. Much has been written about children's development of language in relation to success in reading. Fontenot (1974) suggests a hierarchy of goal acquisitions:

1. language development and verbal meanings
2. perceptual skills
3. attending skills
4. listening skills
5. thinking skills.

Only two of these clearly are language, although it often is postulated that the three others also have language components.

These abilities are considered to form the basis on which children learn to recognize letters, words, and symbols and begin to draw connections between the marks in books and their own mental content. The matches they make between the vocabulary (language and verbal meanings) they have acquired and the language of the school and books determine much of their success in learning to read (Smith, 1971). As the clinician/teacher uses the reading minute to expose nursery school children to patterned language of books, their expectations from the visual display begin to develop and their pragmatics and language expand to include expectations from printed stories.

If this fact is acknowledged, the focus of this book becomes increasingly more significant for both preschool teachers and clinicians and for kindergarten/primary teachers. Studies indicate the desirability of using whole words in working with children, emphasizing the need for use of meaningful language units instead of single letters or other fragments (Gibson & Levin, 1975; Robeck & Wilson, 1974).

The language nursery is intended to provide structured learning situations facilitating acquisition of each of the goals. Attending behavior is a part of pragmatics and intimately related to listening to others. Thinking skills develop as children are encouraged to play in the task situations provided. Similarly, perceptual skills mature with the youngsters' growth in cognition and language.

Listening

The importance of hearing and listening cannot be overstated in considering the development of children's communicative abilities. It is believed that all the auditory stimuli in the youngsters' environment feed data into the brain, producing the background upon which they build. They hear different people using the same words in many different frequencies, rates, inflectional patterns, and contexts. With this variety of sounds stimulating their ears, only the pattern remains constant and some authorities suggest that the children store these patterns because they construct schemata from them.

Robeck and Wilson (1974) describe a study of phenomena by which people recognize tunes even when played on different instruments, transposed into different keys, or sung. They note that people respond to the patterns rather than the specific notes. Robeck & Wilson conclude that "the learner abstracts the common characteristics in the perceptual data he receives from repeated experiences of the same or similar stimuli" (p. 212). They think that the pattern of relationships between and among frequencies, intensities, and quiet periods is the constant element that children can relate to.

Experience and Internalizing

Much experience in listening is necessary for children to internalize particular patterns in oral language that they may translate into the written language later. The number of repetitions of a given pattern necessary for an individual to abstract the common elements varies greatly from child to child, depending upon their individual characteristics such as acuity of hearing, perception of differences between sounds and patterns, interest in listening to people and things, and experience in successful communication with those who matter to the youngster.

If children have heard only a limited range of voices producing a limited number of patterns, they have had insufficient data for formulating a variety of generalizations. If the limited number of patterns available have been spoken in dialect as well, the problem of translating to standard written language is multiplied (Robeck & Wilson, 1974). Oral language patterns are based upon the listening children do, and of course reflects the language they are exposed to while in the formative years.

In addition to the problems involved in learning to listen, children in some cultures are admonished, "Don't talk, just listen." Thus they cannot practice the forms they have perceived. When they are not practicing the forms or patterns, for whatever reason, the possibility of feedback, reinforcement of correct forms, or correction of incorrect forms, is reduced greatly. The authors speculate from the data available that a large number of repetitions of a particular pattern is necessary for a child to abstract the elements that are irreducible, i.e., the essence of the pattern.

Receptive Language a Necessity

Adequate receptive language is a cornerstone upon which expressive language is built. Teachers and clinicians in the preschool language nursery face an interesting challenge in attempting to guide each child into developing adequate listening habits. Many homes are so structured with radio, television, and other competing signals that very young children often have learned to tune out most sounds until past experience with bodily discomfort suggests that they pay attention to their mother's call to "Come and eat!" or "Go to bed, or else!"

A further complication arises in the home, where the number of people is limited, usually to the immediate family (now frequently three or four people at most). This means that most listening situations (other than in public) are face to face and require direct reactions to the message received. It is far different when children go to nursery school or, later, kindergarten. Even after language-impaired preschoolers have learned to listen to other persons, problems arise when they become members of a much larger group, with the necessarily higher noise level and possibly even less teacher involvement with the youngsters' listening abilities or habits.

With the variety of oral abilities present in groups of language-impaired children, and with the play atmosphere, getting children to listen to teachers or clinicians becomes a task requiring much ingenuity and one that is unlikely to be completed before they "graduate" from the language nursery program.

Teachers/clinicians must be concerned with three highly interrelated values when dealing with very young children who may not have learned to listen at home:

1. They must make a major effort to help children understand the importance of receiving verbal and nonverbal communication signals.
2. They must help even the very young children become aware of the interrelatedness of speaking/listening and reading/writing.
3. Perhaps most important of all, children every day should hear many models of the best language available to them, used in the best communicative situations possible.

In many typical homes, teaching children to listen or speak the language is a natural, unplanned, and somewhat haphazard occurrence. It is not at all surprising that children who have any complicating factors often do not develop any systematic approach to language; it is enough that the amazing task of learning the basic language systems occurs at all.

The Focus Upon Arrival at the Nursery

When the language-impaired children arrive in the nursery, it is essential to focus on their reception and use of the language code. Receptive language must be developed carefully to approximate normal levels by the time the children begin formal schooling. With a modicum of planning by the teacher, each snack time or play activity can become a listening experience. In addition, the many activities, games, finger plays, songs, jokes, and riddles that children love (Allen & Allen, 1982; Burns & Bassett, 1982; Coody & Nelson, 1982) focus on teaching children aspects of language and how to follow directions.

Interrelatedness of speaking/listening and reading/writing (Allen, 1976) should receive some attention in the nursery school. The authors are not advocating that the teacher begin reading instruction but do urge a solid, varied, language usage program as part of the daily nursery school activity.

Building Reading Readiness

An essential part of such a program, devoted to showing the interrelationships, is accomplished by surrounding the children with meaningful language activities (Smith, 1971, 1978). Even at the nursery school level, roll should be taken so that the children learn to respond to their own name. As they develop, charts can be maintained with their names or photographs and various activities listed so the names can be changed as individuals move from one activity to another.

In situations when the teacher directs changes of activities, use of children's names orally should be accompanied by change of names on the charts with attention called to the activity as in, "Jason, look! I'm putting your name by the picture of the sandbox. You will be there with Amy and Greg." This establishes the relationship between the various aspects of communication used. It reinforces the children's sense of self as agent and starts to build an awareness of print, essential to beginning reading instruction later.

The primacy of listening/speaking skills in young children must reinforce the teacher/clinician's regard for and use of appropriate language modeling. As they interact with children, teachers and therapists must consider the language systems the youngsters are developing: phonology, semantics, syntax, and pragmatics (Johnston, 1978) and provide carefully chosen modeling for expansion of each.

Pilon (1978) comments, "Despite the amount of time we spend in listening, it is evident that we do not always listen efficiently. Every teacher knows that many children have problems in following spoken directions, retaining information delivered orally and in interpreting and appreciating features of spoken discourse" (p. 55). Few writers have devoted attention to the details of children's language that are basic to beginning reading and that must come from more structured communication situations. The language nursery school seems to be the logical place to begin work on reducing the problems noted by so many teachers when children enter the public schools.

Children cannot learn to abstract features of spoken discourse unless exposed to situations where this becomes important. Unless faced with the opportunity to acquire the pragmatics of social group behavior, they do not learn to interact appropriately. This failure will have very specific negative implications for later schooling.

Oral Language

The reciprocal of listening is oral language. Children must practice the structures they hear if their language is to grow in complexity. The most important part of any language clinician's task is providing an informative, stimulating environment that will ensure youngsters the opportunity to practice oral language in communicative situations. Since language is a social phenomenon, it can be learned effectively only in a social setting. Too often in the past, teachers have been unaware of the importance of language practice, in meaningful situations, possibly because of misplacement of priorities.

Experience of All Types a Key Factor

Much experience in language usage of all types is necessary before typical children are ready to begin reading instruction. Allen (1976) summarizes the concept: "children must recognize words by ear before they can recognize them by sight" (p. 359). As an illustration of the connection between the receptive language areas of listening and reading, Allen's statement has much broader implications and importance to the therapist of young language-impaired children. Each of the communication systems described elsewhere in this book, both linguistic and extralinguistic, must be well under control if the children are to be ready for reading instruction. The way they get ready is through sufficient practice with each system in a communicative context.

Children, as noted earlier, construct their cognitive structures based upon experience with their world. Language systems are built in the same way. Diagnostic observations of children's language hypotheses take many forms. Modification and refinement of the various systems can occur only as the youngsters try to use elements of the systems and receive reinforcement (positive or negative) and encouragement (or the lack of it) for their efforts. Chapter 2 cites an example of learning pragmatically appropriate registers. Each of the systems must undergo similar refinement and modification if progress in communication abilities is to grow at a normal rate.

The phonological system is prerequisite to reading for hearing children because they must understand the relationship between speech sounds, oral language, and print before they can learn to read. Much research has been done regarding the phonological system in language as it is used in teaching reading but much misinformation still exists as to how best to use the phoneme/grapheme relationship. The phonetic inventory is readily available to any teacher who will listen to a child for a minute or so.

The phonological system, as with each of the others, is developed primarily through play/experience. In vocal play, children use the sound elements already learned, combine them into new relationships, and reveal to a listener the poorly developed specific sounds or mispronounced words. Vocal play, whether the cooing or babbling of the preword infant or the sophisticated word games of the kindergarten child, provides a means of practicing the sound inventory either in isolation or in meaningful units such as words, phrases, sentences, or paragraphs.

Practice in many different communication situations, or even alone, leads to overlearning of the systems and patterns to the point of automaticity. Play is superior to work situations for learning because it is less structured, more creative, and more self-directed (Robeck & Wilson, 1974).

Words and Subwords

Allen (1976), as noted, comments that children must know words vocally before beginning reading instruction. Much subword information may be even more important before they enter school. Anastasiow (1979) points out, "The child in beginning reading will be able to decode only those specific words already mastered in the child's own language and will recognize only those ideas already learned" (p. 13).

The necessity of understanding that children must transfer much information contained in their personal oral language (Hildreth, 1964) to graphic representations is implied. Such transfers require intuitive mastery of the phonological rule system of the language, a mastery that Gibson & Levin (1975) note is influencing kindergarten pupils already. Children do not go to school with the ability to segment the words in their vocabulary into individual sounds, although they can be taught to segment to the syllable level at about this time (Gibson & Levin, 1975) and to the individual phoneme/grapheme soon after.

Children arrive in kindergarten generally controlling the phonemes of their language; that is, they have learned to hear and recognize the significant contrasting of meaningful differences among the phonemes in the words recognized and to ignore the unused differences in the sounds (Robeck & Wilson, 1974).

This very complex learning always takes place at home and sometimes, in language situations in nursery school, where the children can hear many repetitions of many different words in varying tones, rates, and inflections. Such repetition provides the data from which they abstract the contrasting features of sounds, described by Gibson & Levin (1975): "the acquisition of the sound system of a language can be best understood by a theory of distinctive features. Significant sounds in a language are each unique bundles of a reasonably small inventory of features. Development involves the abstraction and use of the set of features" (p. 115). The features that are meaningful in reading include the order of occurrence in particular words. Gibson and Levin add: "the order of sounds which are put together to form an utterance is rule governed. That is, certain sounds may occur in sequence, others may not" (p. 117).

Refinement and Modification

Each of the language systems receives refinement and modification in essentially the same way as the children use oral language. The growth in vocabulary often is more noticeable than the other systems, but as important as vocabulary is, the growth of other language schemata must take precedence in importance (Robeck & Wilson, 1974).

Two considerations support this concept: (1) the positional nature of English and (2) the markers attached to words that help to delineate the values. Development of the positional understanding seems necessary to vocabulary growth because so many words in English have their full value or perform their complete syntactic function only in the correct slot in a sentence. Examples include several common words such as "read" and "wind," and the whole class of words that depend largely on their position in the sentence for the proper pronunciation and the determination of whether they are noun or verb, e.g., "desert" and "contest." Many other examples could be developed to show how the schema of position precedes and supports the acquisition of vocabulary.

Children learn to conceptualize better, whether at the word or sentence level, by being involved in language situations in which a given pattern occurs again and again. The vocabulary is related to something they can interact with while listening to others discuss it and talking about it themselves. Children abstract essential characteristics of words and language as well as objects by having things put into groups or categories and discussing common attributes with teachers, clinicians, parents, or other youngsters. The role of adult becomes one of confirming the children's good guesses and arranging materials and situations so that they easily perceive similarities and differences (Robeck & Wilson, 1974).

Constructive use of language in the nursery program, coupled with therapy as necessary, reduces the need for more extensive therapy later. The authors believe it greatly enhances children's school performance, especially reading, when they advance to that level.

Perception

The relationship between auditory processing and oral language was discussed in Chapter 2. While this relationship was questioned, no clear or causative answers could be found. The practice of teaching to the so-called auditory processing skills was found to be questionable (Bloom & Lahey, 1978; Neuman, 1981). Others more concerned with the development of reading (Frostig, 1968; Kerfoot, 1967; Wepman, 1960) have identified what they believe to be a clear relationship between the ability to hear minimal differences between phonemes and their relationship to each other and learning to read.

Their evidence clearly indicates a need for children to have a high level of control of their perceptual abilities, both auditory and visual, before they are likely to learn to read (Smith, 1971, 1978). To be ready to learn to read, they must be able to focus on the page with the idea that the marks they perceive have a story to tell (Nelson, 1981). Focusing on the page, however, is not sufficient to enable children to extract meaning unless they can perceive the most minute differences visually and at the same time can integrate them with the auditory system so there is a direct link with the readers' oral language (Gibson & Levin, 1975).

Children who have not been oriented to books, who possess no concept that the visual display at hand can be exciting, informative, or safely frightening, probably have little if any motivation to examine the differences, to try to distinguish between "cat" and "sat," to expect anything at all from reading when the time comes for them to learn it.

Reading or Telling Stories Vital

The authors suggest that it is impossible to overemphasize the importance of a teacher in the preschool settings, regardless of type, reading to children or telling stories while leafing through picture books, showing the pictures and getting the youngsters to respond at whatever level they can. While it may be difficult to arrange physically, the teacher should sit in such a way that the majority of the children can follow the story on the page during the reading.

No effort is made in the language nursery school to teach reading but the opportunity is provided for the children to note similarities and differences, left-to-right progression of written language, and clusters of letters separated by spaces. It is not clear exactly at what point they begin to pick up cues from print but it is clear that those who are not exposed to stories (told, retold, read, and reread) probably are slower to learn to read when instruction does begin.

For example, 15-month-old Greg, absorbed in his favorite book with his grandfather, contributed a robust "G-R-R-R-R!" at the appropriate place in the story when the reader paused. Whether the cue was the flow of a well-known and well-loved story that was interrupted, or the large black lettering that stood out from the surrounding text, is unimportant. The incident illustrates that at a very early age there is a flow and sequence in language that in some way can be triggered by print.

Learning to read is an extension of the language skills already developed (Smith, 1971, 1978; Smith, Goodman, & Meredith, 1976). However, in keeping with the higher level of abstraction of language usage that reading represents, a substantial refinement of many peripheral skills seems necessary (Waterhouse, 1980).

Perceptual Skills

Writers concerned with the development of language in young children agree that it is unnecessary to be involved in teaching isolated perceptual skills or other fringe areas (Bloom & Lahey, 1978). On the other hand, perceptual ability still is necessary, and those concerned with teaching children to read seem solidly in agreement that beginning reading instruction requires that they have a high level of skill in visual and auditory discrimination (Gibson & Levin, 1975; Robeck & Wilson, 1974).

Children who cannot hear the difference between "house" and "mouse" almost certainly will have difficulty in distinguishing the words when encountered in print. Just as certainly, those who do not see the difference in "house" and "horse" in print, even though they have learned clear differentiation in oral language, will experience difficulty in beginning reading. Harris and Sipay (1979) suggest an approach to the question when they write: "The child who does well must already have reached a satisfactory level of development in such abilities as visual discrimination of letter forms, auditory discrimination of letter names, interest in learning, and associative learning" (p. 45).

Linguists have pointed out that most children arrive in school speaking a perfectly adequate, rule-governed language. It follows, therefore, that most of them have adequate levels of auditory discrimination (Smith, 1971, 1978). The teacher's task then is to teach them to apply the skills they already possess in a new and perhaps frustrating environment and, to some children, in novel media and/or materials.

The Language Impaired

This is not the case with the language-impaired children who are the focus of this book. From their early severe dysfunctions, they have been brought along as far as possible by the teachers and clinicians of the language nursery program. They may have achieved a portion of the language and perceptual development of normal children by the time they enter school. The teacher's task at that point is to continue with the developmental process until the youngsters reach the level at which they are ready to begin to learn to read. Obviously the more the preschool nursery has prepared them in reading readiness as well as visual and auditory perceptual development and has provided the foundations for later literacy, the more prepared they will be to go on to school.

It seems to the authors that a realistic view of readiness for learning to read requires an appropriate level of cognitive development (Zaijka, 1981) supporting an active, free, happy use of language in many meaningful, varied situations. Children without adequate cognitive development have difficulty developing language to a level at which it becomes an effective tool and therefore also have difficulty in extending the language to the level of abstraction necessary for reading and writing (Smith, Goodman, & Meredith, 1976).

Reading instruction as practiced in schools visited regularly by the authors presupposes certain abilities, some of which, as indicated, do not seem really necessary (Smith, 1971, 1978). A proper approach, then, would seem to be an environment in which children are encouraged to interact with many items and materials, including print (Clay, 1977; Durkin, 1966; Holdaway, 1979).

Enjoyment of language activities, stories, rhymes, riddles, and jokes in the preschool years sets the stage for further development of language. It motivates children to use language in meaningful situations. Its use while they are engaged in a variety of activities organized around a variety of objects, toys, and situations seems to facilitate the growth of the intellectual and perceptual abilities necessary for beginning reading.

Cognition and Reading

According to Wardhaugh (1976), there are three major theories regarding the development of language: behaviorist (Jenkins & Palermo, 1964; Skinner, 1957; Staats, 1968), nativist (Lenneberg, 1967; McNeill, 1966, 1968, 1970), and cognitive (Bloom & Lahey, 1978; Schlesinger, 1971; Slobin, 1966). Each of these can be extrapolated to provide some insights into the teaching of reading. Each also breaks down to some extent as an explanation of language acquisition or as a basis for reading.

The authors accept the cognitive approach to language development because it is more compatible with the Piagetian view of the growth of intellect and the purposive psychology of Adler that are involved in organizing the child management techniques used. A further reason for accepting this as the more powerful theory lies in its capacity to explain more completely the stages children must go through to acquire the overlaid use of language called reading.

Several of the characteristics of the cognitive theory of language acquisition described by Wardhaugh (1976) seem to lead directly into reading. Prerequisites to this process of constructing language include:

- the ability to deal with the world
- the ability to retain items in short-term memory for a period of time, then move them to long-term memory
- the ability to segment utterances into sound and meaning units and then to recombine the units into the same or different relationships
- the ability to isolate meaning units from sound or other units; that is, to deal with the semantic level of an utterance with little concern for either the syntax or phonology
- the ability to make wide generalizations.

The purpose of the Language Nursery Program is not to prepare children for reading instruction or to build reading readiness; rather it is to help them become fully communicating human beings in their own nursery world. Reading, also a language function, is an immensely important extension of communication. The authors do try to provide situations and guidance that can facilitate the children's development of the elements of language that later will feed into reading instruction and make it more rewarding.

Oral and Visual Acquisition

While reading must begin with the language possessed by the children, major differences exist between the acquisition of their spoken language and later learning to read. Wardhaugh (1976) mentions several, including the fact that language acquisition is gradual and almost unconscious (to the normally developing population, but not to this population of severely language-impaired children) while reading begins quite suddenly.

Children entering school often have been told about reading, possibly even already instructed by well-meaning parents, grandparents, or older siblings, to the point that some anxiety accompanies each move the youngsters make.

For example, Pete, just 6 years old, got off the bus after the first day of school and walked the long country road home, sobbing bitterly. Arriving at the door, he paused, wiped tears from his eyes, and announced to his mother in his most grown-up, apologetic voice: "You said I'd larn ta read 'n school! Well, I didn't! Guess there ain't no use me goin' back."

Language acquisition is informal and casual but reading instruction is formal, deliberate, and reasonably systematic. The reward for language acquisition is communication with the meaningful adults and other children in the youngsters' lives but the reward for reading success often is so abstract and long range that children may not see it at all.

Reading instruction, dealing with a different aspect and use of language, must be concerned with other aspects of children's developing intelligence. It must take into consideration the need for highly specialized, visual discrimination not necessary in other aspects of growth. Reading instruction must make provisions for the abstract, highly controlled, and somewhat artificial material beginning readers must deal with as basic word recognition techniques are taught. A more important consideration, and one the authors think must be remedied, is that, as Wardhaugh (1976) says, "Reading methods themselves are almost unrelated to theories of language acquisition" (p. 62). The authors do not believe this should be the case.

The broad range of reading materials includes such diverse offerings as Distar (SRA, 1968), which is based on behaviorist theory; *Merrill Linguistic Reading Programs* (1980), which are based on the theories of Fries (1963), and many reading books by major publishers that often are reviewed by linguists before publication but are not necessarily linguistically or language based.

Much attention has been paid to the developmental theories of Piaget (1963, 1969, 1974; Piaget & Inhelder, 1969b) as they might be used to explain and facilitate language and reading development. Piaget is known to have made only one reference to reading instruction, and that in passing (Hall, 1970). He noted, "The idea of reading readiness corresponds to the idea of competence in embryology. If a specific chemical inductor hits the developing embryo, it will produce an effect if the competence is there, and if it is not, the effect will not occur. So the concept of readiness is not bad, but I am not sure it can be applied to reading. There could easily be a difference of aptitude between children independent of mental age" (p. 31).

It was noted in Chapter 2 that the purpose of the language nursery was to develop language competence in language-impaired children. This will enhance the probability that the desired effect of reading will occur when instruction begins. Piaget (1970) was not sure readiness could be applied to reading, however, others, convinced of the power of this theory of cognitive development and feeling the lack of relationship to language and reading, have since replicated much of Piaget's work (Elkind, 1965, 1966, 1967, 1969, 1974) and later drawn many implications for reading instruction or have taken the work of Piaget himself and applied the concepts and processes to reading instruction (Almy, 1967; Kirkland, 1978; Raven & Salzer, 1971).

The Graphic Format

Study of the literature reveals many applications and parallels drawn between children's acquiring the ability to communicate in the graphic format (Samuels, 1971), clearly an extension and use of the basic cognitive structures, and the development of the structures themselves. In addition, studies provide an impressive body of empirical evidence to support the theoretically developed positions that see a necessity for firm possession of the basic cognitive development and abilities before reading instruction can be successful (Durkin, 1966, 1978; Robinson, Strickland, & Kullinan, 1977).

Writers who have studied reading and prereading experiences of children from the developmental standpoint agree in large measure on many aspects of the relationships (Gibson & Levin, 1975; Robeck & Wilson, 1974). Every aspect of growth in cognition seems to be important for emerging elements of reading or, at the very least, interest in reading as someone else does it. Those important foundations of intelligence developing during the sensorimotor period create the structural foundation for all subsequent cognitive development (Waller, 1977), including language development and reading instruction.

The language nursery program implements a philosophy stated by Almy (1967): "An environment that provides the child with many opportunities for varied sensory and motor experiences is essential. So, too, is the presence of people who talk with (not merely to or at) the child, people who read and write and who share these activities with children'' (p. 93). The authors believe that children cannot be too young to be exposed to a variety of experiences and to hear people talking about them in language they generally can understand and relate to. A further requirement of the play situation in the nursery (Almy, 1967) is that "theory implies the necessity that the child discover his own errors in thinking in such fashion that he, himself, attempts to correct them" (p. 92).

Organization of the environment is made with the activities of the children in · mind at all times, based upon their diagnosed needs (see Chapters 3 and 4). Continuous monitoring of progress is maintained to ensure their scheduling and participation in the most appropriate activities.

Preoperational Events

Since the authors' primary concern is language development, the major emphasis in the language nursery program is the events of the preoperational period, generally recognized as the time during which language develops. Even so, attention must be paid to both the sensorimotor period, which is the primary prerequisite for language development, and the crucial transitional time between these two, which is marked by the acquisition of symbolic function. It is there that the ability to let one thing stand for another begins. This includes the possibility of allowing squiggles on paper to stand for words, ideas, or meanings (Waller, 1977).

The program implementing the Piagetian Preschool Language Nursery emphasizes interaction with a wide variety of materials, activities, and situations, including books and reading. In the authors' program children are exposed regularly to the same or similar activities to produce enough data to allow construction of the routines of the language and, eventually, of reading.

Even 2-year-old children have their favorite stories and picture books. Again and again they request that the teacher read particular ones or look at (read) the same picture book during free-choice periods (see Chapter 4).

Unfortunately, numerous children with language problems are among those who lack this "literacy set." Studies of prereaders and beginning readers have shown (Clay, 1977; Holdaway, 1979; Waller, 1977) that:

> [Many] 5-year-olds do not always know what is in a book, that it contains stories, that there is a reason for reading. Worse, they frequently cannot discriminate a phoneme from any other sound or a word from a nonword. In effect children do not grasp the abstract nature of written language and, specifically, do not understand technical vocabulary of reading. (Waller, p. 10)

These skills or subskills—understanding of a word, a story, a poem, or even a sound, and the ability to deal with parts and wholes and their relationships in language—all require basic cognitive development or skill to exist or at least to coexist (Kirkland, 1978; Raven & Salzer, 1971; Waller, 1977). They may well be built during a nursery school program focused on language development as a component of other, more basic cognitive abilities.

Foundation and Familiarity

Language nursery programming for teachers, that includes some specific reading activities with children in every day's program for even the 2-year-olds, is intended to (1) establish a firm foundation for later preoperational and concrete operational learning and (2) begin building a familiarity with books, stories, and the patterned language that nursery rhymes and children's stories abound in.

There are few sources that provide better material for children to assimilate than the old, well-loved stories with their repeating patterns and words and their catchy rhymes. Children are not expected to learn the stories, poems, riddles, etc., but simply to enjoy them, and no preschooler is expected to learn to read.

As the exposure to modeled language continues (Loban, 1967), accompanied by the many carefully organized play activities designed to develop the full range of preoperational abilities, children do learn the language patterns and often play language games with their teachers and peers.

Studies by Almy (1967), Downing (1970), Elkind (1967, 1969, 1974) and others, are summarized by Waller (1977) to determine the specific relationships between various Piagetian tasks and readiness for reading. They suggest a high correlation between achievement levels in these areas.

Their conclusions include the findings that scores obtained on conservation tasks correlate nearly as well (.48) as general intelligence scores (.50) (both only medium level correlations) and better than those on perceptual-motor tasks (.24). They further note correlations ranging from a low of .26 to a high relationship of .82 out of a possible 1 for seriation on various Piagetian tasks and readiness measures.

Six Underlying Abilities

These studies emphasize the necessity that children accomplish particular tasks at specific levels if they are to profit from later reading instruction. Classification, seriation, directionality, reversibility, decentration, and conservation (Ehri, 1978; Kirkland, 1978; Raven & Salzer, 1971; Waller, 1977) have been studied extensively and specific efforts have been made to relate them to various types of reading tasks or requirements.

Classification

The ability to classify elements is necessary to the development of the phoneme/ grapheme relationship (Kirkland, 1978). Grouping letters into words and words into sentences requires the ability to classify words as nouns, verbs, and/or other forms or into their semantic correlates of agent, action, patient, attribute, etc. At a lower level, classification of letters as vowel or consonant also is necessary to both the receptive and expressive uses of oral language or reading.

Children not only must be able to see a letter as representing a vowel or consonant sound, they also must see that in one position in a word, the letter is a vowel while in another it is a consonant (y). Similarly, they must have the mental equipment to understand that in one position the sound represented by the letter " g " is used as / g / in "gun" while in another it represents / j / as in "gym."

Clearly this requires much experience at lower levels in classifying different types of information, holding the order in mind, and shifting from one conceptualization to another as the perception of further data makes necessary. At the same time the children are holding the classification of letters and sounds in mind, they also must remember the resulting words as sentence constituents, observing both their semantic and syntactic roles. Each word also has the entire bundle of semantic attributes that relate to its meaning that must be maintained in proper order and relationships.

Seriation

According to Waller (1977), an essential part of early reading is children's ability to learn to dissect spoken words into component sounds, to keep the sounds in proper sequence, and to keep the order of letters in words, words in sentences, and sentences in paragraphs. Seriation is necessary at an even higher level if the user is to maintain the order necessary to faithfully represent complex semantic relationships or syntactic elements of the sentences chosen.

This ability to order elements also can be traced to successful understanding of left-right progression (Waller, 1977). As an example, prereading children can learn this important task while playing with blocks or dolls or cars and trucks as a parent or teacher says, "Find me the tallest or shortest or smallest" or "Stand the ducks in a line from the biggest to the smallest duck." In this way basic understanding begins, to be expanded later into language reading usage.

Directionality

Another ability beginning to develop during the preoperational stage is directionality (Kirkland, 1978). Its operation can be identified as it works to organize, to point to direction of movement, in essence to allow the children to progress along a line of print. It is especially important for those who have no particular orientation to print because it represents a type of information that may serve to guide them in gaining this all-important orientation.

Preschool children must be exposed to much experience in which concepts such as top and bottom, first and last, over and under, up and down are important to their processing of a game or other activity. Then, when the kindergarten teacher says to start at the top and work down to the bottom, or compare the first picture with the last in the line, the youngsters have some concept of what is meant. In a finer and more complex situation, children lacking in directionality could have trouble in distinguishing between letters where the essential difference may be at the top or the bottom of the item under consideration.

A further consideration of directionality learning is described by Kirkland (1978) in her statement that the ability to focus hearing on sounds in words, to focus listening to a particular source for directions, and to focus attention on the task at hand are contingent upon mastery of directional concepts and tasks at a higher level.

Reversibility

One of the important abilities for children soon to enter kindergarten and first grade reading instruction is reversibility. With the necessity for learning the phoneme/grapheme relationships as quickly as possible and advancing to the mastery level, those who cannot reverse perceptions could not be expected to go from grapheme to phoneme by memorizing the most common or likely sound represented by each letter and then checking the process by turning the whole situation around and considering the range of sounds that could be represented by the one grapheme (Kirkland, 1978).

The same idea is expressed by Waller (1977) when he says that children must learn the patterns of highly probable correspondences between letters and sounds; the one-to-many and the many-to-one correspondences. Prereading behavior illustrating this development might consist of a child's returning to a toy, tool, or task after leaving it out of sight for some time.

For example, a nursery school teacher or parent may say, ''Children, please put the toys away and come to the story circle.'' At the conclusion of the story time, the children may return immediately to the toys, tools, or tasks they had set aside. Many such experiences can pave the way for the children's expansion into reading-related uses of cognitive and communication abilities.

Decentration

The ability to decenter has been studied at some length to determine its relationships to reading readiness. Children must take into account and simultaneously coordinate several dimensions of a situation to extract the relevant information (Ehri, 1978; Elkind, Larson, & Van Doornick, 1965; Waller, 1977).

For example, a child looking at a word in the earliest stages of reading readiness could become locked into one identity of a word, perhaps see only the graphic features and not be able to understand that it also involves the syntactic identity (the word is a noun in a specific syntactic relationship), the semantic identity (the word is an agent in a specific semantic relationship and represents "cat"), and so forth (Ehri, 1978).

Children must be able to see more than one aspect at a time or they cannot be expected to be able to solve the line puzzle (a string of letters and spaces in a specific order) and also assign appropriate meanings to the display, whether a picture or a line of print.

Conservation

According to Waller (1977), this area has evoked the greatest number of studies and various investigators have considered its many aspects. Raven and Salzer (1971) maintain that children must realize substantial change may take place in a system without altering its fundamental characteristics. Waller (1977) carries this a step further and states that children must learn to recognize and discriminate letters in their various forms and relationships, uppercase, lowercase, exposed at the beginning of a word, or masked by other letters. Kirkland (1978) carries the relationship even further in suggesting that children must conserve to hold the rules of phoneme/grapheme relationships in mind while synthesizing meaning from larger units of language. This latter idea clearly is not necessary for those of nursery age but is dependent upon mastery of earlier levels leading to conservation.

Each of the tasks that has been studied has its own importance to the children's cognitive development and can be examined separately but it must be remembered that cognition is neither a one-dimensional phenomenon nor a set of separable skills. Each of these abilities must be developed within its relationship to the others. Each area has roots deep in the children's early cognitive development and must have progressed to an appropriate level of control before the unique contribution of each task to this immensely complex bundle of abilities and skills called reading can be realized.

Learning to speak and communicate in a specific language is not the same as learning to read that language despite the enormous overlapping in usages. Just as young readers acquire a level of both visual and auditory perceptual ability and continued refinements on them (Gibson & Levin, 1975; Robeck & Wilson, 1974), they also must learn to think about their use of language if they are to learn to read (Ehri, 1978; Fischer, 1980; Ryan, 1980).

Fischer (1980) says, "If reading crucially involves a conscious awareness of primary linguistic activities, which I think it does, then perhaps it awaits the child's maturing to nonconcrete, context-independent language processing" (pp. 34–35). Children who are communicating in a meaningful situation with peers, parents, or teachers are operating in a situation where factors termed "extralinguistic" by Fischer (1980) determine the forms as well as the content of communicative efforts (Bates & Johnston, 1979).

Even young children are adept at matching their level of conversational complexity to the needs of the situation, as Fischer (1980) says: "Four-year-olds speak in simpler sentences to 2-year-olds than they do to other 4-year-olds" (p. 34). Children in a reading situation do not have the context of the environment and peers in face-to-face interaction to help them react in a proper way with the proper level of language. Therefore, they must have a much higher level of knowledge about their use of language to make up for the difference in the context (Holdaway, 1979).

If learning to read requires the development of "active, deliberate, meaning-seeking behaviors" (Ryan, 1980, p. 38) that the psycholinguists postulate, then clearly the level of language control must be at or near a conscious level. Because it is a deliberate language activity with purposes quite removed from conversation, and because the rewards may be quite different from those attending speech or lacking entirely for some children (Ryan, 1980), "reading may require a degree of linguistic awareness not necessary for speaking and listening effectively in everyday interactions" (p. 39).

This level of control of the language can come only from a situation in which the children have been exposed to many opportunities to use their language in meaningful interactions. It becomes necessary, also for them to become aware of language as a tool (Bates, 1976) and as amenable to deliberate manipulation and use (Bates, 1976; Bates & Johnston, 1979). This is unlikely to be completed in the language nursery program because language-impaired children usually are not capable of achieving this level of metalinguistic awareness until a later age.

Ehri (1980) in a study of young children's ability to segment sentences into words and syllables finds that preschool and kindergarten prereaders perform less well than first graders. However, the linguistic foundations for such control, no matter how basic, can be laid down in the nursery school, as has been described. This program provides a place where well-trained, knowledgeable adults focus on the language of individual children in a fluid group setting requiring linguistic interaction as the youngsters go about the business of playing.

Studies of early readers (Clay, 1977; Durkin, 1966, 1978; Holdaway, 1979) consistently have shown that children who have better, higher levels of conscious control of language usage—what Fischer (1980) and Ryan (1980) call metalinguistic awareness—make more rapid and higher quality progress in learning to read than those lacking this level of control. For many children this level of control develops naturally as they ask about words, signs, and even letters.

The normal continuing linguistic interaction with children (Holdaway, 1979) takes care of this as parents, older siblings, or other adults answer questions such as, "What does it say?" "How do you spell?" "Show me!" Gibson and Levin (1975) say that parents or others who cannot be bothered answering such questions are "killing curiosity, the spontaneous urge to learn that is the foundation of all adaptive behavior" (p. 553). Children usually seen in this language program already have missed out on some of these behaviors and are running late in language and perhaps in cognitive development.

The Piagetian Nursery Program situation is so organized that in addition to the systematic instruction (therapy) planned for each child, the meaningful adults do take time to answer these and other questions. In addition, they consciously provide occasions conducive to eliciting the questions by leading children through the play situations that have been structured to make interaction necessary.

READING: THE VOYAGE OF DISCOVERY

Part of each day is devoted to reading, which Gibson and Levin (1975) say "provides the best opportunity for discovering that books have something interesting and meaningful to say; it increases knowledge about other places and other people; above all, it can increase a child's language skills" (p. 553). Reading to the children is intended to make them more aware of language (Fischer, 1976), at a more formal and stylized level, to show some of the flow, system, and cadences but above all it is designed to be fun.

As teachers, the authors remember with Clay (1977) that the consciousness of language desired "takes place only in the presence of print and when the child actively seeks to discover how oral and written language are related" (p. 5). It is required that the teachers in this preschool situation be like parents with their children just learning the oral language, not explaining every word or elaborating on each concept but reading and allowing meanings, ideas, and concepts, to build in a natural way as in oral language (Holdaway, 1979). He says that reading in this way provides, "rich exposure beyond immediate needs" (p. 40) and that children are capable of attending for surprising periods or until semantic completeness is achieved.

The complex range of attitudes, concepts, and beliefs that can be developed should raise the children's expectations of print because the more modeled language and the more fully developed ideas, coupled with the more completely developed, logically organized flow of written language, cause children to develop a "literacy set [that] begin[s] to operate immediately and automatically in appropriate ways whenever they are faced with print" (Holdaway, 1979, p. 49).

Children who are read to again and again from a wide range of books develop a deep familiarity with the story language of their favorites, often joining in as the teacher or parent reads particular patterns, and sharply correcting lapses from the printed text. This indicates a level of familiarity with print that allows many children to enter a reading situation with high expectations that they will succeed in learning to read and that it is well worth the effort involved. As they join with the adult reader in familiar patterns, they are experimenting with book language in its primary, oral form while they still are working to gain control of their spoken grammar and phonology (Holdaway, 1979).

These children of 2, 3, or 4 years of age are at the most powerful learning stage they ever will experience. The sensorimotor and preoperational bases are developing rapidly, as is the home, oral language. Exposure to written language in settings and interactive situations similar to those necessary for oral language, and with the same type of emotional support and encouragement, can lay a solid foundation for later literacy.

Holdaway (1979) points out: "Infants are not born with the ability to understand and use cognitive structures and logical processes—these must be learned. Written language is distinct in using a wider range of such structures, more rigorously developed, more crucial to understanding, and more sophisticated in their refinements, than occurs anywhere in conversational language" (p. 54).

As with the other learning tasks of this period, the children work assiduously at building these complex cognitive structures, whether in the play situation with a rich variety of toys that can be manipulated, sorted, classified, and put into varying kinds of order; in the oral language situation where the pragmatics, semantics, syntax, and phonology systems must grow; or in the written language situation where exciting stories told in patterned language with its own ebb and flow, its own logic and complex structures, challenge the mind.

SUMMARY

Children are scheduled into the Piagetian Language Nursery Program for various reasons. The level of competence in language they should acquire to be "graduated" or assigned to other facilities also varies as need indicates and availability dictates. Primarily, the decisions for releasing a child are made by the staff of the facility based upon considerations of level of language achieved, age, inability of this placement to further help the individual, and availability of needed services from other agencies.

Pragmatic development, although extralinguistic in itself, is essential to children's development of communication at all levels and of all types, oral or written, expressive or receptive. Children lacking in pragmatic abilities have difficulty in using language appropriately. Therefore their making mistakes might well delay their growth because feedback and reinforcement would seem to be misdirected. In dealing with the written code, appropriate pragmatics enables the youngsters to build realistic expectations for the higher level of abstraction represented.

Listening and oral language usage bear the responsibility for developing language. Patterns heard over and over become internalized and schemata are begun.

As the children begin to reproduce the patterns orally, the adults of their world (parents or clinicians/teachers) reinforce appropriate efforts and ignore inappropriate usage so the youngsters have help in refining and practicing home language.

The children seen in the language nursery program, because their needs are greater, must have situations structured carefully to elicit the necessary attempts at communication. Clinicians/teachers also must monitor them more intently so they can direct their feedback specifically to the diagnosed point of greatest need, ensuring progress in phonological, syntactic, semantic, and pragmatic performance.

The nursery school emphasizes the fact that the clinician/teacher has an extremely important role in guiding children in need of building the basic language and cognitive structures that will support their later efforts to learn to read. Listening and oral language development is fundamental in building readiness for beginning reading.

Language is even more basic to reading than the various types of perception that so often are studied and taught in reading readiness programs. Analysis of perception studies to determine an appropriate value in the hierarchy of abilities necessary for children learning to read concludes that a high level of control of auditory and visual perception is necessary but that it is more important to concentrate on building language and cognitive skills. As these develop in complexity and utility, interest in communicating should grow with them and this probably will carry the requisite perceptual skills along with it.

Consideration of the role played by cognition in learning to read reveals several differences in acquisition of oral language and literacy related to rate of onset, attendant tensions, rewards for success in the endeavor, and the systematic nature of the instruction involved in the effort to teach the children. As part of the language nursery school program, careful attention is paid to providing happy experiences with print, in nonpressure situations, so the children can begin building the literacy set so important to later success in reading instruction.

The implications for language development, with its expansion into reading instruction, and the various Piagetian developmental tasks—classification, seriation, directionality, reversibility, decentration, and conservation—were examined. Substantial data on each of these tasks clearly indicate the differing levels of control necessary for success in reading instruction. It appears that mastery of the tasks must be at a level where children actually can think about their use of language, i.e., classification must be mature enough to allow them to see and hear sounds and letters as being of the class of vowel or consonant.

The requisite mastery of cognitive and language structures can be developed by adding to the children's normal growth in oral language communication. This provides ample opportunities for their becoming familiar with the more structured, abstract, patterned, and sophisticated language of books.

DISCUSSION QUESTIONS

1. What are the differences in the way the term ''pragmatics'' is used here and your previous understanding of the word?
2. Do you agree or disagree that a high level of mastery of listening and oral language usage is necessary for beginning reading instruction? Why, or why not?
3. Which of the developmental tasks is most important to language development and reading in your opinion? Why?

REFERENCES

Allen, R.V. *Language experiences in communication*. Boston: Houghton Mifflin Co., 1976.

Allen, R.V., & Allen, C. *Language experience activities* (2nd ed.). Boston: Houghton Mifflin Co., 1982.

Almy, M.C. Young children's thinking and the teaching of reading. In J.L. Frost (Ed.), *Issues and innovations in the teaching of reading*. Atlanta: Scott, Foresman & Company, 1967.

Anastasiow, N. *Oral language, expression of thought*. Urbana, Ill.: University of Illinois, 1979. (ERIC Document Reproduction Service No. ED)

Bates, E. *Language in context: The acquisition of pragmatics*. New York: Academic Press, Inc., 1976.

Bates, E., & Johnston, J. Paper presented to the Southwestern Ohio Speech and Hearing Association, Cincinnati, 1979.

Bloom, L., & Lahey, M. *Language development and language disorders*. New York: John Wiley & Sons, Inc., 1978.

Burns, P.C., & Bassett, R. *Language arts activities for elementary schools*. Boston: Houghton Mifflin Co., 1982.

Clay, M. *Reading, The patterning of complex behaviour*. London: Heinemann Educational Books, Ltd., 1977.

Coody, B., & Nelson, D. *Successful activities for enriching the language arts*. Belmont, Calif.: Wadsworth Publishing Co., 1982.

Distar Instructional Systems. Chicago: Science Research Associates, Inc., 1968.

Downing, J. Children's concepts of language. *Learning to Read, Educational Research, 1970, 12,* 106–112.

Durkin, D. *Children who read early*. New York: Teachers College Press, 1966.

Durkin, D. *Teaching them to read* (3rd ed.). Boston: Allyn & Bacon, Inc., 1978.

Ehri, L.C. Beginning reading from a psycholinguistic perspective: Amalgamation of word identities. In F.B. Murray (Ed.), *The recognition of words*. Newark, Del.: International Reading Association, 1978.

Elkind, D. Non-verbal exercises for remedial reading instruction. *Colorado School Journal,* March 1966, 37–38.

Elkind, D. Piaget's theory of perceptual development: Its application to reading and special education. *The Journal of Special Education, 1967, 1,* 357–361.

Elkind, D. Developmental studies of figurative perception. In L.P. Lipsett and H.W. Reese (Eds.), *Advances in child development and behavior*. New York: Academic Press, 1969.

Elkind, D. *Cognitive development and reading.* Claremont, Calif.: Claremont Reading Conference Proceedings, 1974.

Elkind, D., & Deblinger, J.A. Perceptual training and reading achievement in disadvantaged children. *Child Development,* 1969, *40,* 11–19.

Elkind, D.; Horn, J.; & Schneider, G. Modified word recognition, reading achievement, and perceptual decentration. *Journal of Genetic Psychology,* 1965, *107,* 235–251.

Elkind, D.; Larson, M.; & Van Doornick, W. Perceptual decentration, learning and performance in slow and average readers. *Journal of Psychology,* 1965, *56,* 50–56.

Fischer, K.M. Metalinguistic skills and the competence performance distinction. In F.B. Murray (Ed.), *Language awareness and reading.* Newark, Del.: International Reading Association, 1980.

Fisher, C.J. Children's literature and oral discussion in developing oral language of kindergarten, first and second grade children. *Language Arts,* 1976, *53,* 344–346.

Fontenot, R. *Developing prerequisites for reading: A search for rationale.* Paper presented at the International Reading Association, New Orleans, 1974.

Fries, C.C. *Linguistics and reading.* New York: Holt, Rinehart & Winston, 1963.

Frostig, M. Visual modality, research and practice. In H.K. Smith (Ed.), *Perception and reading.* Newark, Del.: International Reading Association, 1968.

Gibson, E.J., & Levin, H. *The psychology of reading.* Cambridge, Mass.: The MIT Press, 1975.

Hall, E.A. A conversation with Jean Piaget and Barbel Inhelder. *Psychology Today,* 1970, *3,* 25–31, 54–56.

Harris, A.J., & Sipay, E.R. *How to teach reading.* New York: Longman, Inc., 1979.

Heilman, A.W.; Blair, T.R.; & Rupley, W.R. *Principles and practices of teaching reading.* Columbus, Ohio: The Charles E. Merrill Publishing Co., Inc., 1981.

Hildreth, G. Linguistic factors in early reading instruction. *The Reading Teacher,* 1964, *18,* 172–178.

Holdaway, D. *The foundations of literacy.* Sydney, Australia: Ashton Scholastic, 1979.

Jenkins, J., & Palermo, D. Mediation processes and the acquisition of linguistic structure. *Monographs of the Society for Research in Child Development,* 1964, *29* (1, Serial No. 92).

Johnston, E.B. *Development of the communicative abilities test for young children.* Unpublished doctoral dissertation, University of Cincinnati, 1978.

Kerfoot, J.F. The relationship of selected auditory and visual readiness measures to first grade reading achievement and second grade spelling achievement. *Journal of Reading,* 1967, *10*(5), 307–308.

Kirkland, E.R. A Piagetian interpretation of reading instruction. *The Reading Teacher,* 1978, *31*(5), 497–503.

Lenneberg, E.H. *Biological foundations of language.* New York: John Wiley & Sons, Inc., 1967.

Loban, W. Oral language proficiency affects reading and writing. In J.L. Frost (Ed.), *Issues and innovations in the teaching of reading.* Atlanta: Scott, Foresman & Company, 1967.

MacAulay, B.D. A program for teaching speech and beginning reading to nonverbal retardates. In H.N. Sloan & B.D. MacAulay (Eds.), *Operant procedures in remedial speech and language training.* Boston: Houghton Mifflin Co., 1968.

McNeill, D. Developmental psycholinguistics. In F. Smith and G.A. Miller (Eds.), *The genesis of language: A psycholinguistic approach.* Cambridge, Mass.: M.I.T. Press, 1966.

McNeill, D. On the theories of language acquisition. In T.R. Doxon and D.L. Horton (Eds.), *Verbal behavior and general behavior theory.* Englewood Cliffs, N.J.: Prentice-Hall, 1968.

McNeill, D. *The acquisition of language: The study of psycholinguistics.* New York: Harper and Row, 1970.

Merrill Linguistic Readers. Columbus, Ohio: Charles E. Merrill, Inc., 1980.

Nelson, N.W. An eclectic model of language intervention for disorders of listening, speaking, reading and writing. *Topics in Language Disorders*, 1981, *1*(2), 1–21.

Neuman, S.B. Effect of teaching auditory perceptual skills on reading achievement in first grade. *The Reading Teacher*, 1981, *34*(4), 422–426.

Piaget, J. *[The origins of intelligence in children]* (M. Cook, trans.). New York: W.W. Norton & Co., Inc., 1963.

Piaget, J. *[The language and thought of the child]* (M. Gavain, trans.). Cleveland and New York: World Publishing Co., 1969(a).

Piaget, J., & Inhelder, B. *[The psychology of the child]* (H. Weaver, trans.). New York: Basic Books, Inc., 1969(b).

Piaget, J. *[The construction of reality in the child]* (M. Cook, trans.). New York: Ballantine Books, 1974.

Pilon, A.B. *Teaching language arts creatively in the elementary grades*. New York: John Wiley & Sons, Inc., 1978.

Raven, R.J., & Salzer, R.T. Piaget and reading instruction. *The Reading Teacher*, 1971, *24*, 630–639.

Robeck, M.C., & Wilson, J. *Psychology of reading, Foundations of instruction*. New York: John Wiley & Sons, Inc., 1974.

Robinson, V.B.; Strickland, D.S.; & Kullinan, B. The child ready or not. In L. Olilla (Ed.), *The kindergarten child and reading*. Newark, Del.: International Reading Association, 1977.

Ryan, E.B. Metalinguistic development and reading. In F.B. Murray (Ed.), *Language awareness and reading*. Newark, Del.: International Reading Association, 1980.

Samuels, S.J. Letter name vs. letter sound knowledge in learning to read. *The Reading Teacher*, 1971, *24*(7), 604, 608–662.

Schlesinger, I.M. Production of utterance and language acquisition. In D.I. Slobin (Ed.), *The ontogenesis of grammar: Facts and theories*. New York: Academic Press, 1971.

Skinner, B.F. *Verbal behavior*. New York: Appleton-Century-Crofts, 1957.

Slobin, D.I. The acquisition of Russian as a native language. In F. Smith and G.A. Miller (Eds.), *The genesis of language: A psycholinguistic approach*. Cambridge, Mass.: M.I.T. Press, 1966.

Smith, F. *Understanding reading*. New York: Holt, Rinehart & Winston, Inc., 1971.

Smith, F. *Reading without nonsense*. New York: Teachers College Press, 1978.

Smith, E.B.; Goodman, K.S.; & Meredith, R. *Language and thinking in school*. New York: Holt, Rinehart & Winston, Inc., 1976.

Snow, C.E. Mother's speech to children learning language. *Child Development*, 1972, *43*, 549–565.

Snow, C.E. Paper presented to the Ohio Speech and Hearing Association, Cincinnati, 1981.

Staats, A.W. *Language, learning and cognition*. New York: Holt, Rinehart & Winston, 1968.

Waller, T.G. *Think first, Read later*. Newark, Del.: International Reading Association, 1977.

Wardhaugh, R. Linguistic insights into the reading process. In S.L. Sebesta & C.J. Wallen (Eds.), *The first R: Readings on teaching reading*. Chicago: Science Research Associates, 1973.

Wardhaugh, R. Language acquisition in relation to beginning reading. In H. Singer & R. Ruddell (Eds.), *Theoretical models and processes of reading* (2nd ed.). Newark, Del.: International Reading Association, 1976.

Waterhouse, L. The implications of theories of language and thought for reading. In F.B. Murray (Ed.), *Language awareness and reading*. Newark, Del.: International Reading Association, 1980.

Wepman, J.M. Auditory discrimination, speech and reading. *Elementary School Journal*, 1960, *60*, 325–333.

Zaijka, A. The child as symbol user: The origins of reading in infancy and early childhood. In M.P. Douglass (Ed.), *Claremont reading conference*, 45th Yearbook. Claremont, Calif.: Claremont Graduate School, 1981.

Developmental Chart of Normal Preschool Behavior

Motor Skills

Age	Gross Motor Skills	Fine Motor Skills
0–12 months	Sits without support Crawls Pulls self to standing and stands unaided Walks with aid Rolls a ball in imitation of adult	Reaches, grasps, puts object in mouth Picks things up with thumb and one finger (pincer grasp) Transfers object from one hand to other hand Drops and picks up toy
12–24 months	Walks alone Walks backward Picks up toys from floor without falling Pulls toy, pushes toy Seats self in child's chair Walks up and down stairs (hand held) Moves to music	Builds tower of three small blocks Puts four rings on stick Places five pegs in pegboard Turns pages two or three at a time Scribbles Turns knobs Throws small ball Paints with whole arm movement, shifts hands, makes strokes
24–36 months	Runs forward well Jumps in place, both feet together Stands on one foot, with aid Walks on tiptoe Kicks ball forward	Strings 4 large beads Turns pages singly Snips with scissors Holds crayon with thumb and fingers, not fist Uses one hand consistently in most activities Imitates circular, vertical, horizontal strokes

Source: Mainstreaming Preschoolers: Children with Hearing Impairments (U.S. Department of Health, Education, and Welfare, Office of Human Development Services, Administration for Children, Youth and Families Head Start Bureau, Publication No. [OHDS] 78-31116.) Washington, D.C.: U.S. Government Printing Office, 1979.

295

Age	Gross Motor Skills	Fine Motor Skills
		Paints with some wrist action; makes dots, lines, circular strokes
		Rolls, pounds, squeezes, and pulls clay
36–48 months	Runs around obstacles	Builds tower of nine small blocks
	Walks on a line	Drives nails and pegs
	Balances on one foot for 5–10 seconds	Copies circle
	Hops on one foot	Imitates cross
	Pushes, pulls, steers wheeled toys	Manipulates clay materials (for example, rolls, balls, snakes, cookies)
	Rides (that is steers and pedals) tricycle	
	Uses slide without assistance	
	Jumps over 15 cm (6″) high object standing, both feet together	
	Throws ball overhead	
	Catches ball bounced to him or her	
48–60 months	Walks backwards toe-heel	Cuts on line continuously
	Jumps forward 10 times without falling	Copies cross
	Walks up and down stairs alone, alternating feet	Copies square
	Turns somersault	Prints a few capital letters
60–72 months	Runs lightly on toes	Cuts out simple shapes
	Walks on balance beam	Copies triangle
	Can cover 2 meters (6′6″) hopping	Traces diamond
	Skips on alternate feet	Copies first name
	Jumps rope	Prints numerals 1 to 5
	Skates	Colors within lines
		Has adult grasp of pencil
		Has handedness well established (that is, child is left- or right-handed)
		Pastes and glues appropriately

Communication Skills

Age	Understanding of Language	Spoken Language
0–12 months	Responds to speech by looking at speaker	Makes crying and noncrying sounds
	Responds differently to aspects of speaker's voice (for example, friendly or unfriendly, male or female)	Repeats some vowel and consonant sounds
		Babbles when alone or when spoken to
	Turns to source of sound	Interacts with others by vocalizing after adult
	Responds with gesture to ''hi,'' ''bye-bye,'' and ''up'' when these words are accompanied by appropriate gesture	Communicates meaning through intonation
		Attempts to imitate sounds

Age	*Understanding of Language*	*Spoken Language*
	Stops ongoing action when told "No" (when accompanied by appropriate gesture and tone)	
12–24 months	Responds correctly when asked "where" when accompanied by gesture Understands prepositions on, in, and under Follows request to bring familiar object from another room Understands simple phrases with key words (i.e., "Get the door" or "Get the ball") Follows a series of two simple but related directions	Says first meaningful word Uses single words plus a gesture to ask for objects Says successive single words to describe an event Refers to self by name Uses "my" or "mine" to indicate possession Has vocabulary of about 50 words for important people, common objects, and the existence, nonexistence, and recurrence of objects and events (i.e., "more" and "all gone")
24–36 months	Points to pictures of common objects when they are named Identifies objects when told their use Understands question forms of "what," "where." Understands negatives "no," "not," "can't," "don't" Enjoys listening to simple storybooks and requests them again	Joins vocabulary words together in two-word phrases Gives first and last name Asks "what" and "where" questions Makes negative statement (i.e., "Can't open it") Shows frustration at not being understood
36–48 months	Begins to understand sentences involving time concepts (for example, "We are going to the zoo tomorrow.") Understands size comparatives such as "big" and "bigger." Understands relationships expressed by "if . . . then . . . because" sentences Carries out a series of two to four related directions Understands when told "Let's pretend"	Talks in sentences of three or more words that take the form agent-action-object (I see the ball) or agent-action-location (Daddy sit on chair.) Tells about past experiences Uses "s" nouns to make plurals Uses "ed" on verbs to include past tense Refers to self using pronouns "I," "me" Repeats at least one nursery rhyme and can sing a song Has speech understandable to strangers but there are still some sound errors
48–60 months	Follows three unrelated commands in proper order Understands comparatives like "pretty, prettier, and prettiest" Listens to long stories but often misinterprets facts	Asks when, how and why questions Uses modals like "can," "will," "shall," "should," and "might" Joins sentences together (i.e., "I like chocolate chip cookies and milk.") Talks about causality by using

Age	Understanding of Language	Spoken Language
	Incorporates verbal directions into play activities Understands sequencing of events when told them (i.e., "First we have to go to the store, then we can make a cake, and tomorrow we will eat it.")	"because" and "so" Tells the content of a story but may confuse facts
60–72 months	Demonstrates preacademic skills	Shows a few obvious differences between child's own grammar and adult's grammar Needs to learn such things as subject-verb agreement and some irregular past tense verbs Can take appropriate turns in a conversation Gives and receives information Communicates well with family, friends, or strangers

Cognitive Skills

Age	Action Indicating Cognition
0–12 months	Follows moving object with eyes Recognizes differences among people; responds to strangers by staring or crying Imitates gestures or actions (i.e., shakes head no, plays peek-a-boo, waves bye-bye) Responds to and imitates facial expressions of others Responds to very simple directions (raises arms when someone says "Come," and turns head when asked "Where is Daddy?") Puts small objects in and out of container with intention
12–24 months	Imitates actions and words of adults Understands and follows simple, familiar directions (i.e., "Give me the cup," "Show me your doll," "Get your shoes") Responds to words or commands with appropriate action (i.e., "Stop that," "Get down") Is able to match two similar objects Looks at storybook pictures with an adult, naming or pointing to familiar objects on request (i.e., "What is that?" "Point to the baby") Recognizes difference between "you" and "me" Has very limited attention span Accomplishes primary learning through own exploration
24–36 months	Responds to simple directions (i.e., "Give me the ball and the block," "Get your shoes and socks") Selects and looks at picture books, names pictured objects, and identifies several objects within one picture Matches and uses associated objects meaningfully (for example, given cup, saucer, and bead, puts cup and saucer together)

Age	*Action Indicating Cognition*
	Stacks rings on peg in order of size
	Recognizes self in mirror, saying ''baby'' or own name
	Can talk briefly about what he or she is doing
	Imitates adult actions (for example, housekeeping play)
	Has limited attention span; learning is through exploration and adult direction (as in reading of picture stories)
	Is beginning to understand functional concepts of familiar objects (for example, that a spoon is used for eating) and part-whole concepts (for example, parts of the body)
36–48 months	Recognizes and matches six colors
	Intentionally stacks blocks or rings in order of size
	Draws somewhat recognizable picture that is meaningful to child if not to adult; names and briefly explains picture
	Asks questions for information, (''Why'' and ''How''), questions requiring simple answers
	Knows own age
	Knows own last name
	Has short attention span, learns through observing and imitating adults and by adult instruction and explanation, is very easily distracted
	Has increased understanding of concepts of functions and grouping of objects (i.e., can put dollhouse furniture in correct rooms), part-whole concepts (i.e., can identify pictures of hand and foot as parts of the body)
	Begins to be aware of past and present (i.e., ''Yesterday we went to the park, today we go to the library'')
48–60 months	Plays with words, creates own rhyming words, says or makes up words having similar sounds
	Points to and names four to six colors
	Matches pictures of familiar objects (for example, shoe, sock, foot, apple, orange, banana)
	Draws a person with two to six recognizable parts (such as head, legs, arms), can name or match drawn parts to own body
	Draws, names, and describes recognizable picture
	Rote counts to five, imitating adults
	Knows own street and town
	Has more extended attention span; learns through observing and listening to adults as well as through exploration; is easily distracted
	Has increased understanding of concepts of function, time, part-whole relationships; function or use of objects in addition to names of objects
	Expands time concepts, can talk about yesterday or last week (a long time ago), today, about what will happen tomorrow
60–72 months	Retells story from picture book with reasonable accuracy
	Names some letters and numerals
	Rote counts to ten
	Sorts objects by single characteristics (by color, shape, or size if the difference is obvious)
	Is beginning to use accurately time concepts of ''tomorrow'' and ''yesterday''
	Uses classroom tools (such as scissors and paints) meaningfully and purposefully

Age	Action Indicating Cognition
	Begins to relate clock time to daily schedule
	Increases attention span noticeably; learns through adult instruction; can ignore distractions when interested
	Increases concepts of function as well as understanding of why things happen; expands time concepts into an understanding of the future in terms of major events (i.e., Christmas will come after two weekends)

Self-Help and Social Skills

Age	Self-Help Skills	Social Skills
0–12 months	Feeds self cracker Holds cup with two hands, drinks with assistance Holds out arms and legs while being dressed	Smiles spontaneously Responds differently to strangers than to familiar people Pays attention to own name Responds to "No" Copies simple actions of others
12–24 months	Uses spoon, spilling little Drinks from cup, one hand, unassisted Chews food Removes shoes, socks, pants, sweater Unzips larger zipper Indicates toilet needs	Recognizes self in mirror or picture Refers to self by name Play, by self, initiates own play Imitates adult behaviors in play Helps put things away
24–36 months	Uses spoon, little spilling Gets drink from fountain or faucet unassisted Opens door by turning handle Takes off coat Puts on coat with assistance Washes and dries hands with assistance	Plays near other children Watches other children, joins briefly in their play Defends own possessions Begins to play house Uses objects, self symbolically in play Participates in simple group activity (i.e., sings, claps, dances) Knows gender identity
36–48 months	Pours well from small pitcher Spreads soft butter with knife Buttons and unbuttons large buttons Washes hands unassisted Blows nose when reminded Uses toilet independently	Joins in play with other children; begins to interact Shares toys; takes turns with assistance Begins dramatic play, acting out whole scenes (i.e., traveling, playing house, pretending to be animals)
48–60 months	Cuts easy foods with a knife (i.e., hamburger patty, tomato slice) Laces shoes	Plays and interacts with other children Performs dramatic play closer to reality, pays attention to detail, time, and space Plays dress-up

Age	Self-Help Skills	Social Skills
		Shows interest in exploring sex differences
60–72 months	Dresses self completely	Chooses own friend(s)
	Ties bow	Plays simple table games
	Brushes teeth unassisted	Plays competitive games
	Crosses street safely	Engages in cooperative play with other children involving group decisions, role assignments, fair play

Identification of
Communication Handicaps

Possible Signs of Hearing Loss

1. Before 6 months the child does not startle, blink eyes, or change immediate activity in response to sudden, loud sounds.
2. Before 6 months the child is not soothed or does not show other responses to mother's voice.
3. By 6 months the child does not imitate gurgling and cooing sounds and show response to noise-making toys.
4. By 6 months the child does not turn eyes and head in search of sound that comes from behind or the side.
5. By 10 months the child does not make some kind of response to own name.
6. By 12 months the child does not respond to household sounds such as a spoon rattling in a cup, running water, the noise of a washing machine, or footsteps from behind.
7. By 12 months the child engages in high shrieking and sustained production of vowels.
8. By 12 months the child does not respond to someone's voice by raising head and turning it, if necessary, to look directly at the speaker.
9. By 15 months the child does not imitate sounds and simple words.
10. People consistently have to raise their voices to get the child's attention.
11. At any age after talking has begun but child frequently says "huh" or "what" when someone is speaking.
12. The child responds inconsistently to sound, sometimes hearing it, and sometimes not.
13. The child has a history of ear infections, often getting earaches.
14. The mother had rubella (German measles) during pregnancy.

Source: Reprinted from Communicative Disorders (2nd ed.) by Curtis E. Weiss and Herold S. Lillywhite with permission of The C.V. Mosby Company, © 1981.

15. There is a history of Rh incompatibility, birth trauma, or high fevers.
16. There is a familial history of hearing difficulty.
17. At any age the child watches the speaker's face carefully.
18. At any age the child turns head so that one ear is facing direction of sound source.
19. At any age the child prefers low-pitched to high-pitched sounds.
20. At any age the child complains of not hearing.
21. At any age the child consistently talks in unusually soft or loud voice.
22. At any age the child often turns the sound on television up loud (adolescents and teenagers excluded when listening to their favorite music).

Possible Signs of Receptive Language Problems

1. By 15 months the child does not understand and respond to name, "no no," "bye-bye," and "bottle."
2. By 21 months the child does not respond correctly to "Give me that," "Sit down," "Stand up."
3. By 24 months the child does not understand and point, on command, to mouth, nose, hair, and ears.
4. By 30 months the child does not understand and demonstrate, on command, in, on, under, front, and back.
5. By 48 months the child cannot answer correctly the questions: "What do we sleep in?" "What do we sit on?" "What do we cook on?" "What is your name?" "What do you do when you are hungry?" "What do you do when you are thirsty?"
6. By 48 months the child cannot distinguish boy from girl, big from little, one object from two or more objects.
7. By 60 months the child cannot tell the use of book, stove, house, and key.
8. By 60 months the child cannot distinguish soft from hard, smooth from rough, and tell why we have a chair, house, dress, and window.
9. By 72 months the child cannot tell the reason for having eyes, ears, and legs.
10. By 72 months the child does not have number concepts up to 5.
11. By 84 to 96 months the child does not know differences (such as between a bird and a dog), cannot tell youngest from oldest (and vice versa), and cannot recognize likenesses (such as how an apple and an orange are alike).

Possible Signs of Expressive Language Problems

1. By 18 months the child is not saying at least six words with appropriate meaning.

2. By 24 months the child is not combining words into phrases, such as "Go bye-bye," "Want a cookie."
3. By 30 months the child is not using short sentences such as "Mommy see dolly," "Daddy go bye-bye."
4. By 36 months the child has not begun asking simple questions.
5. By 48 months the child's sentences are telegraphic, reversed, or confused, such as, "Me car go" "Baby loud crying," "Candy me want."
6. By 48 months the child is not using auxiliary verbs such as, "is," "have," and "can" with main verbs.
7. By 60 months the child is not using the personal pronoun "I," saying "Me (instead of I) want a cookie," or name instead of pronoun, such as "Bobby (instead of I) want a drink."
8. By 60 months the child consistently uses incorrectly past tenses, plurals, and pronouns such as "Them throwed a balls."
9. By 60 months the child's expressive vocabulary is limited and shallow, fewer than 200 to 300 simple words.

Possible Signs of Speech Problems

1. The child uses mainly vowels in babbling or speech after 12 months of age.
2. The speech is not more than 50 percent understandable by age 24 months.
3. There are many consonant omissions by 36 months, such as / æ[1] i / for daddy or /A[1] for puppy.
4. There is a predominance of vowels in the speech after age 36 months.
5. The speech is not 100 percent understandable by 48 months; this does not mean all phonemes are used correctly, just understandably.
6. The child omits most initial consonants after age 3.
7. The child omits, substitutes, or distorts any phonemes after age 7.
8. Phonemes are more than six months late in appearing, according to the normal developmental sequence.
9. The speech has not become noticeably more understandable and more fluent in the last six months, up to the age of 7.
10. The child is concerned or teased about his speech at any age.
11. The child repeats, hesitates, stops, and starts over frequently.
12. The child has been disfluent for more than six months.
13. The child appears to be struggling to say words, blinks eyes, and grimaces when speaking.
14. The disfluency becomes noticeably more severe at any time.
15. The child fears speaking situations at any age.
16. The rate of speaking is too fast, too slow, jumbled, or telegraphed.
17. The voice quality is nasal (talks through the nose).

18. The voice quality, pitch, or loudness is abnormal (conspicuous).
19. The voice is monotone, dysphonic, or whiney most of the time.
20. The child has persistent, recurring hoarseness, pitch breaks, or breathiness.

Activities and Principles for Mother in Preventing Communication Handicaps

Activities and Principles for Preventing Hearing Loss

1. *Prenatal*
   a. Provide Rh immunity
   b. Receive rubella vaccine
   c. Identify high-risk persons
   d. Receive influenza vaccine
   e. Obtain genetic counseling with history of hereditary hearing impairment
   f. Encourage and support research aimed at preventing hearing impairment

2. *During Pregnancy*
   a. Treat maternal syphilis adequately
   b. Carefully monitor the mother's health
   c. Avoid irradiation
   d. Avoid oxygen deprivation
   e. Avoid ototoxic drugs
   f. Receive intrauterine transfusions for fetus showing signs of erythroblastosis

3. *Postnatal*
   a. Practice early detection through infant testing and observation
   b. Plan early educational intervention
   c. Avoid ototoxic drugs
   d. Receive counseling concerning aural hygiene

Source: Reprinted from *Communicative Disorders* (2nd ed.) by Curtis E. Weiss and Herold S. Lillywhite with permission of The C.V. Mosby Company, © 1981.

    e. Provide adequate nutrition
    f. Avoid exposure to high noise levels
    g. Avoid measles, scarlet fever, meningitis, and influenza if at all possible
    h. Receive effective, early treatment of diseases that could not be prevented
    i. Avoid foreign objects in the ear
    j. Receive prompt medical care for otitis media and other ear diseases
    k. Use protective devices in noisy environments
    l. Seek better utilization of residual or remaining hearing
    m. Receive early communicative intervention, amplification, speech reading, and auditory training to minimize the effects of the hearing loss

Activities and Principles for Preventing Language Disorders

1. Maintain good physical and mental health during pregnancy.
2. Maintain good health in the child.
3. Establish a realistic level of expectation.
4. Provide the child with a number of toys and pictures and explain their functions, size, shape, and color.
5. Use many gestures when the child is first learning language.
6. Use simple language—short sentences and easy-to-understand words and sentence structures.
7. Be a good language model.
8. Name or label objects, toys, and furnishings inside the home for the child just beginning to talk.
9. Describe or narrate what you or the child is doing at the time it is being done.
10. Expand telegraphic sentences spoken by the child by adding the missing word or words as you repeat them.
11. Help the child to associate objects, pictures, actions, and other behaviors by supplying the appropriate words.
12. Be constantly aware of the need for a rich verbal environment for the child.
13. Provide ample opportunity and time for the child's self-expression.
14. Teach the child how to ask and answer questions.
15. Do not overlook the importance of the quality as well as the quantity of language.
16. Begin with short, easy-to-say words that are quite concrete such as nouns and verbs, and only later progress to more abstract words such as adjectives or adverbs.
17. Expose the child to visits to the zoo, circus, library, and other highly stimulating places.

18. Discourage others from talking for the child; be sure the child has a need to talk so that talking receives greater rewards than not talking.
19. Reward the child's linguistic efforts.

Activities and Principles for Preventing Articulation Problems

1. Do not accept the advice that the child will "outgrow" the misarticulations.
2. Begin early, shortly after the child is born, to stimulate speech.
3. Provide a number of toys, objects, pictures, and books for stimulating communication in the child.
4. Plan teaching activities that are appropriate, creative, flexible, and enjoyable; plan these activities in consultation with a speech-language pathologist.
5. Sequence the steps to learning articulation in order of difficulty from sounds in isolation to nonsense syllables, single words, phrases, sentences, and finally conversation.
6. Keep daily records of progress that are understandable and meaningful to the child.
7. Be sure to provide for the child's psychological, emotional, and physical needs (good parenting).
8. Motivate the child to become interested in communication by rewarding speech efforts.
9. Be a good listener—pay close attention to the child's communication.
10. When baby babbles, babble back (some of the time); encourage vocal play early in the infant's life.
11. As a parent or "teacher," become familiar with the landmarks of normal articulatory development.
12. "Play" rather than "work" with the child.
13. Whenever possible minimize family upheaval and emotional stress.
14. Be a good model of articulation—talk clearly and slowly with careful phrasing and inflection.
15. When talking, emphasize specific sounds—those with which the child has particular difficulty.
16. Use a variety of facial expressions when talking to the child.
17. Imitate or echo correctly what the child said incorrectly.
18. Provide many opportunities for the child to practice making sounds.
19. Teach the child to talk by using all of the sensory modalities.
20. Parents, teachers, and other adults, as well as the child, should increase their awareness of speech sounds in regard to how they are made and how they sound.

21. Generally teach the easier (earlier developing) sounds or readily identifiable distinctive features first.
22. Teach sound pairs—those sounds made the same way, except that one is made with the vocal folds vibrating and the other is not.
23. Provide ample ear training or discriminative listening so that the child can learn the difference between sounds made correctly and those made incorrectly.
24. Do not try to teach more than two sounds at one time or one distinctive feature at a time.
25. Do not teach "new" sounds until the "old" sounds are habitually (subconsciously) used in conversational speech by the child.
26. Encourage the child to "feel a need to improve" articulation.
27. Begin by bombarding the child with the sound or sounds to be learned.
28. Set realistic goals and expectations, daily as well as long term.
29. Read to the child daily.
30. Consider a preschool experience for the child with delayed communicative development.

Activities and Principles for Preventing Speech Problems

1. Detect a voice deviation or vocal abuse or misuse early.
2. Receive counseling on good vocal hygiene by a speech-language pathologist.
3. Get a thorough laryngeal examination if the child's throat is sore (for more than two weeks) or if the voice becomes hoarse, husky, or breathy, or changes in some other way so that a more serious voice problem will be prevented from developing.
4. Have the child's hearing checked if a voice deviation is present (this is good advice for all children regardless of the communicative problem).
5. Talk with appropriate pitch levels—not too high or too low—and encourage the child to do the same.
6. Talk with appropriate loudness levels—not too loud or too soft—and encourage the child to do the same.
7. Limit the amount of talking when laryngitis is present.
8. Be especially careful in considering removal of the adenoids (you might want to seek a second opinion).
9. Seek early surgery or other medical treatment when organic conditions are present such as cysts, tumors, and disease of the vocal folds.
10. Consider a speech appliance (obturator) if the child talks through the nose.
11. Encourage the use of a "silent" cough or throat clearing (without vocal fold vibration) whenever possible to reduce the amount of vocal abuse.

12. Increase your level of awareness as well as that of the child about abusive vocal fold use and misuse.
13. Count the abusive vocal fold uses and misuses daily while trying to reduce the number.
14. Be aware that some children are more vulnerable or susceptible than others to vocal disorders caused by vocal abuse or misuse.
15. Control upper respiratory problems as much as possible since they can cause structural changes to the vocal folds.
16. Seek and obtain the cooperation of the classroom teacher, parents, peers, and others for encouraging good vocal hygiene.
17. Be especially aware of those children who tend toward hoarseness such as loud, outgoing children who are active in athletics and other activities.
18. Obtain psychological counseling in regard to voice problems whenever indicated.
19. Try to help the child avoid other abusive habits such as smoking (and possibly drinking).
20. Refer the child to a speech-language pathologist if the child's voice calls attention to itself, such as when it seems to be going through the nose, sounds monotonous, or has excessive pitch breaks.

Activities and Principles for Preventing Fluency Problems

1. Early counseling with a speech-language pathologist is indispensable.
2. An evaluation for every child who is disfluent for more than six months is recommended.
3. Avoid the use of the label ''stuttering'' or ''stammering.''
4. Provide the child with a structured, consistent environment; keep family relationships and schedules as harmonious as possible.
5. Do not call any attention to the child's speech, either good or bad.
6. Be a good listener; this requires considerable effort.
7. Praise the child lavishly (for nonspeech performances or behaviors).
8. Guard the child's physical and psychological health.
9. Play ''talking'' games that disguise ''talking'' by emphasizing ''play.''
10. Play ''talking'' games that emphasize rhythm.
11. Never force the child to talk or perform verbally.
12. Note secretly the times when the child is most dysfluent.
13. Avoid teasing the child.
14. Avoid the use of ''gimmicks'' to help the child talk fluently.
15. Never make threats or promises to alleviate the speech dysfluencies.
16. Have reasonable expectations of the child; do not expect too much too soon.

17. Become as sensitive as possible to the child's many ways of communicating both verbally and nonverbally.
18. Tune in more to the feelings being expressed; what is being said should be more important than how it is said.
19. Learn what it takes for normal speech fluency to develop.
20. Provide good fluency models for the child.
21. Make certain that the child and you have plenty of opportunities to express feelings openly.
22. Encourage speech spontaneity in the child by strengthening self-confidence and a desire to share ideas and feelings.
23. Avoid suggestions such as "talk slowly," "take a deep breath," "say it again," "stop that," and "your brain is going faster than your mouth." They are not helpful; in fact, they are harmful to fluency.
24. As a listener do not show emotional reaction when a child is having difficulty with fluency, in "getting the word out."
25. Do not interrupt or say the word for the child at the time the child is trying to say something.

New Principles
of Child Raising

1. Encourage the child
2. Avoid punishment and reward
3. Use natural and logical consequences
4. Be firm without dominating
5. Respect the child
6. Induce respect for order
7. Induce respect for the rights of others
8. Eliminate criticism and minimize mistakes
9. Maintain routine
10. Take time for training
11. Win cooperation
12. Avoid giving undue attention
13. Sidestep the struggle for power
14. Withdraw from the conflict
15. Act! Keep your mouth shut
16. Don't shoo flies
17. Use care in pleasing—have the courage to say "No"
18. Avoid that first impulse—do the unexpected
19. Refrain from overprotection
20. Stimulate independence
21. Stay out of fights
22. Be unimpressed by fears
23. Mind your own business
24. Avoid the pitfalls of pity
25. Make requests reasonable and sparse

Source: Children: The Challenge by Rudolf Dreikurs with permission of E.P. Dutton, Publishers ©
1964.

26. Follow through, be consistent
27. Put them all in the same boat
28. Listen!
29. Watch your tone of voice
30. Take it easy
31. Downgrade "bad" habits
32. Have fun together
33. Talk with them, not to them
34. Establish a Family Council

Index

Note: Pages numbers in italics indicate exhibits, figures, and tables.

About the Authors

Elizabeth B. Johnston received her Ed.D. degree from the University of Cincinnati in 1978, in the area of language/cognition. She is the designer and originator of the Preschool Language Nursery Group, part of the Miami University Speech-Language and Hearing Clinic, Miami University, Oxford, Ohio. She has been the coordinator of Clinical Services for the Speech and Hearing Clinic at Miami University-Oxford and has taught courses in language development and disorders and in diagnosis since 1972. Dr. Johnston also has been a presenter of numerous workshops in language therapy and preschool language. Her research interests involve the study of high-risk infants and factors relating to their later development of language.

Andrew V. Johnston obtained a Ph.D. degree from the University of Oregon in 1963 in elementary education, language arts. Since 1967, he has been a consultant and advisor for reading and language arts, and has taught at the undergraduate and graduate levels at Miami University. He has presented at state, regional, and national levels in language acquisition and reading. His research interests have included problems facing beginning teachers and how teachers use readability information in selecting instructional materials. He now is focusing on children's use of language in reading and learning to read.